Preface

We believe that the material in this resource manual will help all instructors establish or improve their teaching practices. This manual builds upon the writing and editing of many faculty who have contributed to this manual over several years. This provides a range of teaching styles and ideas from which you can select elements you consider most suitable to you in your classroom.

Chapters in the manual correspond to chapters in *Biology: Concepts and Applications*, 8th Edition by Starr/Evers/Starr. In addition, there is an appendix with suggestions for writing essays and term papers (these can be copied and handed out to students).

Each chapter of the manual has the following twelve sections:

- **Chapter Outline:** An outline of the headings within each textbook chapter, giving an overview of its contents.
- **Objectives:** General objectives related to the main elements of each text chapter.
- **Key Terms:** A listing of the boldfaced terms in the chapter, arranged in the order in which they appear in the text.
- **Lecture Outline:** A detailed, sequentially annotated outline of the chapter to aid instructors in preparing lecture notes.
- **Suggestions for Presenting the Material:** Helpful suggestions for presenting certain topics covered in the text. As in other sections, hints have been gathered from several classroom teachers. Common Student Misconceptions is also a bulleted point that will give you an idea of the concepts with which students struggle.
- **Classroom and Laboratory Enrichment:** A useful collection of visual demonstration ideas to help make the lecture a lively learning experience for your students; most of the ideas utilize common laboratory or household equipment.
- **Revisited Classroom Discussion Ideas from Section One of Each Chapter:** These discussion points are directly linked to the first section of every chapter.
- **Additional Ideas for Classroom Discussion:** In contrast to questions at the end of each chapter in the text, these questions are written specifically to evoke a range of responses from your students in a group setting.
- *How Would You Vote?* **Classroom Discussion Ideas:** This section includes discussion topics directly linked to the *How Would You Vote?* question. These topics will truly allow the students to debate amongst each other regarding current biology topics.
- **Term Paper Topics, Library Activities, and Special Projects:** For those instructors who want their students to "dig a little deeper" into the chapter content, a list of topics that require extra effort and research are included.
- **Responses to** *Data Analysis Activities*:
- **Possible Responses to** *Critical Thinking* **Questions:** The response to each of the Critical Thinking questions is only a sample of a common response. This may not either be the "correct" response, or the only possibility.

We hope our contribution to this Instructor's Resource Manual has provided an improved product that will facilitate your teaching the fascinating subject of biology.

1

INVITATION TO BIOLOGY

Chapter Outline

Objectives

1. Define the organization of life at various levels of complexity, and recognize the aspects of life that emerge at each level.
2. Explain those properties shared by all living things.
3. Understand and utilize the modern system of classification for living things.
4. Understand the components of the scientific method.
5. Recognize how research can be used to reveal cause-and-effect relationships in science.

Key Terms

biology	organ	nutrient	development
emergent properties	organ system	producers	reproduction
atoms	population	photosynthesis	inheritance
molecules	community	consumers	biodiversity
cell	ecosystem	homeostasis	nucleus
organism	biosphere	DNA	bacteria
tissue	energy	growth	archaeans

eukaryotes	taxon, taxa	variables	statistically significant
protists	critical thinking	independent variable	scientific theory
fungi	science	dependent variable	law of nature
plants	hypotheses	experimental group	
animals	inductive reasoning	control group	
species	prediction	data	
taxonomy	deductive reasoning	scientific method	
genus, genera	model	sampling error	
specific epithet	experiments	probability	

Lecture Outline

1.1   The Secret Life of Earth
   1.   Biology is the study of life.
   2.   The Earth has an amazing diversity of life, some of which is yet to be discovered.
   3.   The Earth is also suffering the loss of species at an alarming rate.

1.2   The Science of Nature
   A.   Life Is More Than the Sum of its Parts
      1.   Life emerges from the interaction of simpler component parts.

   B.   A Pattern in Life's Organization
      1.   The organization of life is commonly considered from the very small to the very large.
         a.   atoms
         b.   molecules
         c.   cell
         d.   organism
         e.   tissue
         f.   organ
         g.   organ system
         h.   population
         i.   community
         j.   ecosystem
         k.   biosphere

1.3   How Living Things Are Alike
   A.   Organisms Require Energy and Nutrients
      1.   Energy is the capacity to do work, while a nutrient is a substance needed by an organism that it is unable to synthesize.
      2.   Producers make their own energy, while consumers eat other organisms to obtain energy.
      3.   Energy flows through life, while nutrients are cycled.

   B.   Organisms Sense and Respond to Change
      1.   Organisms respond to changes in their internal and external environments.
      2.   Homeostasis is the maintenance of favorable internal conditions.

   C.   Organisms Use DNA
      1.   DNA (deoxyribonucleic acid) guides an organisms metabolic activities.
      2.   Inheritance is the passage of DNA from parents to offspring.

1.4 How Living Things Differ

    A. Organisms may or may not have their DNA housed in a nucleus.
        1. Bacteria and archaeans do not have a nucleus.
        2. Eukaryotes do have a nucleus.

    B. Eukaryotes are subdivided into four major groups.
        1. Protists are the most simple eukaryotes.
        2. Fungi are multicellular eukaryotes that secrete digestive enzymes externally.
        3. Plants are multicellular eukaryotes that are generally producers, capable of photosynthesis
        4. Animals are multicellular eukaryotes that are consumers.

1.5 Organizing Information About Species

    A. Taxonomy is the system of naming and organizing species
        1. The Linnaean system provided a standardized means for science to describe species.
        2. In order of decreasing inclusiveness, the taxon of the Linnaean system are: domain, kingdom, phylum, class, order, family, genus, species.

    B. A Rose by Any Other Name…
        1. Individuals of a species share morphological, physiological, and behavioral traits.
        2. Differentiating species can be difficult and is partially subject to human judgment.
        3. A classic and useful, though imperfect, definition of a species is that members of a species can produce fertile offspring, but cannot with other groups.

1.6 The Nature of Science

    A. Thinking About Thinking
        1. Critical thinking involves judging the quality of information before accepting it.

    B. How Science Works
        1. Develop hypotheses (educated guesses) using all known information.
        2. Make a prediction of what the outcome would be if the hypothesis is valid.
        3. Test the predictions by experiments, models, and observations.
            a. Experiments are tests designed to support or falsify a prediction. In experiments conditions are carefully controlled.
            b. Variables are the factors manipulated and measured in an experiment.
            c. Experimental and control groups are used to measure the effects of the variable being tested. The experimental group experiences all the same conditions as the control group except for the variable being studied.
        4. Repeat the tests for consistency.
        5. Report objectively on the tests and conclusions.

1.7 Examples of Biology Experiments

    A. Potato Chips and Stomachaches
        1. A suburban Chicago theater was chosen as a "laboratory" to determine if the synthetic fat called Olestra® caused gastrointestinal cramps.
        2. Both control and experimental groups were random samples of moviegoers who had no idea which fat-impregnated chips they were eating.
        3. Later, the moviegoers were called at home to determine the extent of distress: 15.8 percent for Olestra, 17.6 percent for regular chips; no significant difference.

    B. Butterflies and Birds
        1. The peacock butterfly has a long life span for a butterfly. When it rests it folds its wings so that only the underside shows; and it flicks its wings in a specific pattern when a predator approaches.

2. Scientists formed hypotheses to better understand why the peacock butterfly flicks it wings. They tested two hypotheses by isolating and controlling both variables.
3. Data supports that birds are deterred by the sounds the wings make when they flick as well as the wing spots.

  C. Asking Useful Questions
    1. Scientists prefer quantitative reports of experimental tests to guard against bias.
    2. Science is a competitive and collaborative process. Using critical thinking skills and changing one's mind in the light of new evidence is a strength in science.

1.8   Asking Useful Questions
  A. The Trouble With Trends
    1. Scientists must be careful not to make broad generalizations from limited experiments.
  B. Problems With Probability
    1. To avoid sampling error, large sample sizes are favored.
    2. Statistics can be used to assess the probability that sampling error is an issue.
  C. Bothering With Bias
    1. Scientists must be cautious in their experimental design and data analysis to avoid skewing the data towards their desired outcome.

1.9   Philosophy of Science
  A. About the Word "Theory"
    1. A theory is a related set of hypotheses that form an explanation about some aspect of the natural world.
      a. A theory has broader application than a hypothesis.
      b. A theory is not "absolute truth"; scientists are relatively certain it is (or is not) correct.
    2. The fact that an idea, or even a theory, might be subject to change is a strength of science, not a weakness.
  B. The Limits of Science
    1. Science does not provide subjective answers or address the supernatural.
    2. Science does allow us to communicate our experience and understand nature without bias.

Suggestions for Presenting the Material

♦ Although Chapter 1 is a general introduction to biology and to this textbook, it will be viewed very differently by instructor and student. For the student, this chapter is a *preview*. That means the instructor must take extra care not to "intimidate" the students during early lectures. Obviously, it would be very easy to lose the attention and enthusiasm of newly enrolled students if *too much* is presented *too soon*.

♦ The chapter contents terms unfamiliar to most students. These might include: *DNA* and *homeostasis*. Decide if these terms need explanation now or are to be deferred until later.

♦ Figure 1.3 (levels of organization) is an excellent "road map" and can be used throughout the course to guide the progression along the organizational ladder. It can also be used in the exercise listed in the Enrichment section below.

♦ The diagram in Figure 1.4 (one-way energy flow) also has relevance to future lectures. When introducing it here, you should stress the *flow of energy* and the recycling of *raw materials*.

♦ Explain carefully the necessity for control groups in scientific investigations. Using human clinical trials, discuss the difficulty of determining which groups of human patients will *not* receive a valuable drug (the controls) and who will receive a possibly life-saving medication. Discuss the ethics behind this situation.

♦ The basic concept of the scientific method can, and should be, introduced early in the course. Find common experiences that can be analyzed using the scientific method to allow students to appreciate its precision and power.

♦ **Common Student Misconceptions:**

    o Address misconceptions with terms such as *theory*. Emphasize the meaning of these words from a scientific point of view.

    o Sometimes students think that methods of scientific investigation are used only by scientists. Show that this is not true by discussing the use of these methods in a routine investigation of "why won't the car start?" (See the Enrichment section below.)

Classroom and Laboratory Enrichment

♦ Bring in several organisms and ask your students to name characteristics that identify each item as living or nonliving (for some organisms, this may be difficult to do without specialized equipment, such as a microscope). Ask the students to identify equipment or experiments that would help to determine if an item is a living organism.

♦ Show a representative variety of plants, animals, and decomposers. Ask students to characterize them as *producer, consumer,* or *decomposer*.

♦ Show the videotape "Life on Earth" by David Attenborough (available at retail outlets) as a general introduction to biological diversity.

♦ Give examples of several scientific names for local plants and animals that are well known to the students. Interpret the meanings of each Latin specific epithet.

♦ Show a phylogenetic tree of vertebrates (or any other group of organisms for which a phylogenetic tree is available) to demonstrate the phylogenetic system of classification. Present students with a set of diverse organisms; ask them how they would classify these organisms.

♦ Present fossil evidence showing how a group of related organisms or a single genus (for example, *Equus*) has evolved and changed through time.

♦ Show how we use the scientific method in everyday problem solving as illustrated by this example:

Event		Method Step
a.	Auto will not start............................a.	Observation
b.	Battery dead..................................b.	Hypothesis
	Ignition problem.........................	Hypothesis
	Out of gas................................	Hypothesis
c.	Turn on headlights.........................c.	Experiment
	Check spark plug...........................	Experiment
	Check gas gauge...........................	Experiment
	Dip long stick into gas tank	Experiment
d.	Headlights burn brightly (battery OK).........d.	Analyze results
	Strong ignition spark.....................	Analyze results
	Gauge says half tank but no gas on stick.........	Analyze results

e. Gas gauge is not accurate; car needs gas
   to run...e.   Generalize; form principle

The Secret Life of Earth (revisited)

♦ Go to the website www.eol.org to examine the updating database of information on species. Have each student present information on a species with which they were not familiar.

♦ Ask students to discuss whether or not they feel it is important to spend resources to explore new areas and discover new species.

Additional Ideas for Classroom Discussion

♦ During your first lecture, ask students to name as many characteristics of living things as possible. While this may at first seem like an obvious and overly simple exercise, students will be surprised at some of the less obvious characteristics, such as homeostasis.

♦ How does our modern definition of "life" differ from the definition of life that a seventeenth-century biologist might have used?

♦ What is metabolism? What metabolic steps in humans are different from those found in green plants? What metabolic steps in humans are the same as those found in green plants?

♦ What are some examples of homeostasis? Why must living organisms be able to perform it?

♦ Present a list of 10 random organisms (or, better yet, let your students do this). Identify ways in which all of the organisms are similar, then ways in which all of the organisms are different. How would you classify (that is, place into meaningful groups) these organisms?

♦ Why is it important for a species to be able to change? Wouldn't a species be more successful if it could be assured of remaining the same from one generation to the next?

♦ Name some organisms you might find in a grassy area nearby. Using arrows, arrange the organisms in a diagram depicting energy flow and the cycling of materials (for help, see Figure 1.4). What are some organisms that may be invisible to the eye but are essential for the recycling of nutrients during decomposition?

♦ An animal carcass infested with insect larvae is not an attractive sight. Yet it is a biological necessity. Explore the role of these and other "recyclers."

♦ Is there such a concept as the "balance of nature"?

♦ Humans are able to manipulate certain aspects of nature for their own benefit. However, it is often said that "humans are the only animals that engineer their own destruction." Give examples to support this allegation.

♦ Death and decay are considered by religious fundamentalists as part of God's curse on mankind. What would the earth be like without these two processes?

♦ Why is the term *scientific creationism* an oxymoron? Describe why this body of thought cannot be considered a science.

♦ Does belief in the principle of evolution exclude belief in religion? Why or why not?

♦ What is artificial selection? How does it differ from natural selection?

♦ Distinguish among independent, dependent, and controlled variables. Can you identify each if presented with an actual experimental design?

- Why is it difficult to obtain a control group when selecting volunteers to test a new anticancer drug?
- Those who wish to berate certain scientific principles sometimes say, "It's only a theory." This statement is used by creationists when referring to evolution. Does the use of theory in biology mean the concept is in doubt? Explain using examples.

How Would You Vote? Classroom Discussion Ideas

- Monitor the voting for the online question. Ask your students to explain their reasons for or against the protection of unexplored areas and endangered species.
- At what point does the benefit of protecting unexplored areas become unethical to the economic advancement of local peoples?
- Is it valuable to protect all endangered species, even those with no obvious value to humans?
- Have students complete classroom polling using the JoinIn clickers.

Term Paper Topics, Library Activities, and Special Projects

- Discover more about how the first cells are thought to have evolved. How do biologists draw the line between that which is living and that which is nonliving?
- Describe how any one of several modern scientific investigative tools (such as electron microscopy, radioactive labeling, gas chromatography, or gel electrophoresis) has made it possible to discover similarities and differences among living organisms.
- The pupal stage of insect metamorphosis is erroneously called the "resting stage." Actually, there is a complete transformation of larval tissues to adult tissues. Consult several entomology and biochemistry texts to learn the current status of our knowledge concerning these transformations.
- The supply of easily obtainable energy sources is a matter of debate today. Some persons see a bleak future; others are optimistic. What are the issues that each of these camps sees?
- How do today's biologists reconcile their personal faith in an organized religion with their belief in evolution? Research the viewpoints of some famous scientists on this issue.
- Learn more about the discovery of fossils of *Archaeopteryx* and the reactions of the scientific community to them.
- Select an advertisement for a weight loss or sports nutrition supplement and research the scientific validity behind the product.

Responses to *Data Analysis Activities*

1. A is the control group for D, testing the impact of spot visibility. B and C are the control group for E and F, testing the impact of wing noise.

Possible Responses to *Critical Thinking* Questions

1. A person can be considered dead with only a small fraction of their cells being dead as those cells are responsible for coordinating the action of the all the other cells, and ultimately maintaining the homeostasis of the organism as a whole.

2. When understanding the complete scientific name you see that the genus defines what each of these organisms is: American black bear, New Jersey tea, garden toad, or a snowshoe hare. At a café, you are probably interested in the tea (*Ceanothus americanus*)!

3. "Facts change." That is true in scientific research because science is open to new data and new interpretations of old data, which can lead to discarding or modifying formerly-held tenets. This is a strength of science, not a weakness. It is this willingness to accept *change* that makes the phrase "scientific creationism" meaningless. Creationists have accepted as fact a set of immutable ideas, which are then supported by carefully chosen facts from the realm of science.

4. It is unfortunate that the respectable journal did not catch any experimental fraud; however, this is an example of "facts change." The process of science did work, and when the results could not be confirmed the article was retracted. It is important to hold scientists accountable for their work, and this scientist was held accountable and lost his research privileges. As in all professions, just because one person is unethical it is not fair to judge the work of everyone in that profession based on one person's actions.

2

LIFE'S CHEMICAL BASIS

Chapter Outline

Objectives

1. Understand how protons, electrons, and neutrons are arranged into atoms and ions.
2. Explain how the number and arrangement of electrons in an atom or ion determines the number and kinds of chemical bonds that can be formed.
3. Know the various types of chemical bonds, how they form between atoms, and the relative strengths of each type.
4. Understand the essential chemical properties of water that make life possible.
5. Understand the importance of pH and the relationships of acids and bases.

Key Terms

atoms	mass number	mixture	cohesion
protons	radioisotopes	ionic bond	evaporation
neutrons	radioactive decay	covalent bond	temperature
electrons	tracer	polarity	concentration
charge	shell models	hydrogen bond	pH
nucleus	ion	solvent	acids
atomic number	electronegativity	solutes	bases
elements	chemical bond	salt	buffer
periodic table	molecule	hydrophilic	
isotopes	compounds	hydrophobic	

Lecture Outline

2.1   Mercury Rising

     A.   Mercury is gradually being released to the atmosphere
         1.   This is due to both natural processes and human activities.

     B.   Mercury in the body can damage a variety of vital organs

2.2   Start With Atoms

     A.   Atoms are assembled from protons, neutrons and electrons.
         1.   Protons (positive) and electrons (negative) impact the charge of an atom.
         2.   Elements are pure substances, with all atoms have the same number of protons, and therefore the same atomic number.
         3.   The periodic table arranges atoms in order of their atomic number and with regard to their behavior.

     B.   Isotopes and Radioisotopes
         1.   Atoms with the same number of protons (for example, carbon with six) but a different number of neutrons (carbon can have six, seven, or eight) are called isotopes (^{12}C, ^{13}C, ^{14}C).
         2.   Radioisotopes spontaneously emit subatomic particles or energy when their nucleus breaks down.
         3.   Decay occurs independent of external factors like temperature, pressure, or chemical bonds with other atoms. This process occurs at a constant rate.
             a.   They can be used to date rocks and fossils.
             b.   Some can be used as tracers to follow the path of an atom in a series of reactions.

2.3   Why Electrons Matter

     A.   Energy Levels
         1.   Electrons are subatomic particles governed by different forces.
             a.   In general, atoms have the same number of electrons as protons.
             b.   Electrons travel in different orbitals, defined as volumes of space around the center of the atom.
         2.   Orbitals can be thought of as occupying shells around the nucleus.
             a.   The shell closest to the nucleus has one orbital holding a maximum of two electrons. Orbitals closest to the nucleus are lowest in energy level.
             b.   The next shell can have four orbitals with two electrons each for a total of eight electrons. Orbitals further from the nucleus have successively higher energy levels.
         3.   A chemical bond is a union between the electron structures of atoms.
             a.   Atoms with "unfilled" orbitals in their outermost shell tend to be reactive with other atoms.
             b.   The number or the distribution of its electrons changes when an atom gives up, gains, or shares electrons.

     B.   Swapping Electrons
         1.   Ions are atoms that carry a charge—negative by acquiring electrons or positive by donating electrons.
         2.   A measure of an atom's ability to pull electrons away from another atom is called electronegativity.
         3.   Electronegativity is dependent upon the atom's size and electron vacancies. It is not a measure of an atom's charge.

C. Sharing Electrons
1. A molecules forms when two or more atoms of the same or different elements join in chemical bonds.
2. A chemical bond is an attractive force between atoms resulting from the interaction of their electrons.
3. A compound consists of two or more different elements, where the relative percentages of the elements do not vary.
4. In a mixture, two or more elements intermingle, and their proportions may vary.

2.4 Why Atoms Interact
A. Ionic Bonds
1. When an atom loses or gains one or more electrons, it becomes positively or negatively charged—an ion.
2. Two atoms with a large difference in electronegativity have a strong mutual attraction and form an ionic bond.

B. Covalent Bonds
1. A covalent bond holds together two atoms that share one or more pairs of electrons.
2. Covalent bonds can be much stronger than ionic bonds, but not always.
3. In a nonpolar covalent bond, atoms share electrons equally.
4. In a polar covalent bond, atoms share the electron unequally, resulting in a slight difference in charge between the two poles of the bond; water is an example.

C. Hydrogen Bonds
1. A hydrogen bond is an attraction between a hydrogen atom and an electronegative atom, both of which are taking part in separate polar covalent bonds.
2. These are not chemical bonds; they do not form new molecules. They are weaker than ionic or covalent bonds, easily forming and breaking.
3. These bonds are critical to life and impart structure to liquid water, and stabilize nucleic acids and other large organic molecules.

2.5 Water's Life-Giving Properties
A. Each Water Molecule is Polar
1. Water is a polar molecule due to the slight negative charge at the oxygen end and a slight positive charge at the hydrogen end caused by the unequal sharing of electrons.
2. Water molecules often form hydrogen bonds with each other.

B. Water is an Excellent Solvent
1. The solvent properties of water are greatest with respect to polar molecules with which they interact by pulling on ions or molecules, dispersing them.
2. Polar substances are hydrophilic (water loving); non-polar ones are hydrophobic (water dreading, like oils) and are repelled by water.

C. Cohesion
1. Hydrogen bonding of water molecules provides cohesion, a property that helps the molecules resist separating, which imparts surface tension.
2.   In evaporative processes the input of heat energy increases molecular motion so that hydrogen bonds are broken faster than they form and water molecules escape into the air, thus cooling the surface..
3. Cohesion contributes to pulling water through plant tissues.

D. Water Stabilizes Temperature
1. Temperature is a way of measuring the energy of molecular motion.

2. Water's hydrogen bonding slightly restricts molecular "jiggling," absorbing some energy. This property means that water acts as an energy reservoir, stabilizing surrounding air temperatures.
3. In freezing, the hydrogen bonds resist breaking and lock the water molecules in the bonding patterns of ice.

2.6 Acids and Bases
  A. The pH Scale
    1. pH is a measure of the H^+ concentration in a solution; the greater the H^+ the concentration the lower the pH scale.
    2. The scale extends from 0 (acidic) to 7 (neutral) to 14 (basic).
    3. Each one unit change reflects a 10-fold change in H^+ concentration.
  B. How Do Acids and Bases Differ?
    1. A substance that releases hydrogen ions (H^+) in solution is an *acid*—for example, HCl.
    2. Substances that release ions such as (OH^-) are called *bases*.
  C. Buffers against Shifts in pH
    1. Buffers are chemicals, often weak acids or bases and its salt, that help keep the pH of a solution stable.
    2. Buffer molecules act by combining with, or releasing, H^+ to prevent changes in pH.
    3. Bicarbonate is one of the body's major buffers.

Suggestions for Presenting the Material

♦ First and foremost the instructor must consider that the abstract nature of Chemistry and the associated terminology are tremendous obstacles to learning. This is highly intimidating—especially to nonscience majors. While the chapter materials are considered elementary and certainly critical to the topic of biology, care must be taken in developing a well grounded presentation. As this topic most often comes early in the semester, take care to ensure students are not overly discouraged if they struggle.

♦ The extensive use of examples of common chemical compounds and their properties will help provide context.

♦ Use common examples and references highlighted throughout the text, for example: isotopes, electron excitation, bonding, buffers, and water, to stress the importance of reading.

♦ Use and have students reference in class the numerous diagrams and illustrations in the text.

♦ Use of the ball-and-stick models (see the Enrichment section below) is very helpful. Larger examples can be made using inexpensive materials like tennis balls and dowels. This is especially effective when illustrating properties of polar molecules in a large lecture hall.

♦ Stress the foundational nature of the material and its importance in biology.

♦ Play the animation of Figure 2.11, which illustrates the ionic pull of polar water molecules as an example of water's solvent properties. Refer students back to this as a review tool.

♦ Figure 2.14 provides an excellent reference for explaining acid, base, and pH scale. Note particularly the pH values of common household products. Emphasize that acids and bases are not necessarily terms that describe *corrosive* substances!

♦ The properties of water are important to life on Earth. Describe the polarity of water molecules; then proceed to the influence that water molecules have on cells and cellular environments.

♦ **Common Student Misconceptions:**

  o Students misunderstand and get confused when discussing atomic structures. Quiz students on the basic terms to prod them to commit these to memory.

Classroom and Laboratory Enrichment

♦ Students are often intimidated by chemistry, especially if they lack sufficient high school background in this area or if they have been out of school for several years. The more you ground your presentations using everyday examples the more comfortable your students will be. When possible, emphasize the biological significance of chemistry. Give students frequent opportunities to use new terms. Use illustrations or diagrams, pause often, and interject questions to gauge their level of understanding.

♦ Most undergraduates have trouble visualizing abstract items such as atoms and molecules. To help them visualize atoms and molecules, use ball-and-stick models that are very large and easy to see. Models help students understand the size relationships among molecules. Overhead transparencies of ball-and-stick models are especially useful when covering the larger carbon compounds.

♦ Reinforce chemical bonding patterns through the use of common examples. Present sketches or illustrations of each type. Use a pair-share activity to have students identify chemical bonding types with classmates.

♦ Simple ball-and-stick models are also useful for demonstrating the hydrogen bonding that occurs between water molecules and the latticework structure of ice.

♦ Fill a large jar with water, then add salad oil. Shake the bottle, then allow it to sit on the front desk. Ask students to explain what has happened. Add a few drops of methylene blue (a polar dye) and sudan III fat stain (a nonpolar dye) to the jar and shake. Students will see that the water layer is blue and the oil layer is red; ask them to speculate about how this occurs.

♦ Draw a pH scale on the board (or use an overhead transparency of Figure 2.14), and discuss pH values of familiar substances. Use examples of pH in nature, their own bodies, or food.

♦ If your class is small, demonstrate the use of a pH meter. For larger groups or in lab, pH paper can be used to give each student a chance to quickly determine the pH of sample solutions.

♦ If you are teaching in a room with a periodic table of the elements hanging on the wall, point out the major elements, or use an overhead transparency to show the same items. Relate subatomic particles with the atomic number and mass.

♦ Prepare a glass of iced tea (instant mix) with added sugar and lemon. Which ingredients are compounds? What are the components of the mixture?

♦ Bring a package of buffered and regular aspirin to class. Ask students to investigate the difference(s) in ingredients.

♦ Using the names of the active ingredients on an antacid package, explain how they act as *buffers* to stomach acid.

Mercury Rising (revisited)

♦ Have students estimate how much mercury they consume by analyzing their diet.

♦ What body systems does mercury most impact?

♦ Why is mercury so harmful to the developing brain?

- Beyond Chinese coal-fired energy plants, investigate the other major contributors to mercury emissions.

- Are there other chemical substance that humans are responsible to releasing at high levels that could be toxic? Have the students split into groups and investigate this.

Additional Ideas for Classroom Discussion

- Show diagrams of subatomic particles, atoms, and molecules to student groups. Have them identify what they are and what their properties are.

- Form small groups and have them discuss chemical bonding types. One at a time, call on individual groups and have them explain one type to the whole class.

- Show a copy of a soft drink ingredient label to the class. Have them explain why soft drinks have such a low pH. What ingredient is responsible for this low pH?

- What is acid precipitation? What chemical reaction is responsible for the mildly acidic pH of normal rainwater? What chemicals are responsible for acid precipitation?

- Discuss with the class why water is so critical to life. Assess student understanding of the properties of water by using an open-ended question-and-answer format. Have students explain what is meant by water being the "universal solvent" for Earth.

- What would happen to fish and other aquatic organisms in temperate climates if water sank when it froze instead of floated?

- What is the difference between the composition of a molecule of a substance and an atom of that substance?

- If atoms are beyond the reach of visualization even by electron microscopes, how do we know so much about their structure?

- Some pain relievers are advertised as "tribuffered." What is meant by this statement? Do you think it is an important advantage or just a sales gimmick?

- Television commercials portray the "acid stomach" as needing immediate R-O-L-A-I-D-S. Is the stomach *normally* acidic? Have students find the pH of stomach acids (gastric fluids) on the chart Figure 2.14. How do you know when there is too much acid down there?

How Would You Vote? Classroom Discussion Ideas

- Monitor the voting for the online question. Ask students to justify their answer, considering topics such as corporate responsibility, consumer education, and relative risk.

- Have students investigate other chemical contaminants in food, and how these are handled by different manufactures.

Term Paper Topics, Library Activities, and Special Projects

- From the InfoTrac® College Edition site, have students search for and download an article on elements (atoms) or biomolecules. Have them summarize the article and give a short presentation in lab or prepare a short paper summarizing the information.

- Have students investigate and prepare a short paper on common elements used in food additives for humans, livestock, or plant fertilizers.

- Why are the cells lining the stomach able to withstand pH ranges between one and three?

- Have students investigate and explain the functional relationship between acids and bases. What are the homeostatic mechanisms that help the human body regulate blood pH? Also, how does the body measure blood pH?

- Discuss strategies currently being considered by the United States and other nations to remedy acid rain. What suggestions would you make to help solve this problem?

- Describe some of the roles played by ions in the human body.

- Many elements have radioactive isotopes that are useful as tracers in biological systems. Show how $^{14}CO_2$ can be used to follow the fate of carbon as it is incorporated into carbohydrate.

- The structure of atoms can be deduced using nuclear magnetic resonance (NMR) and mass spectrometer machines. Have students prepare a short report on each of these instruments.

- Using a pH meter or test paper, examine the degree of acidity/alkalinity of common household products. If the substance is not a liquid, mix it with water according to package directions before testing.

- Most of the content of human blood is water. However, synthetic blood has been made and tested. What is the base in this fluid? Is it a feasible substitute? Report on its advantages and disadvantages.

Responses to *Data Analysis Activities*

1. Approximately 2200 tons of mercury were released world-wide in 2006.

2. Fossil fuel combustion was responsible for the largest fraction of mercury released. Artisanal and small-scale gold production was second on the list.

3. Asia emits the largest volume of mercury from producing cement.

4. Gold production in South America released just over 100 tons of mercury.

Possible Responses to *Critical Thinking* Questions

1. Medieval alchemists understood the transformative processes of heat and other simple chemical reactions but lacked a fundamental understanding of matter at the atomic level. Specifically, they were attempting to remove protons from lead (Pb) to create gold (Au), a process that would be incredibly difficult and require massive quantities of energy as lead represents a particularly stable element.

2. The shell model for an uncharged nitrogen atom would have two electrons in the first orbital, and five electrons in the second orbital.

3. If 210Po emits an alpha particle, it is losing two protons. Given that Po contains 82 protons, and investigation of the periodic table finds that the element with two less protons is Pb (lead).

4. Lab workers are told to wipe off splashes with a towel before washing as in undiluted form, the acid may not appreciable damage to the exposed surface. However, exposure to water can increase the corrosive nature of the acid to the point where it will significantly degrade the surface it is exposed to.

3

MOLECULES OF LIFE

Chapter Outline

Objectives

1. Understand how cells make and modify the structure and how the presence/absence of functional groups are related to a molecules function. Recognize and identify the six common functional groups in biological molecules and know the properties they confer when attached to organic molecules.
2. Understand the basic structure of carbohydrates, and recognize their roles as energy reservoirs and structural materials.
3. Recognize the diverse roles of lipids and their unifying hydrophobicity.
4. Understand the basic structure of proteins and why their complex structure is so important to their function.
5. Recognize and understand the special role that nucleotides and nucleic acids play in cellular operations, coding, and transfer of genetic information.

Key Terms

organic	condensation	phospholipid	denature
hydrocarbon	hydrolysis	wax	prion
functional group	carbohydrates	steroids	nucleotides
monomers	lipids	proteins	RNA
polymers	fatty acids	amino acids	DNA
metabolism	fats	peptide bond	
enzymes	triclyceride	polypeptide	

Lecture Outline

3.1   Fear of Frying

    A. The average American diet not only contains a large amount of fat, but more dangerously a large amount of trans fats.

    B. Trans fats have been associated with high cholesterol levels and hardening of the arteries.

3.2   Molecules of Life—From Structure to Function

    A. The Molecules of Life are organic compounds that contain carbon and at least one hydrogen atom. Most have one or more functional group covalently bonded to carbon atoms, which form the backbone of most organic compounds. Familiar examples include: carbohydrates, fats, proteins, and nucleic acids—molecules used for energy, structural materials, metabolic workers, and carriers of genetic information.

    B. Functional Groups

        1. Atoms or clusters of atoms that covalently bond to carbon in organic molecules.

        2. The number, kind, and arrangement of these groups give rise to specific properties such as polarity and acidity.

    D. What Cells Do to Organic Compounds

        1. Metabolism is a term that refers to activities where cells acquire and use energy to stay alive, grow, and reproduce. Inside cells, organic molecules are constructed, split, or re-arranged to form new organic compounds. There are five common classes of reactions that involve organic molecules. Refer to Table 3.1.

        2. Most metabolic reactions require enzymes (specialized proteins) that speed up these chemical reactions.

        3. Condensation and hydrolysis are two common metabolic activities. In condensation, two molecules covalently bond to form a larger one. Enzymes remove an –OH group from one and an H from another to expose bonding sites. Water forms as a by-product of this reaction. Hydrolysis is the reverse reaction; large molecules are split by the action of enzymes and the addition of H and –OH from water molecules.

3.3   Carbohydrates

    A. Carbohydrates are used for structural materials and energy. Most consist of C, H, and O in a 1:2:1 ratio

    B. Simple Sugars

        1. Single sugar unit monosaccharides are the simplest carbohydrates.

        2. Most are water soluble, easily transported in fluids, and taste sweet.

        3. Simple sugars, like glucose, are used by cells for energy and as a structural building block.

        4. Other sugars are part of the nucleotide monomers of RNA and DNA.

C. Short Chain Carbohydrates
   1. Oligosaccharides are covalently bonded short chains of sugar monomers.
   2. Examples include our table sugar, a disaccharide called sucrose, and the lactose sugar found in milk. Oligosaccharides are often bonded to lipids or proteins that have roles in cell membrane functions and immunity.

D. Complex Carbohydrates
   1. Called polysaccharides, straight or branched chains of many (often hundreds or thousands) sugar monomers of the same or different types covalently linked together.
   2. Common polysaccharides made from glucose monomers covalently bonded together in different ways include starch, cellulose, and glycogen.
      a. Plants store glucose in large spiral-shaped, hydrophobic molecules called starch. Hydrolysis breaks these molecules down when sugar is needed.
      b. Cellulose, tightly bundled chains of glucose produced in plants, used to form structural elements in cell walls.
      c. Glycogen is a stored form of glucose common in animal tissues.
      d. Chitin, a polysaccharide modified with nitrogen-containing groups, strengthens the exoskeleton in many animals like crabs and insects. In most fungi, chitin reinforces the cell wall.

3.4   Lipids
   A. Lipids function as the body's main energy reserve as well as form structural materials in locations like cell membranes. Lipids are fatty, oily, or waxy organic compounds that are insoluble in water – hydrophobic
      1. Fats can be saturated, with only single carbon-to-carbon bonds, or unsaturated with double carbon-to-carbon bonds.
      2. Unsaturated fats may be cis or trans depending on the arrangement of hydrogens on either side of the double bond.

   B. Fats
      1. Fats, or triglycerides, have three fatty acid tails linked to a glycerol and include examples such as butter and vegetable oils.
      2. Triglycerides are the most abundant energy source in vertebrates, stored in adipose (fat) tissue that insulates and cushions parts of the body.
      3. At 9 kcal/gram, fats contain more than twice the energy of carbohydrates.
      4. Saturated fats have fatty acid tails with carbon backbones that have only single covalent bonds. This permits the fatty acid tails to pack together tightly, allowing animal fats to remain solid at room temperature.
      5. Fatty acid tails in unsaturated fats have one or more double covalent bonds, making the tails more rigid and preventing them from packing together tightly. Most vegetable oils are unsaturated and remain liquid at room temperature.

   C. Phospholipids
      1. Phospholipids are fats in which one fatty acid has been replaced with a phosphate group.
      2. These partly hydrophobic, partly hydrophilic molecules are found in cell membranes.

   D. Waxes
      1. Waxes are fats with long fatty acids bound to long-chain alcohols or carbon rings.

   E. Steroids
      1. Steroids are lipids with four carbon rings and no fatty acid tails.
      2. Cholesterol is the most common type of sterol in animal tissues.
      3. Sterols form the basis for diverse molecules like bile salts and hormones. Estrogen and testosterone are two familiar examples.

3.5   Proteins—Diversity in Structure and Function.

    A. Proteins are large biological molecules that are very diverse in form and function. Proteins are used as structural elements and as enzymes, and help move materials around and in communication between cells.

    B. Amino Acids

        1. Amino acids are small organic compounds with an amino group ($-NH_3^+$), a carboxyl group ($-COO^-$, the acid), a hydrogen atom, and one or more atoms of an R group. In most cases, these components are all attached to the same carbon atom (remember the carbon can form up to four covalent bonds).

        2. The R group represents the variable portion of the 20 different amino acids. In simple amino acids the R group is a single hydrogen atom, while in complex amino acids it consists of one or more carbon atoms with various functional groups attached.

    B. Building Proteins

        1. Proteins are build via the formation of a peptide bond between amino acids.

        2. A protein may be build of hundreds or thousands of amino acids.

    C. Protein Structure

        1. Each protein is made from a unique sequence of amino acids. This is called its primary structure. Amino acids are joined together using a type of covalent bond called a peptide bond.

        2. Secondary structure results from twists, bends, loops, and folds in the primary structure. While primary protein structures are unique, there are common patterns of coils, sheets, and loops that occur in most proteins.

        3. Tertiary structures represent "domains," parts of a protein that are organized as structurally-stable units. Domains are a compact section of a protein that result from coils, loops, or sheets that fold up.

        4. A quaternary structure results from two or more polypeptide chains that bond together or are closely associated with one another.

        5. A protein's structure is often further modified by the action of enzymes that attach short, linear, or branched oligosaccharides to new polypeptide chains, creating large molecules called glycoproteins. Other molecules like lipids also get attached to many proteins, further modifying their structure.

3.6   The Importance of Protein Structure

    A. Proteins Undone—Denaturation

        1. Protein shapes define (dictates) its biological activity. Therefore, proteins function as long as they maintain their complex shapes. Heat, shifts in pH, salts, and detergents may all act to disrupt bonding patterns and alter a protein's shape.

        2. Denaturing is the process by which bonding patterns are broken, altering the secondary, tertiary, or quaternary shape of the protein.

        3. Denaturing causes the protein to loose its function and is often irreversible.

    B. Prions

        1. Prions are proteins that induce spontaneous denaturation in other similar proteins.

        2. These proteins can be shared by consumption of infected tissue.

3.7   Nucleic Acids

    A. Nucleotides are small organic molecules that function as energy carriers, enzyme helpers, andmessengers.

        1. Nucleotides are composed of one sugar, at least one phosphate group, and one nitrogen-containing base. These organic molecules vary from one another based on the type, number, and orientation of these components.

2. DNA (deoxyribonucleic acid) is a double stranded polymer comprised of four different nucleotide monomers (adenine, guanine, thymine, and cytosine). DNA encodes the genetic information for all living things based on the sequence of the nucleotide monomers.

3. RNA (ribonucleic acid) is similar to DNA. Most RNA, however is comprised of a single stranded polymer of four nucleotide monomers (uracil instead of thymine). RNA is involved in the conversion of the genetic code in DNA to create proteins.

Suggestions for Presenting the Material

♦ It is critical to remember that molecules are a completely abstract notion for most undergraduates, certainly for non-science majors. It is vital to place biological molecules in a familiar context for students to understand the key concepts in this chapter.

♦ Students are familiar with carbohydrates, proteins, and fats from their diets and have heard about DNA. Their lives are filled with personal interactions with biomolecules. Build on this basic framework of knowledge to generate interest in how these molecules are constructed and interact. Keep in mind that human nutrition is covered in-depth in Chapter 36.

♦ Use, and have students review, the digital animations available in the electronic textbook supplements to help them visualize these abstract concepts. Find a 3-D protein animation on the web; this helps students understand the significance of molecular shape.

♦ We each have differing requirements for students to learn about molecular structure. At a minimum, students should comprehend the significance of a molecule's shape and how that dictates function. The critical role of shape in proteins allows for numerous illustrations of this key concept.

♦ Students should understand that atoms (like C, H, and O that make up a bulk of organic molecules) have their own distinct properties (such as chemical bonding patterns) that contribute to molecular form and function. This builds on knowledge transfer skills students have by reinforcing materials from Chapter 1 and 2.

♦ Asking students to be able to recognize (draw or construct in lab) the basic molecular shapes of biomolecules reinforces their understanding of shape dictating function.

♦ Grounding the role of functional groups in metabolic reactions helps students comprehend how biomolecules interact. Stress the importance of functional groups' locations on a molecule that give it certain properties.

♦ As shown in Figure 3.5, use an overhead transparency or series of PowerPoint slides to demonstrate condensation and hydrolysis reactions to illustrate how cells construct/de-construct larger molecules.

♦ Stress the key role of monomer units in constructing carbohydrates, proteins, and nucleic acids. Lipids are difficult, and you may choose to define this group based on solubility or perhaps functional role.

♦ Denaturing and its irreversibility are illustrated in the lab using a fried egg white.

♦ Introduce the importance of genetic coding and the impact of mutations on the construction of biological molecules.

♦ You may choose to enhance the presentation of this information from a nutritional standpoint by including information on water, vitamins, and minerals discussed later in the text (Ch 36).

- **Common Student Misconceptions:**
  - o Students are very anxious about the abstract nature of chemistry and molecules. Continue to reinforce and ground students with molecules they are already familiar with from their diets.

Classroom and Laboratory Enrichment

- Show the six individual animations provided during class and/or laboratory sessions to help students visualize the key concepts presented in the chapter.

- Using a "think-pair-share" exercise in lecture (or group exercise in lab), have your students interpret a nutritional label on a food item (something simple like a candy bar or can of soda). Have students identify and quantify the amount of biomolecule in the product by category. Have them relate calories to energy discussed in Chapter 2.

- In lab groups, have students use basic ball-and-stick chemistry models to build a carbohydrate monomer and discuss in larger groups how the monomers would be joined to form larger polymers.

- In similar exercises, have lab groups construct a sterol, amino acid, and nucleic acid. You can have lab groups collaborate and speculate about how the structure relates to function.

- To assess student learning, have students (or lab groups) construct structures of the macromolecules as illustrated throughout this chapter.

- A simple, inexpensive way to illustrate the levels of protein structure in a lecture format is to use foam swim tubes, colored duct tape, and large stick-on Velcro patches. The straight foam swim tubes can be wrapped at intervals in colored duct tape to represent the differing sequence of amino acids, illustrating a protein's primary structure. Using several foam tubes of different colors, with strategically placed stick-on Velcro patches, you can quickly illustrate secondary, tertiary, and quaternary protein structures.

- In lab using a DNA double helix model (or in lecture using an unlabeled overhead of this structure), ask students to identify the building blocks for nucleic acids, describe the bonding patterns between and across the molecule, and summarize how these biomolecules "capture" genetic information.

- In class, pair students and ask them to make comparisons and describe contrasts between DNA and RNA molecules.

Fear of Frying (revisited)

- Challenge students to find trans fats in natural foods.
- Have students investigate those foods that are rich in trans fats.
- Have students analyze their own diets to determine how much trans fats they are consuming each day. Additionally, find out how many foods that may contain trans fats below the federally mandated listing rule that they are consuming.

Additional Ideas for Classroom Discussion

- Compare the caloric values for carbohydrates, fats, and proteins. Discuss what a calorie is. In pairs or small groups, have students discuss/speculate about why the caloric value differs for these categories of molecules.

- Discuss what is meant by solubility. What happens at the molecular level when a substance dissolves in water? Challenge students to think about why some fats are soluble and others are not. For an extended discussion you may ask students to speculate about the role of saturated and unsaturated fats in our diets.

- Why are sugars controversial as a component of our diets? Discuss the trend toward and motivation for removal of soda and candy vending machines in schools and public buildings.

- Discuss how plants and animals acquire and store carbohydrates. How are these molecules modified for use as structural components?

- Obtain the nutritional information for a popular fast-food sandwich. Present the biological molecule breakdown to the class. Have the students calculate the energy yield for each and speculate about the fate of these molecules in their bodies.

- Have students speculate why malnutrition influences the fate of biomolecules at the cellular level. What chemical reactions take place to bring molecules out of storage or to modify larger molecules?

- Have students discuss the special properties of carbon that enhance its capacity to interact with other organic compounds.

- In a pair-share format, ask students to explain the common features of amino acids and proteins. To expand the exercise, include nucleotides.

- In a pair-share format, ask students to explain to one another what makes a complex carbohydrate complex. To expand the exercise, include a short list of terms on an overhead that students must define for one another.

- Using small groups, ask students to explain what is meant by the term "functional group." To expand this exercise, use acetate overheads; one by one, present pictures of functional groups and have students identify them and explain their properties.

- Biomolecules in the News! Each day newspapers and popular magazines have articles (or advertisements) that describe (or make claims about) scientific findings related to biological molecules. Have student groups search newspapers or magazines for articles that discuss this topic. Using a small group discussion format, have students apply their understanding of biomolecules to the major point(s) addressed in the article.

- What is a steroid? What effect do they have on our bodies? Why are steroids such an important issue in both amateur and professional sports?

- Using illustrations from the book, discuss the similarities and differences in the way living organisms make use of specific biomolecules. For example, have students speculate on the presence/abundance of phospholipids in cell membranes in plants, or on the differences between terrestrial and aquatic organisms.

How Would You Vote? Classroom Discussion Ideas

- Monitor the voting for the online questions. Ask your students to present their reasons for having trans fats (hydrogenated vegetable oils) banned from all foods.

- Ask students to form groups and form lists both Pro and Con for the use of trans fats in foods.

- Is it the responsibility of food manufacturers to produce healthy foods, or simply to make obvious on their packaging the presence of potential health hazards? Have students debate this controversial topic.

Term Paper Topics, Library Activities, and Special Projects

- Discuss the scientific basis for the use of LDL and HDL measurements of cholesterol obtained in blood samples as predictors of health.

- Investigate why termites are able to digest plant-produced compounds like cellulose and humans are not.

- Describe the development and use of artificial fats in popular snack foods. Investigate the Food and Drug Administration's recommendation for the use of these artificial fats in our diets.

- Research and describe the trend toward banning of trans-fat at fast food restaurants. How are such bans being sold to the public? Are they effective?

- Interview a range of athletes and determine the range of biomolecule intake compared to your own. How do you compare? What types of nutritional supplements are they taking and why?

- Search a range of health or bodybuilding magazines for diet supplement advertising. What claims are being made? Have scientific studies been conducted to support the claims?

- Why do women typically have a higher percentage of body fat than men? What adaptive value does this serve?

- Visit a local art museum and complete a report on plant fibers used in art, clothing, and other textiles on display.

- Investigate how artificial sweeteners work. Why are they so much sweeter than natural sugars? Research the history of their development and investigate how many types are available at a local grocery store. What types of products do you find artificial sweeteners in?

Responses to *Data Analysis Activities*

1. LDL levels were highest in the group consuming saturated fat.
2. HDL was lowest in the group consuming trans fatty acids.
3. The trans fatty acid group had the highest LDL to HDL ratio.
4. With regard to their impact on heart disease, the ranking of diets from best to worst would be cis fatty acids, saturated fats, and lastly trans fatty acids.

Possible Responses to *Critical Thinking* Questions

1. Normally, a person's exposure to chlorine atoms from sucralose is very small. Only 7 percent of the sucralose molecules (each containing three chlorine atoms) are digested, the vast majority passing through the body without being metabolized. As sucralose is 600 times sweeter than natural table sugar, only very small amounts get used in food products, greatly reducing the exposure levels. While chlorine (a gas element of the halogen group) is toxic when combined in certain organic molecules (like pesticides), sucralose has been scientifically tested and approved by the Food and Drug Administration (FDA) for use in food and drink products. In fact, we consume chlorine every day in salt and in the water we drink. Over 100 scientific studies have shown the safety of using this artificial sweetener. As a result, the FDA does not require any warning label.

4

CELL STRUCTURE AND FUNCTION

Chapter Outline

Objectives

1. Understand the essential structure and function of the cell, and that cells are the smallest unit of life.
3. Recognize how microscopes are used to reveal cell structure.
4. Understand the basic structure and function of cell membranes.
4. Recognize the basic features of the simplest cells; the bacteria and the archaea.
5. Describe the features of eukaryote cells with respect to structure and function.

Key Terms

cell	plasmids	central vacuole	centriole
plasma membrane	nucleoid	lysosomes	basal body
cytoplasm	flagella	peroxisomes	extracellular matrix,
organelles	pili	Golgi body	ECM
nucleus	cell wall	mitochondrion	cuticle
surface-to-volume	biofilm	plastids	primary wall
ratio	nuclear envelope	chloroplasts	secondary wall
cell theory	nucleoplasm	cytoskeleton	lignin
lipid bilayer	nucleolus	microtubules	cell junctions
fluid mosaic	endomembrane	microfilaments	tight junctions
adhesion proteins	system	cell cortex	adhering junctions
recognition proteins	endoplasmic	intermediate	gap junctions
receptor proteins	reticulum, ER	filaments	plasmodesmata
transport proteins	vesicles	motor proteins	
ribosomes	vacuoles	cilia	

Lecture Outline

4.1   Food for Thought

   A. Bacteria are Prolific

   B. Generally Harmless, Exceptions Exist

      1. The E. coli strain O157:H7 can cause serious infection, potentially leading to death, in humans following ingestion.

      2. O157:H7 is sticky, making it difficult to remove once present.

4.2   What Is a Cell?

   A. Traits Common to All Cells

      1. The cell is the smallest unit with the properties of life: metabolism, response to environment, growth, and reproduction.

      2. All cells have three features in common:

         a. A plasma membrane separates each cell from the environment, regulates the flow of molecules across the membrane, and contains receptors that can affect the cell's activities.

         b. A nucleus or nucleoid region localizes the DNA, which can be copied and read.

         c. The cytoplasm contains membrane systems, particles (including ribosomes), filaments (the cytoskeleton), and a semifluid substance.

   B. Constraints of Cell Size

      1. Cell size is constrained by the surface-to-volume ratio.

         a. As a cell expands in diameter, its volume will increase more rapidly than its surface area will.

         b. A cell that is too large will not be able to move materials into and out of the cell interior fast enough to keep the cell alive.

      2. Surface to volume constraints influence the body plans of multicellular species.

C. Cell Theory
   1. The cell theory has four generalizations:
      a. All organisms are composed of one or more cells;
      b. The cell is the structural and functional unit of all organisms;
      c. All cells come from the division of previously existing cells; and
      d. Cells contain hereditary material, passed to offspring during division.

4.3 Spying on Cells
A. Microscopes Allow us to View Cells in Detail
   1. Light microscopes still rely on visible light and an arrangement of glass lenses to focus and magnify images.
B. Modern Microscopes
   1. Fluorescence microscopes use focused laser energy to help capture light emitted by cells or molecules in samples.
   2. Electron microscopes use electrons instead of visible light to illuminate samples. They achieve magnifications many thousands of times greater to see the fine detail in cell structure, as small as 0.2 nanometers in size.

4.4 Membrane Structure and Function
A. Fluid Mosaic Model
   1. Phospholipids are the most abundant components of the cell membrane.
      a. Each molecule has a phosphate-containing head and two fatty acids attached to a glycerol backbone.
      b. The head is hydrophilic and the tails are hydrophobic, causing phospholipids to spontaneously form a lipid bilayer when exposed to an aqueous environment.
   2. The fluid mosaic model describes a cell membrane of mixed composition.
      a. The *mosaic* refers to the mixed composition of the membrane, consisting of phospholipids, sterols, proteins, and other components.
      b. The *fluid* part of the model refers to the behavior of the phospholipids in a living cell's membrane.
B. Membrane Proteins
   1. Membrane proteins can:
      a. Fasten cells together (adhesion proteins);
      b. Serve as identity tags (recognition proteins);
      c. Bind substances outside the cell (receptor proteins); and
      d. Move substances across membranes (transport proteins).
C. Variations on the Model
   1. In addition to differences in composition, membranes differ in fluidity. In some cases proteins drift through a bilayer, in others they may stay put.

4.5 Introducing Bacteria and Archaeans
A. Prokaryotes Lack a Nucleus
   1. This antiquated term includes both bacteria and archaea.
B. Bacteria and Archaea: Different yet Similar
   1. The two types are similar in outward appearance and size but differ in their structure and metabolic details.
      a. Most are not much wider than a micrometer and a few micrometers long.
      b. Internal structure comes from protein filaments that act as scaffolding.
      c. A single, circular protein is found in a region termed the nucleoid.
      d. A rigid but porous cell wall surrounds the cell of nearly all prokaryotes.

    e. Sticky polysaccharides form an outer capsule, which helps cells attach to surfaces and aides in protection.

    f. Prokaryotes may have one or more slender flagella for motion.

    g. Pili are outer protein filaments that help some bacterial species cling to surfaces.

C. Biofilms

  1. These arrangements are communal groups called biofilms, which may include bacteria, fungi, protists, as well as other microbes.

  2. Biofilm communities are interdependent and organized into neighborhoods with distinct microenvironments.

  3. Some members form scaffolding for others; those at the edges often divide and expand the biofilms. Wherever there is water there are biofilm communities.

4.6   Introducing Eukaryotic Cells

A. Eukaryotic have a Nucleus

  1. Eukaryote translates as "true kernel," taken to refer to the nucleus.

  2. The nucleus is one type of specialized organelle found inside a eukaryote cell.

B. Organelles are the Sites of Metabolism

  1. Substances shuttle from one organelle to another; for example, new polypeptides move from the ribosomes through the ER, on to the Golgi bodies, and eventually to the plasma membrane for export.

  2. Table 4.2 lists the common components found in eukaryotic cells.

4.7   The Nucleus

A. The Nucleus Protects the DNA

    a. The nuclear envelope consists of a double lipid bilayer that is continuous with the membrane of another organelle called the ER.

    b. The nuclear membrane surface contains receptors, pores, and transporters that span the lipid bilayers, controlling the movement of materials in and out of the nucleus.

    c. The nuclear envelope encloses a semifluid matrix called nucleoplasm. In this matrix is the nucleolus, a region where ribosome subunits are assembled.

4.8   The Endomembrane System

A. Endoplasmic Reticulum

  1. The endoplasmic reticulum (ER) is an extension of the nuclear envelope containing interconnected tubes and flattened sacs.

  2. The ER is the site where many new polypeptide chains are modified.

  3. There are two types named for their appearance, distinguished by the presence or absence of ribosomes.

    a. *Rough ER* consists of stacked, flattened sacs with many ribosomes attached; oligosaccharide groups are attached to polypeptides as they pass through on their way to other organelles or to secretory vesicles.

    b. *Smooth ER* has no ribosomes; it is the area from which vesicles carrying proteins and lipids are budded; and it also inactivates harmful chemicals.

B. A Variety of Vesicles

  1. The Endomembrane system includes a range of vesicle types.

    a. Endocytic kinds form as a patch of plasma membrane that sinks into the cytoplasm.

    b. Exocytic kinds bud from the ER or Golgi membranes and transport materials to the plasma membrane for export.

  2. The *central vacuole* of mature plant cells accumulates a watery solution of ions, amino acids, sugars, and toxic substances.

Cell Structure and Function   **27**

3. *Lysosomes* are vesicles that bud from Golgi bodies; they carry powerful enzymes that can digest the contents of other vesicles, worn-out cell parts, or bacteria and foreign particles.

4. *Peroxisomes* are vesicles containing enzymes that break down fatty acids and amino acids; the hydrogen peroxide released is degraded by another enzyme.

C. Golgi Bodies

1. Many vesicles fuse with and empty their contents into Golgi bodies.

2. Membranes of the Golgi are arranged in stacks of flattened sacs.

a. Inside, proteins and lipids undergo final processing, sorting, and packaging.

b. The finished products are sorted and packaged into new vesicles for transport.

4.9 Mitochondria and Plastids

A. Mitochondria

1. Specialized organelle for aerobic respiration, the metabolic pathway that produces many ATP from organic molecules.

2. Each mitochondrion has two membranes, an inner folded membrane (cristae) surrounded by a smooth outer membrane.

3. Inner and outer compartments formed by the membranes are important in the flow of ions and energy transformations.

B. Chloroplasts and Other Plastids

1. Chloroplasts are oval or disk-shaped plastids, bounded by a double membrane and central to the process of photosynthesis.

a. The two outer membranes enclose a semifluid interior called the stroma.

b. A third, called the thylakoid membrane, is folded in a continuous compartment inside the stroma.

c. In the stacked disks (thylakoids), pigments and enzymes trap sunlight energy to form ATP and NADPH.

d. Sugars are formed in the fluid substance (stroma) surrounding the stacks.

e. Pigments such as chlorophyll (green) confer distinctive colors to the chloroplasts.

2. Chloroplasts share many traits with photosynthetic bacteria. Like mitochondria, they may have evolved from bacteria that invaded a host cell. They have their own DNA and some ribosomes, which points to the possibility that they were once independent entities.

3. Other plastids include chromoplasts that store pigments, and amyloplasts that store starch.

4.10 The Dynamic Cytoskeleton

A. Components of the Cytoskeleton

1. The cytoskeleton is an interconnected system of fibers, threads, and lattices that extends between the nucleus and the plasma membrane in eukaryotic cells.

2. It gives cells their internal organization, overall shape, and capacity to move.

3. Some elements are transient, such as the "spindle" microtubules used in chromosome movement during cell division; others are permanent, such as filaments operational in muscle contraction.

4. The main components are microtubules, microfilaments, and intermediate filaments—all assembled from protein subunits.

a. Microtubules are long, hollow cylinders of the protein tubulin; they are responsible for the movement of chromosomes during cell division.

b. Microfilaments strengthen or change the shape of certain animal cells. Crosslinked, bundled, and gel-like microfilaments make up the cell cortex, which is a reinforcing mesh under the plasma membrane.

c. Intermediate filaments, the most stable of the cytoskeleton elements, occur only in animal cells of specific tissues.

5. All eukaryotic cells have similar microtubules and microfilaments. Both elements play a range of roles in the cells by interacting with accessory proteins, like motor proteins that that help move cell parts.

B. Cilia, Flagella, and False Feet
   1. Eukaryotic flagella and cilia are comprised of organized arrays of microtubules.
      a. These structures function in cell movement, like sperm.
      b. Flagella are quite long, not usually numerous, and are found on one-celled protistans and animal sperm cells.
      c. Microtubular extensions of the plasma membrane have a 9 + 2 cross-sectional array that arises from a centriole and are useful in propulsion.
   2. Pseudopods are temporary lobes that project from the cell, used in locomotion and food capture.

4.11 Cell Surface Specializations

A. Matrixes Between and Around Cells
   1. In most multicellular organisms, the cells are surrounded and organized by an extracellular matrix. This nonliving matrix of substances is secreted by cells and varies by the type of tissue. It functions in support, anchors cells, separates tissues, and functions in cell signaling.
   2. Primary cell walls are a type of extracellular matrix. In plants it is made of cellulose, and in fungi it is made of chitin.
   3. For example, cartilage consists of scattered cells and collagen embedded in a "ground substance" of modified polysaccharides; bone is similarly constructed.

B. Cell Junctions
   1. Cells enclosed by cell walls or other cell secretions maintain the capacity to communicate with other cells and their surroundings. In multicellular species this interaction occurs via cell junctions that connect one cell to another.
   2. Animal cells display three types of junctions.
      a. *Tight junctions* occur between cells of epithelial tissues in which cytoskeletal strands of one cell fuse with strands of neighboring cells causing an effective seal.
      b. *Adhering junctions* are like spot welds at the plasma membranes of two adjacent cells that need to be held together during stretching, as in the skin and heart.
      c. *Gap junctions* are small, open channels that directly link the cytoplasm of adjacent cells.
   3. In plants, tiny channels called plasmodesmata cross the adjacent primary walls and connect the cytoplasm.

4.12 A Visual Summary of Eukaryotic Cell Components

   [Diagrams with descriptions of typical organelles of plant and animal cells]

4.13 The Nature of Life
   A. Cells Reflect Life
      1. The properties of cells are representative of the properties of all living things.
      2. Collectively, these differentiate life from non-living things.

Suggestions for Presenting the Material

   ♦ The information in this chapter presents an opportunity for students to reflect on the organization in nature, and the role of specific roles of macromolecules.

- Stress the foundational nature of understanding what cells are and how they function as the basis for higher levels of organization in eukaryotes. This material represents a wonderful introduction to the concept of form fitting function in the living world.

- Don't assume students know, or remember, the definitions of *hydrophilic* and *hydrophobic*.

- Using the animation for Figure 4.4 stress the significance of the surface to volume ratio and the relevance to membrane function.

- Find and use several micrograph examples to highlight the complexity of cells; even at such small scales, students often believe that as you scale down you also lose the capacity for complex structures. The animation of Figure 4.7 provides a springboard for this discussion.

- Use demonstrations of a mosaic artwork to illustrate the cell membrane structure. The animation of Figure 4.8 brings this material to life.

- This is also an excellent time to review the use of the word *theory* as explained in Chapter 1.

- A clear distinction between prokaryotic and eukaryotic cells should be made (see the Enrichment section below for visual aid suggestion).

- Reinforce that the prokaryotic world is highly diverse and fills many unique and vital ecological roles. Section 4.5.C on biofilms helps students visualize some of these roles.

- Students have great difficulty keeping cell organelles straight. Have students keep Table 4.2 handy for reference. Make use of each animation to put the organelles in context.

- Although the descriptions and diagrams of the cell organelles occupy only a small number of textbook pages, it is best to proceed carefully and deliberately. There is a dizzying array of unfamiliar terms here.

- When describing each cell structure, a visual representation of some type should be constantly in view to the student. Each time a new cell part is introduced, the figures in Section 4.12 help the student keep pace with you. The Animation 4.26 plant cell and animal cell should be shown in class and used as a study tool.

- Stress the fact that several cell parts are so complex in function that greater detail will follow in future lectures.

- **Common Student Misconceptions:**
  o Students often have difficulty with the abstract nature of such small structures and the unfamiliar measures of scale. Attempt to use multiple examples to help them grasp how small cells are.

Classroom and Laboratory Enrichment

- Demonstrate the structure of the plasma membrane in as many ways as possible, for example: with a three-dimensional model, overhead transparencies, the Animation 4.8, and in small groups a demonstration using dialysis tubing.

- Use electron micrographs (in the form of overhead transparencies or digital pictures) to add to your description of plasma membrane structure, specifically to the complexity of the protein complexes.

- In the classroom, demonstrate the loss of turgor pressure by flooding a small potted tomato plant with salt water at the beginning of the class period.

- Use models or overhead transparencies to show how channel proteins and transport proteins function during passive transport and active transport, respectively.

30   Chapter Four

© 2011 Cengage Learning. All Rights Reserved. May not be copied, scanned, or duplicated, in whole or in part, except for use as permitted in a license distributed with a certain product or service or otherwise on a password-protected website for classroom use.

- In the lab, students can view plasmolysis under the microscope. Obtain a small *Elodea* leaf and place it in a small drop of distilled water on a microscope slide. Cover it with a cover slip. Now prepare a second slide, only this time mounting an *Elodea* leaf in a drop of 10 percent NaCl solution. Compare the cells of the second slide to those of the first slide.

- Unless a student has an interest in art, he/she may not know what a "mosaic" is. If you can bring an example of such a piece of art, or at least a photo, it will aid your description of the fluid mosaic model.

- Use sketches or models drawn to scale to demonstrate the size difference between prokaryotic and eukaryotic cells. Any example you can provide will help students relate to the small sizes referred to in the microscopy section.

- Show a picture of a diagram or an electron micrograph of any cell. Ask if the cell is prokaryotic or eukaryotic. Is it an animal cell? A plant cell? Some other type of cell?

- Ask students to pair off or work in small groups to match "organelle" with "cellular task." Have the groups present their answers at the board or on an overhead.

- If you present the historical sketch of the cell theory, include pictures of the researchers you are discussing. The pictures may include examples of the equipment they worked with as well as examples of what they would have seen with their simple microscopes. These photos can usually be found in a variety of introductory biology texts or special texts on the history of biology.

- Construct a table (overhead or handout), listing side-by-side comparisons of prokaryotic and eukaryotic cells.

- Most departments possess some type of cell model. These are especially helpful in perception of the 3-D aspects of cell structure. They can also be useful in oral quizzing.

- Arrange for students to see an electron microscope. Have the technician discuss specimen preparation and the operation of the microscope, the costs involved, and the nature of scanning versus transmission electron microscopes.

- If you have access to electron micrographs generated by your colleagues, bring some to class to pass around. Students will appreciate the research references to work being conducted at their school.

Food for Thought (revisited)

- Find examples of foods in your home that have the irradiation symbol.
- Should chemically sterilized foods be required to present a disclosure?
- How does radiation act to sterilize food?

Additional Ideas for Classroom Discussion

- Why do we use the fluid mosaic model to describe the plasma membrane? Ask students to explain the nature of the "fluid" reference.
- Why is the structure of the plasma membrane basically the same among organisms of all five kingdoms? Ask students to reflect on the common evolutionary origins of all life and the similarity we see in the organization of living things.

- What would happen to freshwater unicellular organisms if suddenly released in a saltwater environment?

- Have students quiz one another on the specific role of cell organelles. Have them address some organelles that contain internal compartments or DNA. How do internal compartments assist in the functioning of the organelle?

- Why do unicellular protists (such as *Paramecium*) not burst even though their cell interiors are hypertonic to their freshwater environments?

- How do exocytosis and endocytosis differ from passive transport and active transport? Have students speculate what would happen to cells if they were unable to form vesicles.

- Have students practice their drawing skills by creating their own animal, plant, and bacterial cell sketches. Have them label the parts and describe their functions.

- Use a collection of children's building blocks (like Legos) to illustrate the cytoskeleton fibers that link together to provide cell structure or movement of materials internally.

- Plant cells have a rather rigid wall enclosing their plasma membranes; animal cells do not. Ask students to think about a comparison of consequences when plant and animal cells are placed in different environments that might be isotonic, hypertonic, and hypotonic.

- List a number of the tasks that a cell must do.

- Illustrate the link to later chapters in a discussion of the cell nucleus as the repository for genetic material and why membrane regulation is so critical for this organelle.

- To illustrate the concept of surface to volume ratios and membrane function, have students speculate about why there are no unicellular creatures one foot in diameter?

- Why do bacteria need ribosomes yet lack other organelles critical to eukaryotes?

- What is the difference between scanning electron microscopy and transmission electron microscopy? Have students learn the basics of scale conversion and the order of magnitude differences between light microscopes and electron microscopes.

- Why do you think most plant cells have a central vacuole while animal cells lack this organelle? How do non-plant eukaryotes compensate for this?

- What is the significance of the word *theory* in reference to the basic properties of the cell?

- Why is the term *nucleus* used to describe the center of an atom and the organelle at the center of the cell when these are such different entities? Are cell nuclei typically located at the center of the cells in all Kingdoms?

- In measurement of length, what are the largest cells (when mature) in the human body? What fundamental property of all cells is denied to these?

- What feature makes a eukaryotic cell a "true" cell?

- What organelle could be compared to the control center of an assembly line in a factory?

- Compare the similarities of functions of mitochondria and chloroplasts.

How Would You Vote? Classroom Discussion Ideas

- Monitor the voting for the online question. Ask students their reasons for choosing or not choosing sterilized food.

- In the absence of sterilization, how do students propose that food safety be maintained?

- How was food sterility maintained before radiation or chemical sterilants were available (or in areas where this technology in not available)?

Term Paper Topics, Library Activities, and Special Projects

♦ How do cells "recognize" other cells of the same type during tissue formation?

♦ Have students conduct an internet search for Flash animations that illustrate chloroplast or mitochondrial functions. Have students complete a profile that compares and contrasts these organelles.

♦ Using pipe cleaners or similar materials, construct the oriented and bundled microtubule structures of flagellum. As a follow-on have them research and explain the mechanics of the flagellum operation.

♦ Learn more about plant tissue culture. What mechanisms govern cell differentiation in vitro?

♦ Discuss the development of electron microscopy. What are some of the advances in cell biology that electron microscopy has made possible? How are biological specimens prepared for examination with an electron microscope?

♦ How do antibiotics such as penicillin stop bacterial growth?

♦ Design a hypothetical cell that would function with maximum efficiency under conditions of extreme drought.

♦ Describe the function of liver cell smooth ER in the metabolism of drugs and alcohol. How might the liver cells of an alcoholic differ from those of a moderate imbiber or nondrinker?

♦ Prepare brief biographies of the researchers who are credited with early discoveries of cell structure and function.

♦ Search the library shelves for biology texts of 20, 30, 40, and 50 years ago. Find the diagrams of cell structure. Prepare a sequential composite of these, and compare each to the others and to your present text. What instrument made the difference in the drawings?

♦ Using a special dictionary of Latin and Greek root words, search for the literal meanings for each of the cell parts listed in Table 4.4. (Be careful with Golgi—it is a man's name!)

Responses to *Data Analysis Activities*

1. As shown in Figure 4.22, dynein is the motor protein that is responsible for imparting mobility on the eukaryotic flagella. For individuals with Kartagener syndrome, the abnormal dynein would result in immobile (or poorly mobile) sperm. The males would be infertile unless their sperm was injected into the egg, thus eliminating the need for sperm mobility.

Possible Responses to *Critical Thinking* Questions

1. The idea of a gigantic cell of any kind, or a gigantic creature of any kind, has fascinated Hollywood movie-makers for decades. Movie-goers love this sort of thing. But wet-blanket scientists have to spoil the fun by pointing out the impossibility of gigantic cells based on that surface-to-volume ratio thing. Simply put, a huge cell would have so much volume that the distance from the deepest reaches of the interior of the cell would be too far for nutrients and oxygen to diffuse in, and carbon dioxide and metabolic waste to diffuse out, not to mention the

woefully inadequate surface area for all that diffusion to take place. There are additional complications of why such a large single-celled organism would want to consume starships and planets.

2. As the question (and picture) illustrate, it is a single-celled organism. Most conspicuous is the flagella. However, a variety of internal organelles are present. This strongly suggests that the organism is a protist.

5

GROUND RULES OF METABOLISM

Chapter Outline

Objectives

1. Understand the properties and nature of one-way energy flow in living organisms.
2. Understand how ATP couples energy release to energy use in metabolism.
4. Understand metabolic reactions are influenced by enzymes, which are in turn impacted by multiple factors.
5. Know the mechanisms by which substances are moved across membranes.

Key Terms

energy	exergonic	metabolic pathway	isotonic
kinetic energy	activation energy	feedback inhibition	osmosis
first law of	ATP	allosteric	turgor
thermodynamics	phosphorylation	redox reactions	osmotic pressure
entropy	ATP/ADP cycle	electron transfer	passive transport
second law of	catalysis	chain	active transport
thermodynamics	substrates	concentration	exocytosis
potential energy	active sites	concentration	endocytosis
reaction	induced-fit model	gradient	phagocytosis
reactants	cofactors	diffusion	
products	coenzymes	hypotonic	
endergonic	antioxidant	hypertonic	

Lecture Outline

5.1   A Toast to Alcohol Dehydrogenase

    A. The liver is your body's detoxification center

        1. Polar ethanol molecules move quickly from your stomach to your bloodstream.

        2. Beverage alcohol is degraded by the enzyme alcohol dehydrogenase in the liver.

        3. Bing drinking by college age students damages the liver, and is a strong factor in increased accident rates, assaults, date rape, and unprotected sex.

5.2   Energy and the World of Life

    A. Energy Disperses

        1. Energy is the capacity to do work.

            a. The first law of thermodynamics states that the total amount of energy in the universe is constant. It cannot be created or destroyed; it can only change form.

            b. Energy is either "in play" or in storage, for example the potential energy of a ball balanced on a shelf. ATP is an example of an organic molecule with potential energy.

        2. Energy tends to disperse spontaneously.

            a. The second law of thermodynamics states that the spontaneous direction of energy flow is from high- to low-quality forms.

            b. Each conversion produces energy (usually heat) that is unavailable for work.

            c. As systems lose energy they become more disorganized; the measure of this disorder is called entropy.

            d. Energy flows through life by the making and breaking of bonds in chemical reactions.

    B. Energy's One-Way Flow

        1. The tendency of energy to disperse provides us a sense of the tendency of energy to flow in one direction only.

            a. All living organisms exchange energy and substances with their surroundings.

            b. With each exchange some energy is lost as heat.

            c. Organisms can only stay alive by continuing to resupply themselves with energy from someplace else.

2. Energy enters our web of life as sunlight.
   a. Photosynthetic producers (autotrophs) convert sunlight energy to chemical bond energy when they build glucose and other organic molecules.
   b. Consumers access energy stored in those compounds by breaking and rearranging bonds.
   c. Nearly all living organisms survive by tapping into the one-way energy flow from the sun.

5.3 Energy in the Molecules of Life
   A. Energy In, Energy Out
      1. All chemical bonds possess potential energy.
         a. The amount of energy in any chemical bond depends upon the elements involved.
      2. Molecules enter reactions as reactants, and those remaining at the end are products.
         a. The reaction is a single event in which the reactant bonds are broken by the energy of product bond formation.
         b. Photosynthesis is an example of an endergonic reaction (requiring energy input) for molecular rearrangement to occur.
         c. Endergonic reactions store energy for the cell.
         d. Exergonic reactions yield stored energy from chemical bonds to provide energy for reactions such as aerobic respiration.
   B. Why Earth Does Not Go Up in Flames
      1. Biomolecules are not particularly stable in the presence of oxygen.
         a. Fire is an exergonic reaction in which cellulose is converted to water and carbon dioxide.
         b. The earth is rich in oxygen and thus in potential exergonic reactions.
         c. Reactions like this take activation energy, the amount of energy needed to get a reaction going.
         d. Activation energy is the minimum amount of energy that will get a chemical reaction going.
   C. ATP-The Cell's Energy Currency
      1. ATP accepts energy released by exergonic reactions and delivers it to endergonic reactions.
      2. ATP is composed of a nucleotide and three phosphate groups.
      3. ATP can in turn donate a phosphate group to another molecule, which then becomes primed and energized for specific reactions. This is called phosphorylation.
      4. ADP can be recycled to ATP very rapidly in the ATP/ADP cycle. This cycle drives most metabolic reactions.

5.4 How Enzymes Work
   A. Catalysis is the Process of Accelerating Chemical Reactions
      1. Enzymes are catalytic molecules that speed up the rate of chemical reactions.
      2. Most enzymes are proteins; a few are RNA molecules.
      3. During chemical reactions, enzymes remain unchanged, and so can be reused.
      4. Enzymes recognize, bind, and alter specific reactants.
      5. Enzymes increase the rate of a reaction by lowering the activation energy through extensive bonding of substrate at the active site.
         a. Most enzymes are larger than their substrates, or the specific reactants that an enzyme recognizes and acts upon.
         b. The active site is a crevice where the substrate binds to the enzyme during a reaction, according to the induced-fit model.

6. Remember enzyme mediated reactions included processes like functional group transfer, electron transfers, rearrangements, condensation, and cleavage.
7. Binding energy helps bring about the transition state by four mechanisms:
   a. Helping substrates get together,
   b. Orienting substrates in positions favoring reaction,
   c. Shutting out water, and
   d. Inducing changes in enzyme shape (induced-fit model).

B. Effects of Temperature, pH, and Salinity
1. The temperature, pH, and salinity in an environment influence reaction rates.
2. Because enzymes operate best within defined temperature ranges, high temperatures decrease the reaction rate by disrupting the bonds that maintain three-dimensional shape (denaturation occurs).
3. Most enzymes function best at a pH of between six and eight (pepsin in the stomach is an exception); higher or lower values disrupt enzyme shape and halt function.
4. Most enzymes do not work well when fluids are saltier than their range of tolerance.

C. Help from Cofactors
1. Cofactors are nonprotein atoms or molecules that associate with enzymes and make them more reactive.
2. Catalase is an example of a cofactor. Inorganic metal ions such as Fe^{++} serve as cofactors when assisting the catalase in the breakdown of hydrogen peroxide.
   a. Catalase is an antioxidant whose function is to neutralize free radicals.
   b. Free radicals have unpaired electrons, which make them highly reactive molecular fragments capable of harming our DNA.
3. Coenzymes are organic compounds such as NAD^+, $NADP^+$, and FAD, which can participate as helpers in metabolic reactions, undergoing changes in the process.

5.5 Metabolism: Organized, Enzyme-Mediated Reactions
A. Types of Metabolic Pathways
1. Metabolic pathways are sequences of enzyme-mediated reactions by which cells build, rearrange, or tear down substances.
2. Metabolic pathways may be linear or cyclic.

B. Controls Over Metabolism
1. Feedback mechanisms and other controls that activate or inhibit enzymes allow cells to conserve energy and resources.
   a. This helps cells produce the products they need, and no more, when they need it.
   b. The concentration refers to the amount of substance in its given volume.
   c. Some controls regulate the number of enzyme molecules available by speeding up/slowing down their synthesis, thus regulating the concentrations of enzymes present.
   d. Allosteric enzymes have (in addition to active sites) regulatory sites where control substances can bind to alter enzyme activity.
   e. In feedback inhibition, excess end product of a pathway will bind to an enzyme earlier in the pathway sequence and shut down further synthesis.

C. Redox Reactions
1. Oxidation-reduction reactions are simply electron transfers between molecules.
   a. The donor molecule loses an electron and is oxidized.
   b. The receptor molecule gains an electron and is reduced.

2. In electron transfer chains, molecules accept and give up electrons in an orderly, stepwise fashion to control the release of energy in small, manageable increments.
   a. Electrons are at a higher energy level when they enter the chain than when they leave.
   b. It is helpful to think of the electrons as descending a staircase losing a bit of energy at each step.

5.6 Movement of Ions and Molecules
   A. Concentration Gradients Impact Diffusion
      1. Concentration gradient refers to substance difference in solute concentration between two regions.
      2. Interaction between the molecules drives the movement of molecules.
         a. Molecules constantly collide and tend to move down a concentration gradient (high to low).
         b. The net movement of like molecules down a concentration gradient is called diffusion; each substance diffuses independently of other substances present as illustrated by dye molecules in water.
         c. Any substance tends to diffuse in a direction set by its own concentration gradient.
      3. Several factors influence the rate and direction of diffusion: concentration differences, molecular size (smaller = faster), temperature (higher = faster), electric gradients (a difference in charge), and pressure gradients.
         a. Small molecules diffuse faster than larger ones.
         b. More heat energy makes molecules move faster.
         c. The diffusion rate is higher when there are steeper gradients.
         d. An electric gradient (difference in electric charge between regions) can affect the rate and direction of diffusion.
         e. Diffusion occurs faster at higher pressure.
   B. Diffusion Across Membranes
      1. Tonicity refers to the relative concentration of solutes in two fluids—extracellular fluid and cytoplasmic fluid, for example.
      2. Three conditions are possible:
         a. A *hypotonic* fluid has a lower concentration of solutes than the fluid in the cell; therefore, water moves into the cells immersed in it and swell.
         b. A *hypertonic* fluid has a greater concentration of solutes than the fluid in the cell; cells in it may shrivel.
         c. An *isotonic* fluid has the same concentration of solutes as the fluid in the cell; immersion in it causes no *net* movement of water.
      3. Most free living cells counter shifts in tonicity by selectively transporting solutes across the plasma membrane.
   D. Turgor
      1. Hydrostatic pressure (turgor) is a force directed against a membrane by a fluid; the greater the solute concentration, the greater will be the hydrostatic pressure it exerts.
      2. This force is countered by osmotic pressure, which prevents any further increase in the volume of the solution.
      3. When plants lose water, there is shrinkage of the cytoplasm, which could lead to cellular death.

5.7 Membrane-Crossing Mechanisms
   A. Most molecules cross the cell membrane with the assistance of molecule-specific transport proteins.

B. Passive Transport
   1. In passive transport a concentration gradient, electric gradient, or both drive diffusion across a membrane through a channel inside a transport protein.
      a. No energy input is required to make this happen. This is why it is also known as facilitated diffusion.
      b. Some passive transporters are open channels; others have gates.
      c. The net movement of solutes tends to be toward the side of the membrane with the lower concentration gradient.

C. Active Transport
   1. To move molecules across a membrane against a concentration gradient, special proteins are induced to change shape (in a series), but only with an energy boost from ATP.
   2. Examples of active transport include the sodium-potassium pump of the neuron membrane, and the calcium pump of most cells.
   3. The membranes of all cells (not just animals) have membrane pumps.

5.8   Membrane Trafficking
A. Endocytosis and Exocytosis
   1. Exocytosis moves substances, enclosed in small sacs made of membranes, from cytoplasm.
   2. Endocytosis encloses particles in small portions of plasma membrane to form vesicles that then move into the cytoplasm.
      a. In receptor-mediated endocytosis, receptors at the cell membrane bind to molecules, which are then enclosed in a tiny pit that sinks into the cytoplasm.
      b. In phagocytosis, amoebas and white blood cells digest the contents of the endocytic vesicles by means of enzymes within lysosomes, which fuse with the vesicles.
      c. Bulk phase endocytosis is not selective and will engulf a small volume of fluid.
   3. As long as a cell lives, the process of endocytosis and exocytosis are continually replacing and withdrawing patches of its plasma membrane.
      a. Remember that the composition of the plasma membrane begins in the ER.
      b. In a cell that is no longer growing, the area of the plasma membrane remains fairly constant.

Suggestions for Presenting the Material

♦ Students are unfamiliar with and lack confidence concerning the first and second laws of thermodynamics, so you should distinguish clearly between the two laws; emphasize the central role of the sun as the primary energy source in sustaining life on Earth.

♦ To help students grasp the concept of energy, have them consider their own diet as a means by which they acquire energy. Discuss their body temperature as a function of heat dispersion resulting from their cellular metabolic reactions.

♦ Using a simple ball-and-stick model of the three major ATP functional groups, discuss where the high energy chemical bonds in the phosphate group are located, and how that energy is released or stored as a function of the separation or addition of phosphates.

♦ Finish up with the animation of Figure 5.9 to further cement the role of ATP as an energy molecule for the body.

♦ Find a simple example to illustrate the concept of reactants and products.

♦ Tell students to think of enzymes working like a matchmaker at a party, as a chemical reaction can be very similar. Just like enzymes, the matchmaker must first bring the two people to the same location in the room, then orient them such that they are facing each other, and finally induce interaction by playing up the complimentary features of each.

♦ After presentation of the various capabilities of enzymes, students may think of them as "miracle workers." Remind the students that these are nonliving molecules—albeit amazing ones. Also emphasize the limitations and vulnerability of enzymes, including causes and effects of denaturation.

♦ To enhance student understanding of the controls over enzyme function, have them consider the alternative to little or no control over metabolic reactions. To further this discussion, have students speculate about what happens to these controls when they are sick.

♦ In small groups or in sections, have students discuss the leading role antioxidants play in the marketing of certain foods or supplements. Now that students know the role of antioxidants, have them speculate about the effectiveness of these foods or supplements.

♦ Using figure 5.16 as a backdrop, have students discuss the important links between endergonic and exergonic reactions. Have them answer the question, "What is being reduced in a redox reaction?"

♦ Note that the animated Figure 5.18 greatly assists students in understanding the selective permeability of membranes (as a refresher to the fluid mosaic model discussed in Chapter 4).

♦ Animations, Figure 5.20 on passive transport, and Figure 5.21 on active transport will bring to life these deceptively simple concepts for students. Here they get exposed to the full importance of the transport and channel proteins embedded in the plasma membrane.

♦ The animation of Figure 5.23 and 5.25 illustrates the important role of vesicles in transport processes from and to individual cells to support metabolic reactions.

♦ If you prefer to teach from specific examples, you may want to choose a specific metabolic pathway (of your own or from elsewhere in the book); draw it on an overhead transparency and use it to explain the various terms found in the text.

♦ **Common Student Misconceptions:**

   o Students have a difficult time understanding the enzyme structure and its function. Obtain a three dimensional diagram (overhead, picture, or computer animation) to help illustrate further this critical concept. Use Figure 5.10 to help.

   o The various methods by which molecules move, either through space or through membranes, can be confusing to students because of the subtle differences that distinguish each method. Perhaps you could begin with general, nonmembrane-associated phenomena such as diffusion. Then proceed to membrane-associated mechanisms such as osmosis, facilitated diffusion, and active transport.

Classroom and Laboratory Enrichment

♦ Discuss the terms *isotonic, hypotonic,* and *hypertonic* by showing students three sketches of semipermeable bags in beakers of distilled water (classically available overheads or pictures are available from many sources). Vary the concentrations of the sugar solutions shown in the bags. Ask students what the direction of water movement would be in each case. Then ask what direction the sugar molecules will move in. Many students will believe that the sugar molecules will move across the membrane, even though they previously learned these sugar molecules are too large to cross the plasma membrane readily.

♦ To demonstrate that some molecules will pass through membranes and some will not, prepare two test tubes as follows: In one tube pour dilute Lugol's iodine solution until it is about nine-tenths full; in another tube pour 1 percent starch paste until it is about nine-tenths full. Using dialysis tubing, cover the mouth of each test tube; then secure it tightly by tying with thread or a tight rubber band. Invert the starch paste test tube into a beaker about one-half full of dilute Lugol's solution; invert the test tube containing dilute Lugol's solution into a beaker containing a 1 percent starch paste. Ask students why the well-known blue-black color appears in the starch solution and not in the Lugol's solution. Students may decide that the starch requires digestion to a more soluble form before it can pass through the membrane.

♦ Set up two or more osmometer tubes (glass or plastic thistle tubes covered with a selectively permeable membrane) at the front of the room. Compare rates of osmosis by filling each tube with a colored sugar (you may use corn syrup) or salt solution (vary the concentrations) and placing the base of the tube into a beaker of distilled water.

♦ Living cells can be used to demonstrate the osmotic water passage through semipermeable membranes. Use an apple corer to remove center cylinders of a raw white potato, carefully weighing each piece. Expose the potato pieces to various concentrations of sucrose solution (0%, 5%, 10%, 15% and 20% work well) for 45 minutes, and then re-weigh the potato pieces. Hypertonic and hypotonic solutions can be determined from changes in mass.

♦ To show how molecules move from points of greater concentration to regions of lower concentration, place a tea bag in a beaker of warm water. This provides a very visible illustration of the movement of tea particles.

♦ In the classroom, demonstrate the loss of turgor pressure by flooding a small potted tomato plant with salt water at the beginning of the class period.

♦ In the lab, students can view plasmolysis under the microscope. Obtain a small *Elodea* leaf and place it in a small drop of distilled water on a microscope slide. Cover it with a cover slip. Now prepare a second slide, only this time mounting an *Elodea* leaf in a drop of 10 percent NaCl solution. Compare the cells of the second slide to those of the first slide.

♦ Watch hemolysis by diluting several drops of fresh blood with distilled water. Compare the resulting solution with one in which the same number of red blood cells were diluted with physiological saline (0.09% NaCl). The suspension that has undergone hemolysis will be clear (red blood cells have burst), while the solution made with physiological saline will be visibly cloudy (red blood cells remain intact in the solution). Please use extreme care if using fresh blood.

♦ The diffusion of a gas through other gases (air) can be demonstrated easily as follows: Wet a circle of filter paper with phenolphthalein and insert it into the bottom of a large test tube. Next, invert the test tube over an open bottle of ammonium hydroxide. Ask students to explain the rather rapid color change of the filter paper to red. Set up a control with filter paper soaked in water.

♦ Bring a can of room deodorizer spray to class to demonstrate diffusion (in this case, a liquid in a gas) as a general example of how concentration gradients operate.

♦ The action of an enzyme (salivary amylase) can be easily demonstrated by the following procedure:

a. Prepare a 6 percent starch solution in water and confirm its identity by a spot plate test with iodine solution (produces blue-black color).

b. Collect saliva from a volunteer by having the person chew a small piece of Parafilm and expectorate into a test tube.

c. Place diluted saliva and the starch solution in a test tube and mix.

d. At suitable intervals, remove samples of the digestion mixture and test with iodine on the spot plate (lack of dark color indicates conversion of starch to maltose).

e. Variations can include heating the saliva to destroy the enzyme, adding acid or alkali, and adding cyanide.

♦ The effect of ATP on a reaction can be demonstrated by use of bioluminescence kits available from biological supply houses.

♦ Demonstrate the two models of enzyme-substrate interactions in the following ways:

a. *Rigid "lock and key" model:* Use preschool-size jigsaw puzzle pieces or giant-size Lego blocks.

b. *Induced-fit model:* Use a flexible fabric or latex glove to show how the insertion of a hand (substrate) induces change in the shape of the glove (active site).

♦ The relationship among ATP, ADP, energy, enzymes, and phosphorylation may be illustrated by the use of a toy dart gun with rubber suction cup-tipped darts. It is helpful to have pictures of ADP and ATP structures that can be projected on a screen as the following demonstration is performed:

a. Tell the students that the unloaded dart gun represents ADP and the dart represents inorganic phosphate (P). Show the structure of ADP on the screen.

b. As you insert the dart into the gun, emphasize the need for the expenditure of energy to do this. Tell the students that the addition of P to ADP is, therefore, an endergonic reaction; it is also called a phosphorylation reaction. At this time show the structure of ATP on the screen. Also point out that the spring inside the dart gun is under much tension and as such has a great deal of potential energy. The same can be said for the P group that has been added to ADP.

c. Next, demonstrate the hydrolysis of ATP. The trigger finger represents the necessary enzyme. Aim the gun at some vertical smooth surface (window or aquarium works well) and depress the trigger. The dart should adhere to the surface (a substrate molecule being energized by phosphorylation). The reaction is thus exergonic and some of the energy has been transferred to the substrate molecule.

A Toast to Alcohol Dehydrogenase (revisited)

♦ Show the video clip to the entire class. Pose the question, "What happens to alcohol molecules contained in the alcoholic drinks people consume?" Pose several "what if" questions concerning enzyme action such as: What if the liver becomes damaged due to alcohol consumption and cannot function normally?

♦ Discuss the role binge drinking plays in college society on your campus. What are the "real" negative outcomes?

♦ *Exactly* what causes the liver of a heavy alcohol drinker to diminish in its capacity to metabolize alcohol over a lifetime of drinking?

Additional Ideas for Classroom Discussion

♦ What would happen to freshwater unicellular organisms if suddenly released in a saltwater environment? Have students reflect on why this might happen.

- Distinguish between diffusion and osmosis introduced earlier in the text. Have students give specific examples using familiar molecules.

- Why do unicellular protists (such as *Paramecium*) not burst even though their cell interiors are hypertonic to their freshwater environments?

- How do exocytosis and endocytosis differ from passive transport and active transport?

- Have students prepare a chart that illustrates and lists the various properties and roles of enzymes, cofactors, and coenzymes. Have them explain why temperature, pH, and salinity influence the effectiveness of these molecules.

- After viewing examples of diffusion of molecules across membranes in class or lab, have students consider constructing their own demonstrations.

- Using a chemistry book or an online resource, have students look up the diameter of various familiar molecules and their relative polarity. Have them speculate about their movement across a plasma membrane.

- Based on your knowledge of membranes and solubility, which insecticide preparation would you expect to kill insects faster: one that is water formulated or petroleum-solvent formulated?

- What would be the result on blood cells of a substitution of pure water for physiological saline in an IV bottle?

- In some cases, a 5 percent glucose solution is given intravenously to persons after surgery. If you were the doctor on such a case, would you order the glucose solution to be isotonic, hypertonic, or hypotonic to blood? Explain your decision.

- Ask students what the prefixes *hyper-* and *hypo-* refer to in the text discussions. If they do not understand that these terms refer to solute concentration (not water), they will have difficulty with the concept. Hint – consider helping the students by providing the more common words hyperactive and hypodermic.

- Plant cells have a rather rigid wall enclosing their plasma membranes; animal cells do not. Ask students to think about a comparison of consequences when plant and animal cells are placed in isotonic, hypertonic, and hypotonic solutions.

- Discuss what would happen to life on Earth if the flow of sunlight energy stopped.

How Would You Vote? Classroom Discussion Ideas

- Monitor the voting for the online questions. Discuss elements of lifestyle that eliminate people from organ donation. Discuss "fairness" as an element of access to transplant organs in spite of lifestyle choices that make them a poor candidate.

- Have students reflect on lifestyle choices they make that might put them at risk for liver disease later in life, or eliminate them from an organ transplant list.

Term Paper Topics, Library Activities, and Special Projects

- Research the basis for the first and second laws of thermodynamics. On the basis of what observations did scientists formulate these laws? What experiments can be done in the laboratory to confirm the laws?

- Have students find examples of the functions of the sodium-potassium pump and the calcium pump in other organisms.

- Have students investigate why when whales lose their way and swim up freshwater streams do scientists get so concerned about the health of the animals? What is it about the whale's metabolism that makes freshwater potentially dangerous?

- Look up the composition of "physiological saline." Are there different varieties of this preparation for different animal species?

- The diffusion and transport phenomena discussed in the chapter are based on a property called Brownian movement that is demonstrated by all molecules, whether alive or not. What is the physical manifestation of this property, and what is the derivation of its name?

- Design a hypothetical cell that would function with maximum efficiency under conditions of extreme drought.

- Explain the defect in the metabolic pathway that results in the condition known as phenylketonuria (PKU). How can this condition be treated? Is it curable?

- Have students research and find examples of three-dimensional enzyme illustrations. Have the students write a short summary about the specific properties of these enzymes and the critical nature of binding sites on these enzymes.

- Explain the role of the B vitamins in human metabolism.

- Discuss ways that coenzymes and inorganic cofactors participate in enzymatic reactions.

Responses to *Data Analysis Activities*

1. Eight of the participants experienced a worse hangover with the placebo than with the artichoke extract.

2. Seven of the participants experienced a worse hangover with the artichoke extract than with the placebo.

3. 53% of the participants experienced a greater hangover with the placebo, while 47% experienced a greater hangover with the artichoke extract. The difference between these two values is extremely small.

4. These results do not support artichoke extract as an effective hangover cure as they did not significantly reduce the level of hangover experienced when compared to a placebo.

Possible Responses to *Critical Thinking* Questions

1. First, "you can't win" refers to the nature of energy that cannot be made nor destroyed. The phrase may be taken to refer to the fact that we cannot influence this energy constant. Second, "you can't break even" refers to the fact that you cannot conserve or transfer all the energy when it is moved between sources; some will inevitably be lost to you.

2. Water molecules can be more or less concentrated based on the solute that is present. For example, and solution of nothing but water is 100% water. But, a 1% salt solution would only be 99% water. While the difference may be small, a 99% water solution has less water than a 100% water solution, and thus water would move towards the 99% solution.

6

WHERE IT STARTS — PHOTOSYNTHESIS

Chapter Outline

Objectives

1. Understand that captured light energy provides the energy to drive glucose synthesis.
2. Recognize the photosynthesis has two stages: converting light energy to chemical energy and using energy to drive the second stage.
3. Recognize that ATP provides the energy, NADPH provides the electrons, and CO_2 provides the carbon for carbohydrate production.
4. Understand that light-independent reactions can vary to accomodate different environmental conditions.

Key Terms

autotrophs	stroma	photosystems	stomata
photosynthesis	thylakoid	photolysis	C3 plants
heterotrophs	membrane	electron transfer	Photorespiration
wavelength	light-dependent	phosphorylation	C4 plants
pigment	reactions	Calvin-Benson cycle	CAM plants
chlorophyll a	light-independent	carbon fixation	
chloroplast	reactions	rubisco	

Lecture Outline

6.1 Green Energy

    A. Most autotrophs make use of photosynthesis to make food out of carbon dioxide and water

    B. Heterotrophs break down organic molecules assembled by other organisms

    C. Biofuels are the extraction of energy trapped in chemical bonds by the process of photosynthesis

6.2 Sunlight as an Energy Source

    A. Properties of Light

        1. Visible light represents a part of the electromagnetic spectrum.

            a. One property of radiant energy is that it travels in wavelengths. Wavelength refers to the distance between crests of these waves.

            b. Light energy is packaged as photons, which vary in energy as a function of wavelength.

    B. Pigments: The Rainbow Catchers

        1. Pigment molecules are organic compounds that selectively absorbs light. Wavelengths not absorbed are reflected.

        2. Chlorophyll *a* is the main photosynthetic pigment in plants, algae, and cyanobacteria. It absorbs violet and red light, so it appears green.

        3. Accessory pigments extend the range of wavelengths usable for photosynthesis.

            a. Accessory pigments act as antioxidants.

            b. Accessory pigments do not break down as fast as chlorophyll, and in the fall we see their bright colors of yellow, orange, and red.

        4. The light-trapping part of all pigments consists of an array of atoms where single bonds alternate with double bonds.

            a. Photon energy from sunlight excites the electrons of these atoms increasing their energy level.

            b. This energy is released or transferred, returning these atoms to a lower energy state.

6.3 Exploring the Rainbow

    A. Photosynthesis occurs most efficiently within limited wavelengths.

        1. Theodor Engelmann, a botanist, designed an experiment using a prism to test what parts of sunlight bacteria were using to produce oxygen.

        2. Engelmann's experiment allowed him to develop an early absorption spectrum showing how absorption varies with the wavelength of light.

        3. These absorption spectrums reflect the ability of the pigments of photosynthesis to be excited by specific ranges of light wavelengths.

6.4 Overview of Photosynthesis

    A. Chloroplasts are organelles of photosynthesis in plants and other eukaryotic organisms that harness light. Their structure plays a critical role in their function.

        1. Chloroplasts in plants have three membranes.

            a. Two membranes enclose a semifluid matrix called the stroma. Sugars are built in the stroma.

            b. The third, called the thylakoid membrane, is folded up into flattened disks inside the stroma.

            c. The space within the thylakoid membrane is continuous, forming a single compartment.

2. Overall, the equation for glucose formation is written:

$$12H_2O + 6CO_2 \xrightarrow{\text{sunlight}} 6O_2 + C_6H_{12}O_6 + 6H_2O$$

B. Two Stages of Reactions
1. Light-dependent reactions convert light energy to chemical bond energy of ATP.
   a. Water is split to release oxygen.
   b. NADP+ picks up electrons to become NADPH to be used later.
2. The light-independent reactions assemble sugars and other organic molecules using ATP, NADPH, and CO_2.

6.5   Light-Dependent Reactions
A. Capturing Light for Photosynthesis
1. Photons strike pigment molecules, increasing their energy state.
   a. In the thylakoid membrane this energy is captured by pigment molecules that "pass" the energy from complex to complex until it absorbs it "for keeps."
B. The Noncyclic Pathway
1. At photosystem type II, an electron pair is excited by light energy and ejected.
2. Photosystem type I re-excites the electrons.
C. Replacing Lost Electrons
1. Electrons lost by photosystems are not unlimited and need to be replaced.
   a. Photolysis is a process that pulls replacement electrons from water molecules. The water molecules then disassociate into hydrogen ions and oxygen.
   b. The hydrogen ions contribute to the gradients that drive ATP production; oxygen is diffused out of the cell.
D. Harvesting Electron Energy
   a. Electrons lost from photosystems immediately enter an electron transfer chain that is embedded in the thylakoid membrane.
   b. Electron transfer chains are organized arrays of enzymes, coenzymes, and other proteins that accept and donate electrons in turn.
   c. The entry of the electron into this chain is the first step in the light-dependent reactions. Here light energy is converted to chemical energy.
   d. Electrons release energy bit by bit as they move along the chain. Components of the chain use released energy to move H+ ions across the thylakoid membrane.
   e. As this process progresses an H+ ion concentration gradient is established across the thylakoid membrane. H+ ions move back across the membrane through the interior of ATP synthases. The flow causes these proteins to attach phosphate groups to ADP, creating ATP in the stroma.
   f. Following transfer through type II to type I, the excited electrons are stored in NADPH.
E. The Cyclic Pathway
   A. When NADPH is not being used, it backs up and stalls the noncyclical pathway.
   B. When this happens a cyclic pathway run independently in type I photosystems will kick in and continue making ATP.
   a. In this case electrons lost from photosystem I get cycled back to it.
   b. As the electrons cycle back they pass through an electron transfer chain that shuttles H+ ions into the thylakoid compartment, creating a gradient.
   c. This gradient drives ATP formation just as in the noncyclical pathway, but NADPH does not form.

6.6   Energy Flow in Photosynthesis

   A. The cyclic pathway evolved first in anaerobic organisms

      1. It is simpler and less energy efficient.

      2. It still operates in nearly all photoautotrophs.

      3. No NADPH forms and oxygen is not released. Electrons lost to photosystem I are cycled back and returned.

   B. The noncyclical pathway evolved later and photosystem II became part of it

      1. This created a sequence of reactions powerful enough to strip electrons from water, oxidizing it.

      2. The reaction yields oxygen and H+ ions. The electrons that leave do not return.

      3. In both pathways energy associated with electrons flowing through electron transfer chains shuttle H+ across the thylakoid membrane setting up a concentration gradient that drives ATP production

6.7   Light-Independent Reactions: The Sugar Factory

   A. These reactions constitute a pathway known as the Calvin-Benson cycle

      1. The participants and their roles in the synthesis of carbohydrates are:

         a. ATP, which provides energy;

         b. NADPH, which provides hydrogen atoms and electrons; and

         c. Atmospheric air, which provides the carbon and oxygen from carbon dioxide.

      2. The reactions take place in the stroma of chloroplasts and are not dependent on sunlight.

   B. Carbon dioxide diffuses into a leaf, across the plasma membrane of a photosynthetic cell

      1. Rubisco joins carbon dioxide to RuBP to produce an unstable intermediate that splits to form two molecules of PGA.

      2. Each PGA then receives a P_i from ATP plus H^+ and electrons from NADPH to form PGAL (phosphoglyceraldehyde).

      3. Most of the PGAL molecules continue in the cycle to fix more carbon dioxide, but two PGAL join to form a sugar-phosphate, which will be modified to sucrose, starch, and cellulose.

   C. Most of the glucose produced is converted at once to sucrose or starch by other pathways that conclude the light-independent reactions

      1. Sucrose is the transportable form of carbohydrate in plants.

      2. Excess glucose is stored as starch grains in the stroma of chloroplasts.

      3. When sugar is needed in other parts of the plants, starch is converted to sucrose and exported.

6.8   Adaptations: Carbon-Fixing Pathways

   A. Gases diffuse into and out of plants via stomata, small openings across the surface of the leaf or green stem.

      1. Plants in hot, dry environments close their stomata to conserve water, but in so doing retard carbon dioxide entry and permit oxygen buildup inside the leaves.

      2. These plants are called C3 plants because they fix carbon with the Calvin-Benson cycle in which three-carbon PGA is the first stable intermediate.

      3. At high O_2 levels the enzyme rubisco attaches oxygen instead of carbon to RuBP in a wasteful pathway called photorespiration.

         a. CO_2 becomes a product of photorespiration, causing the plant to loose carbon instead of gaining it.

         b. ATP and NADPH are used to "fuel" this process instead of being used to make sugars. Thus sugar production is limited in C3 plants on hot, dry days.

c. Plants compensate by producing lots of rubisco, it is the most abundant protein on Earth.

B. Bamboo, corn, and other plants that evolved in the tropics also close their stomata when it is hot and dry, but their sugar production does not cease.
   1. We call these plants C4 plants. They fix carbon twice (in mesophyll cells, then in bundle-sheath cells) to produce oxaloacetate, a four-carbon compound, which can then donate the carbon dioxide to the Calvin-Benson cycle.
   2. The C4 cycle keeps CO_2 levels high near rubisco and minimizes photorespiration.

C. CAM is another evolutionary adaptation of plants in hot, dry climates. CAM plants such as cacti, open their stomata and fix CO_2 only at night, storing the intermediate product for use in photosynthesis the next day.

Suggestions for Presenting the Material

♦ The biochemical metabolic reactions associated with the complex process of photosynthesis is terribly intimidating to students. Make a deliberate attempt to introduce each element with lots of time for questions and examples.

♦ Many students think that the only autotrophic organisms are those with green pigments, which are, of course, capable of using light for food manufacture. Highlight the existence of *chemoautotrophs*, which derive their energy from chemicals.

♦ Make use of the animated Figure 6.4 to help students gain an understanding of the differences between wavelength and photosynthetic pigments.

♦ A discussion of the reason colored objects appear the color they do may facilitate the students' understanding of why, for example, green light is ineffective for photosynthesis (not absorbed).

♦ Include the animated Figure 6.7 as a part of your introduction of photosynthesis. It does a great job of placing the dizzying array of terms and abstract functions in context.

♦ As the noncyclic photosynthetic pathway is more common, use the animated Figure 6.8 to bring this metabolic process "to light" for your students. Point out that most existing plants use the noncyclic pathway.

♦ ATP and NADPH were introduced in Chapter 5 as carrier molecules. Their connection between the light-dependent and light-independent reactions is an excellent opportunity for reinforcement of these molecules as bridges and the energy flow that occurs in photosynthesis.

♦ The term *granum* dates from the days when microscopes revealed "grains" within the chloroplast. Now we realize that these grains consist of complex thylakoid membranes.

♦ Photosynthesis is much more complicated than the usual simple equation that a student may have seen in a previous course. Perhaps the best approach to presenting this topic is to follow a stepwise outline and rely heavily on illustrations of the figures in the chapter.

♦ Although the diagram of the Calvin-Benson cycle (Figure 6.9) is intimidating, the most important features are the entry of carbon dioxide and the production of the sugar phosphate, driven by ATP and NADPH from the light-dependent reactions.

♦ The emphasis on C3, C4, and CAM plants can be moderated according to the interests of the instructor. Omitting it will not affect future discussions in the book.

♦ Students enjoy the tie between carbon acquisition by photosynthetic organisms and increasing atmospheric CO_2 rates associated with global climate change. Share with your students the direct tie to activities they engage in and future discussion on ecology.

- ♦ **Common Student Misconceptions**
  - o Students may have previously learned to refer to the two divisions of photosynthesis as the "light" and "dark" reactions. Starr uses the more accurate and currently acceptable terms *light-dependent* and *light-independent,* respectively. You may wish to explain why "dark reactions" is a poor designator and no longer used (the reactions can occur in both the dark and the light).
  - o Students often get confused with the similarities and differences between the ATP synthase mechanism in chloroplasts (Figure 6.7) and mitochondria (Chapter 7).

Classroom and Laboratory Enrichment

- ♦ You can demonstrate the production of oxygen by plants with the following:
  - a. Place *Elodea* (an aquarium plant) in a bowl, and expose it to bright light.
  - b. Invert a test tube over the plant, and collect the bubbles.
  - c. Remove the tube and immediately thrust a glowing wood splint into the tube.
  - d. Result: The splint burns brightly in the high-oxygen air.
- ♦ Separate the pigments in green leaves using paper chromatography. (Consult a botany laboratory manual for the correct procedure.)
- ♦ Many students have never seen the action of a prism in separating white light into its component colors; a demonstration would most likely be appreciated.
- ♦ If a greenhouse facility is readily accessible, provide students with a brief tour and explanation of the devices used to control light, water, air, and heat.
- ♦ Show a DVD that highlights photosynthesis in C3, C4, and CAM plants.
- ♦ Have students view a model of a chloroplast and discuss the nature of the three membranes found in this organelle. Also, remind students that chloroplasts have some of their own DNA and synthesize some of their own proteins.
- ♦ Show an electron micrograph of a chloroplast and indicate where light-dependent reactions, light-independent reactions, and chemiosmosis occur.

Green Energy (revisited)

- ♦ Have students reflect on the true source of food they consume. How many layers of a food web might they identify if challenged?
- ♦ Have a discussion about the role of photosynthesis in extracting CO_2 from the atmosphere, and how burning plant-products can liberate this CO_2.
- ♦ Challenge students to consider how long it takes for CO_2 to be 'trapped' in plant matter, and how quickly it can be liberated.
- ♦ Why are coal, oil, and natural gas called *fossil* fuels?
- ♦ Usually we think of photosynthesis as *producing* carbohydrate and oxygen, but what important role does photosynthesis perform as a "consumer"?

Additional Ideas for Classroom Discussion

- ♦ Introduce students to other greenhouse gasses and show them how CO_2 compares to others in abundance, residence time, and estimated impact on the global environment.

- In what ways could the "greenhouse effect" hurt agriculture? In what ways could it possibly *help,* especially in Canada and the countries of the former Soviet Union?

- Have students consider the current marketing of compact fluorescent light bulbs. How are these linked to atmospheric carbon?

- Suppose you could purchase light bulbs that emitted only certain wavelengths of visible light. What wavelengths would promote the most photosynthesis? The least?

- Assume you have supernatural powers and can stop and start the two sets of photosynthesis reactions. Will stopping the light-independent affect the light-dependent, or vice versa?

- What conflicting "needs" confront a plant living in a hot, dry environment? What is the frequent result in C3 plants? How is the problem avoided in C4 plants?

How Would You Vote? Classroom Discussion Ideas

- Monitor the voting for the online question. Present the results to the class and discuss the dramatic increase in ethanol plant construction in the United States.

- Discuss the relative efficiency of producing fuel from renewable crops such as corn. What are the positive aspects and what are the limitations of such energy programs?

- Have students reflect on the marketing trends for paying a premium for products and vehicles that are "green."

Term Paper Topics, Library Activities, and Special Projects

- One of the hottest and driest summers (1988) in North America in recent years affected the production of food and grain crops. Prepare an analysis of the effect(s) of that summer's drought (or future ones) on future food availability and its cost to the consumer.

- Consult a biochemistry or advanced plant physiology text to learn of a laboratory technique that would clearly indicate whether the oxygen produced by plants is derived from *water* or from *carbon dioxide.*

- Prepare a detailed diagram of the Calvin-Benson cycle showing the introduction of radioactively-labeled carbon dioxide and its subsequent journey through several "turns" of the cycle.

- Of the total amount of sunlight energy impinging on a green plant, what percentage of the energy is actually converted into glucose?

- Have student groups investigate biotechnology developments designed to enhance the efficiency of rubisco or increase the rate of plant adaptations to global climate change. Have them report to the laboratory or classroom group on their findings.

- Discuss why radiation with greater or lesser wavelengths than visible light is not generally used in biological processes.

Responses to *Data Analysis Activities*

1. The ethanol produced from one hectare of corn yield produced approximately 22 x 10⁶ kcal of energy. To produce the corn in that hectare required approximately 18 x 10⁶ kcal of energy.

2. Grass synfuel had the highest ratio of energy output to energy input.

3. Corn grain ethanol would require the least amount of land to produce the greatest amount of biofuel energy.

Possible Responses to *Critical Thinking* Questions

1. Let's look at the possibilities. The gain in weight of the tree could have been unchanged water simply absorbed through the roots and retained in the plant tissues, but not 168 pounds of it! Furthermore, we know that the water molecules are not going to combine *directly* with any other molecules in the tree. Of course we now know much more about the reactions of photosynthesis than van Helmont did, so we can conclude that the gain in weight was from the synthesis of carbohydrate (specifically, cellulose) in the chloroplasts of the leaf cells due to the reacting of carbon dioxide from the air and water from the soil.

2. The bubbling from submerged aquatic plants is quite a common phenomenon and can actually be enhanced by shining a light source on the plants. Of course, what you are observing is the photolysis of water into hydrogen ions (retained) and oxygen gas (diffused outward).

3. By looking at Figure 6.10 in the textbook, we can see in C3 photosynthesis the ^{14}C of the carbon dioxide will join with PGA to form RuBP and then immediately split into two PGAL molecules. Conversely, in C4 photosynthesis, the 14C will initially join glycolate, and will subsequently join RuBP.

7

HOW CELLS RELEASE CHEMICAL ENERGY

Chapter Outline

Objectives

1. Understand the fundamental nature of energy-releasing pathways to life.
2. Recognize the universal role of glycolysis in harvesting energy from carbohydrates.
3. Know the raw materials and products of each of the processes of aerobic respiration.
4. Know the raw materials and products of each of the processes of fermentation.
5. Understand the metabolic pathways used to extract energy from fats and proteins.

Key Terms

photoautotrophs	aerobic respiration	pyruvate	alcoholic fermentation
anaerobic	fermentation	substrate-level phosphorylation	lactate fermentation
aerobic	glycolysis		

Lecture Outline

7.1   When Mitochondria Spin Their Wheels

    A.   Mitochondria are the organelles responsible for releasing the energy stored in foods

        1.   When mitochondria do not work properly, energy releasing molecules are not used efficiently, causing people to have high metabolic rates but low energy levels.

        2.   In Luft's syndrome, the mitochondria are active in oxygen consumption, but with little ATP formation to show for it.

        3.   In Friedreich's ataxia, too much iron in the mitochondria causes an accumulation of free radicals that attack valuable molecules of life.

    B.   Prokaryotes also make ATP via electron transfer chains built into their membranes.

7.2   Extracting Energy From Carbohydrates

    A.   Evolution of Earth's Atmosphere

        1.   As the early atmosphere on earth was oxygen poor, early energy-releasing pathways were likely anaerobic.

        2.   Increasing oxygen levels lead to the evolution of aerobic respiration.

        4.   All energy-releasing pathways begin with the glycolysis reactions, which occur in the cytoplasm and produce two molecules of pyruvate, an organic compound with a three-carbon backbone.

            a.   After initial reactions, fermentation pathways end in the cytoplasm where a molecule other than oxygen accepts electrons at the end of electron transfer chains.

            b.   Aerobic respiration ends in the mitochondria where oxygen accepts electrons at the end of electron transfer chains.

            c.   Aerobic respiration extracts energy from each glucose molecule, yielding a net of 36 ATP. This is far more efficient than the anaerobic pathways that yield a net of two ATP per glucose molecule.

    B.   Overview of Aerobic Respiration

        1.   The aerobic route is summarized:

$$C_6H_{12}O_6 + 6O_2 \rightarrow 6CO_2 + 6H_2O$$

        2.   Aerobic respiration consists of three stages of reactions.

            a.   Glycolysis takes place in the cytoplasm and consists of the breakdown of glucose to pyruvate; small amounts of ATP are generated.

            b.   In the second stage of reactions, enzymes break down the pyruvate to carbon dioxide. These reactions are called acetyl-CoA formation and the Krebs cycle.

            c.   In the first two stages electrons and hydrogen atoms are picked up by coenzymes called NAD+ and FAD. When they carry electrons we call them NADH and $FADH_2$.

            d.   In the third stage, electron transfer phosphorylation processes the H^+ ions and electrons to generate high yields of ATP; oxygen is the final electron acceptor.

7.3   Glycolysis—Glucose Breakdown Starts

    A.   Glycolysis refers to reactions that liberate the chemical energy of sugars

        1.   Cells must invest two ATP to start the reaction or it will not run.

        2.   Glucose is first phosphorylated in energy-requiring steps, then split to form two molecules of PGAL.

        3.   Enzymes attach a phosphate to each PGAL forming two molecules of PGA. In this reaction, H^+ and electrons from PGAL change NAD^+ to NADH, which is used later in electron transfer.

4. In substrate-level phosphorylation, two ATP are formed after enzymes transfer a phosphate group from each PGA to ADP. Two more ATP form when phosphate is transferred from other intermediates to two ADP.

B. The end products of glycolysis are (for each glucose molecule degraded): two pyruvates, two ATPs (net gain), and two NADH.
1. These molecules are now ready to enter the second stage of reactions in which cells break down sugars for energy.

7.4 Second Stage of Aerobic Respiration

A. Acetyl-CoA Formation
1. Pyruvate enters the mitochondria, one carbon is removed and forms CO_2, and the two-carbon fragment joins coenzyme A (CoA) forming acetyl-CoA.
2. Acetyl CoA enters the Krebs cycle and CO_2 diffuses out of the cell.

B. The Krebs Cycle
1. Krebs consists of a series of enzyme mediated reactions. It is termed a cycle because the final reaction regenerates the substrate of the first step.
2. It takes two turns of the Krebs cycle to break down two pyruvates from one glucose molecule.
3. Each acetyl-CoA transfers its two carbon atoms to four-carbon oxaloacetate. The outcome is citrate, which is a form of citric acid. This is why the Krebs cycle is sometimes referred to as the citric acid cycle.
4. In later steps, additional CO_2 molecules are released.
5. Two molecules of ATP are produced by substrate-level phosphorylation along with eight NADH and two $FADH_2$. These coenzymes will deliver electrons to the next stage.

7.5 Aerobic Respiration's Big Energy Payoff

A. Electron Transfer Phosphorylation
1. In this step electron transfer chains put electrons and hydrogen atoms from glucose to use.
2. NADH and $FADH_2$ donate their electrons to transfer (enzyme) systems embedded in the inner mitochondrial membrane.
   a. The energy is used to pump hydrogen ions out of the inner compartment.
   b. Energy from the electrons is given up a little at a time creating an H+ gradient between the inner and outer compartments.
   c. When hydrogen ions flow back through the ATP synthase in the channels, the coupling of phosphate to ADP yields ATP.
3. Aerobic respiration literally translates to taking a breath. Oxygen joins with the "spent" electrons and H+ to yield water.
   a. In oxygen-starved cells the electrons have nowhere to go and create a backup, stalling the transfer chains.

B. Summing Up: The Energy Harvest
1. Electron transfer yields 32 ATPs, glycolysis yields two ATPs, and Krebs yields two ATPs for a grand total of 36 ATPs per glucose molecule.
2. When energy is transferred from glucose to ATP, the efficiency is about 40 percent.
   a. Remember that energy transfer is not entirely efficient, with some energy lost to heat.
3. Shuttling mechanisms differ among cells. In the brain and skeletal muscles the yield is 38 ATP, while in the liver, heart, and kidney cells the yield is 36.

7.6 Fermentation Pathways

A. Fermentation is Extracting Energy from Carbohydrates Anaerobically
1. Fermentation uses only glycolysis to generate ATP.

2. Alternate mechanisms are employed to remove the electrons from NADH, thus regenerating NAD+.

B. Alcoholic Fermentation
   1. Fermentation begins with glucose degradation to three-carbon pyruvate.
   2. Cellular enzymes convert pyruvate to two-carbon acetaldehyde, which then accepts electrons from NADH to become ethyl alcohol.
   3. The last step regenerates NAD+.
   4. Yeasts are valuable in the baking industry (carbon dioxide by-product makes dough "rise") and in alcoholic beverage production such as wine.

C. Lactate Fermentation
   1. In lactate fermentation, enzymes transfer electrons and hydrogen from NADH to pyruvate.
   2. The reaction converts pyruvate to three-carbon lactate (lactic acid) and regenerates NAD+.
   3. Certain lactate fermenting bacteria (as in milk) are used to preserve food. Others ferment and preserve pickles, corned beef, and kimchi. Still others spoil food.

D. Skeletal muscles use aerobic and anaerobic metabolism
   1. Slow twitch muscle fibers have many mitochondria and produce ATP by aerobic respiration.
      a. These muscle fibers dominate during prolonged activity such as distance running.
      b. These cells are red due to the abundance of myoglobin, a pigment related to hemoglobin found in red blood cells. The myoglobin stores oxygen in muscle tissue.
   2. Fast twitch muscle fibers have few mitochondria and no myoglobin; appearing pale.
      a. They produce ATP via lactate fermentation pathways for short bursts of activity.
      b. This pathway cannot be sustained for long periods.
      c. Most human muscles are a mix of slow and fast twitch fibers.

7.7 Alternative Energy Sources in the Body
   A. The Fate of Glucose at Mealtime and in between Meals
      1. After eating a meal, glucose is absorbed into the blood.
         a. Insulin levels rise, causing greater uptake of glucose by cells for entry into glycolysis.
         b. Excess glucose is converted into glycogen for storage in muscles and the liver.
      2. Between meals blood glucose levels fall. If this were not checked it would be bad.
         a. The hormone glucagon prompts liver cells to convert glycogen back to glucose.
         b. Glycogen levels are adequate but can be depleted in 12 hours.

   B. Energy from Fats
      1. Excess fats (including those made from carbohydrates) are stored away in cells of adipose tissue, primarily as triglycerides. Stored fats insulate and pad parts of our bodies in addition to their role as stored energy.
      2. When blood glucose levels fall, fats are digested into glycerol, which enters glycolysis, and fatty acids, which enter the Krebs cycle.
      3. Because fatty acids have many more carbon and hydrogen atoms than carbohydrates, they are degraded more slowly and yield greater amounts of ATP.
      4. Excess glucose can be converted to fat by a diversion of acetyl-CoA into a pathway that synthesizes fatty acids.

   C. Energy from Proteins
      1. During digestion, proteins are split into their amino acid subunits and absorbed into the bloodstream.
      2. In some cases, amino acids are broken down into their subunits and fed into the Krebs cycle.

Suggestions for Presenting the Material

♦ If photosynthesis has already been presented, Chapter 7 can be even more intimidating when the student views the diagrams of complicated biochemical pathways. It would be comforting to your students if you could spend a few minutes presenting an *overview* that specifically links Chapters 6 (energy acquiring) and 7 (energy releasing).

♦ The critical role of ATP must be emphasized. Distinguish clearly between the *transfer* of energy from carbohydrates to ATP (this chapter) and the *synthesis* of the ATP molecule (Chapter 5).

♦ The material in the chapter is most easily and logically presented by skillful use of the figures and the animations of several of them.

    a. The animated Figure 7.4 is an easy to follow flowchart of aerobic respiration that further reinforces the energy currency role of ATP. Point out the entry molecules, exit molecules, and key intermediates as well as the total energy yield (36 ATPs).

    b. For some instructors in a non-science majors course, Figure 7.4 may be of sufficient detail; however, if you choose, other figures in the chapter depict the details of glycolysis (Animated Figure 7.5), Krebs (Animated Figure 7.7), and electron transfer (Figure 7.8). The animated Figure 7.9 makes a great summary.

♦ As you progress deeper into the pathway discussions, it is advisable to refer frequently to Figure 7.4 to maintain an overview. You will need to indicate that fermentation begins with glucose and proceeds from pyruvate.

♦ Summing up the total energy yield per glucose molecule is important. Use Figure 7.9.

♦ You can emphasize the roles of other foods (proteins and lipids) and their relationship to carbohydrates by following the arrows of Figure 7.12. This especially appeals to students interested in nutrition and exercise physiology.

♦ Emphasize to students the importance of knowing the *processes* rather than memorizing all the various *reactions*.

♦ Although the focus in this chapter is the generation of ATP, you may wish to explain to your students that another major function of respiration is the production of intermediates for biosynthetic reactions.

♦ **Common Student Misconceptions**

    o Students often are deceived by the similarities in terms and biochemical pathways between mitochondria, chloroplasts, photosynthesis, and aerobic respiration. While they are similar in many respects, ground students in the overall function of the two different processes.

    o It should be stated that plants do carry-on aerobic respiration. Many students have the mistaken idea that plants *only* photosynthesize.

Classroom and Laboratory Enrichment

♦ Use a computer simulation to illustrate how basal metabolic rate (BMR) is calculated by measuring oxygen consumption. There are numerous free websites available to illustrate this point and tie it to student nutrition.

♦ Select several students who differ in physical stature and exercise conditioning. Allow them to exercise vigorously for several minutes; then determine heart rate and the length of time before breathing rate returns to normal (indicates extent of oxygen debt).

- Survival shows are popular on television; research and provide information on what happens to the human body when deprived of water and nutrients. Have students speculate about the order in which the body reaches in to stored energy molecules.

- Explain the difference between slow-twitch and fast-twitch muscles by comparing marathon runners and sprinters. To further the discussion, call your athletic department and ask an exercise physiologist to talk to the class about the effect(s) of exercise on body metabolic rate.

- Show an electron micrograph of a mitochondrion (Figure 7.1) and point out the matrix (inner compartment), cristae (inner membranes), and outer compartment. Compare and contrast this to the chloroplast studied in Chapter 6.

- If there is a brewery or winery nearby, arrange for a field trip. Brewmasters and winemakers generally are happy to conduct a tour through the facilities and explain the processes involved.

When Mitochondria Spin Their Wheels (revisited)

- Ask students to relate oxygen consumption to metabolic rate. Have them speculate how diseases or poor nutrition might impact the production of energy.

- In *Luft's syndrome* the mitochondria are not producing sufficient amounts of ATP. What series of reactions could be most responsible for the deficiency?

- Mitochondria are so critical for normal metabolism, but from which parent did each human being's original mitochondria come from at conception?

Additional Ideas for Classroom Discussion

- Table wines, that is, those that have *not* been fortified, have an alcoholic content of about 10–12 percent. What factors could limit the production of alcohol during fermentation? Is it self-limiting, or do the vintners have to stop it with some additive? Ask students to consider alcohol toxicity to the yeast engaged in fermentation processes.

- Your text lists two types of fermentation: one leads to alcohol, the other to lactate. Which occurs in yeasts, and why? Which pathway is reversible? What would be the consequences of nonreversible lactate formation in muscle cells?

- Yeast is added to a mixture of malt, hops, and water to brew beer—a product in which alcohol and carbon dioxide are desirable! Why is yeast added to bread dough?

- Analyze the simple equation for cellular respiration by telling exactly *at what place* in the aerobic metabolism of glucose each item in the equation is a participant.

- Why is fermentation necessary under anaerobic conditions? That is, why does the cell convert pyruvate to some fermentation product when it does not result in any additional ATP production?

How Would You Vote? Classroom Discussion Ideas

- Monitor the voting for the online question. One's response to this question depends on the role of compassion for humankind or the economic limitations inherent in our society.

- Pharmaceutical companies are in business to make money for shareholders. Therefore, they cannot profitably invest time and money in developing a drug/treatment for a small number of persons who will be grateful, but not make the company rich. The only alternative is for the government to provide financial incentives, such as tax breaks, to foster this research.

- Should academics receiving research grants be more likely to receive funding if their research can be shown to provide treatment for rare, and therefore unprofitable, disorders?

Term Paper Topics, Library Activities, and Special Projects

- Rotenone is a fish poison and insecticide. Its mode of action is listed on container labels as "respiratory poison." Exactly where and how does it disrupt cellular respiration?

- Prepare a fermentation vat with grape juice and yeast (don't seal it!). Allow the process to proceed for a few days, then strain the fluid into a flask and distill it. What gas is produced during fermentation? What product distills over at 78.5°C?

- Certain flour beetles and clothes moths can live in environments where exogenous water is virtually unobtainable, yet they thrive. What mechanisms do they use for the synthesis and retention of water?

- Have students research and describe the trend in professional athletics to enhance performance of muscle tissues, aerobic respiration, or other metabolic processes.

- Because ATP is the direct source of energy for body cells, why not bypass the lengthy digestion and cellular metabolism processes necessary for carbohydrate breakdown and eat ATP directly?

- Investigate the "set-point theory" of metabolism; discuss how it relates to people who are trying to lose or gain weight.

- Hydrogen cyanide is the lethal gas used in gas chambers. Have students conduct a web-based search to find out how it causes death.

Responses to *Data Analysis Activities*

1. The number of mitochondria was the abnormality most strongly associated with TF.

2. There is no strong correlation between any mitochondrial abnormality and blood oxygen levels. There is a weak correlation between abnormality of shape and low blood oxygen levels.

Possible Responses to *Critical Thinking* Questions

1. Altitude sickness results from a lack of oxygen, but more specifically, it results from the deficiency of oxygen needed to "pull" the train of electrons along the electron transfer chain, which provides the energy necessary to produce ATP. This would explain why the symptoms of altitude sickness would mimic those of cyanide poisoning, namely, the inability to produce enough ATP to power the muscle cells necessary for breathing and pumping blood.

2. Prokaryotes lack mitochondria and the capacity to produce ATP via aerobic respiration. Instead, they are limited to anaerobic energy-releasing pathways that occur in their cytoplasm. Examples of this are the alcohol or lactate fermentation pathways discussed in section 7.6.

3. You would expect the flight muscles to be dark colored as they would contain many red fibers. Red fibers support aerobic metabolism, and for such a lengthy journey with a sustained effort, aerobic metabolism would be the only metabolic means to provide the necessary output of ATP.

8

DNA STRUCTURE AND FUNCTION

Chapter Outline

Objectives

1. Recognize that chromosomes determine essential functions and gender, in addition to serving as anatomical determinants of species.
2. Understand how experiments using bacteria and viruses demonstrated that instructions for producing heritable traits are encoded in DNA.
2. Describe the building blocks of DNA and recognize proper base pairing in a DNA molecule.
3. Understand how DNA is replicated and repaired.
4. Understand various ways that mammals can be cloned and the implications of such cloning.

Key Terms

clones	chromosome number	DNA sequence	somatic cell nuclear
chromosome	karyotype	DNA ligase	transfer
sister chromatid	sex chromosomes	DNA repair	therapeutic cloning
centromere	bacteriophage	mechanisms	
histones	DNA replication	mutation	
nucleosome	DNA polymerase	reproductive cloning	

Lecture Outline

8.1   A Hero Dog's Golden Clones

   A. Cloning mammals is difficult

      1. Not many nuclear transfers are successful; most individuals die before birth or shortly thereafter.

      2. Those that do survive have many problems with individual organs.

   B. The potential benefits of cloning are enormous, despite the ethical controversy

      1. Replacement cells and organs may help those with incurable degenerative diseases.

      2. Extinct animals might be saved from extinction.

      3. Livestock production can be enhanced.

   C. Animal cloning brings us technically closer to human cloning

8.2   Eukaryotic Chromosomes

   A. DNA Storage

      1. DNA is organized into units known as chromosomes.

      2. Chromosomes may be found unduplicated, or duplicated with two sister chromatids connected at a centromere.

      3. Chromosomes are very long, but compact themselves by forming nucleosomes wrapped around histones.

   B. Chromosome Number

      1. Chromosome number is a characteristic feature of each species.

      2. Cells may be diploid (two copies of each chromosome) or haploid (one copy of each chromosome).

   C. Types of Chromosomes

      1. An organized picture of all the chromosomes in a given cell is called a karyotype.

      2. Autosomes are the same in males and females, sex chromosomes differ and determine an individual's sex.

8.3   The Discover of DNA's Function

   A. Early and Puzzling Clues

      1. Johann Miescher is credited with the discovery of DNA in the late 1800s.

      2. In 1928, Fred Griffith was working with S (pathogenic) and R (nonpathogenic) strains of a pneumonia-causing bacterium.

      3. He performed four experiments summarized here.

         a. Injected mice with R cells; mice lived.

         b. Injected mice with S cells; mice died; and blood samples contained many live S cells.

         c. S cells were heat-killed, then injected into mice; mice lived.

         d. Live R cells plus heat-killed S cells were injected into mice; mice died; and live S cells were found in the blood.

      4. Some substance from the S cells had transformed the R cells.

         a. Both proteins and nucleic acids were candidates.

         b. In 1944, Oswald Avery showed that the substance was DNA.

   B. Confirmation of DNA Function

      1. Viruses called bacteriophages use bacterial cells for reproduction.

      2. Because they consist of only a protein coat and a nucleic acid core, these viruses were used in experiments by Hershey and Chase to show which of these was the hereditary material. (It was the nucleic acid.)

a. ^{35}S-labeled proteins in the bacteriophage coat did not enter the bacteria and thus were not participating in providing directions for new virus assembly.

b. ^{32}P-labeled DNA in the viral core did enter the bacteria and directed new virus assembly.

8.4   The Discovery of DNA's Structure

A. DNA's Building Blocks

1. DNA is composed of four kinds of nucleotides, each of which consists of:

a. A five-carbon sugar—deoxyribose;

b. A phosphate group; and

c. One of four bases—adenine (A), guanine (G), thymine (T), or cytosine (C).

2. The nucleotides are similar, but T and C are single-ring pyrimidines; A and G are double-ring purines.

3. Edwin Chargaff, in 1950, noted two critical bits of data.

a. The four kinds of nucleotide bases making up a DNA molecule differ in relative amounts from species to species.

b. The amount of A = T, and the amount of G = C.

3. James Watson and Francis Crick were using chemical bonding to predict the structure of DNA.

4. Rosalind Franklin used x-ray diffraction techniques to produce images of DNA molecules.

a. DNA exists as a long, thin molecule of uniform diameter.

b. The structure is highly repetitive.

c. DNA is helical.

B. DNA's Base Pair Sequence

1. The following features were incorporated into Watson and Crick's models.

a. Single-ringed thymine was hydrogen bonded with double-ringed adenine, and single-ringed cytosine with double-ringed guanine, along the entire length of the molecule.

b. The backbone was made of chains of sugar-phosphate linkages.

c. The molecule was double stranded and looked like a ladder with a twist to form a double helix.

2. The base pairing is constant for all species, but the sequence of base pairs in a nucleotide strand is different from one species to the next.

8.5   Fame and Glory

A. Rosalind Franklin was a superb practitioner of x-ray crystallography.

1. She worked on taking pictures of DNA and theorizing about its structure, but was not aggressive about publishing her results.

2. At one of her talks, she presented a DNA structure that was a helix but with too many chains and the phosphate groups projected outward.

B. Her coworker, Maurice Wilkins, passed some of her images to Watson and Crick, who were able to piece together all of the data and present the correct DNA structure to the world.

8.6   DNA Replication and Repair

A. How DNA Gets Copied

1. First, the two strands of DNA unwind and expose their bases.

a. Then, unattached nucleotides pair with exposed bases.

b. Thus, replication results in DNA molecules that consist of one original template strand and one newly copied synthesized. This is designated semiconservative replication.

2. Several enzymes participate in replication.
   a. DNA helicase unwinds the two nucleotide strands.
   b. DNA polymerases attach free nucleotides to the growing strand.
   c. DNA ligases seal new short stretches of nucleotides into one continuous strand.
   B. Proofreading
   1. Errors happen during DNA replication and are also caused by environmental factors (radiation, pollution, etc.)
   2. DNA repair mechanisms can fix much of the damaged DNA.
   3. DNA polymerases "proofread" the new bases for mismatched pairs, which are replaced with correct bases.
   4. Errors that are not fixed are mutations.

8.7   Using DNA to Duplicate Existing Mammals

   A. Cloning is a laboratory method of making multiple copies of DNA. Cloning also applies to interventions in reproduction or developments.

   B. Embryo cloning is a natural occurrence producing identical twins. Artificial twinning has been used to give birth to cloned livestock.

   C. Adult or reproductive cloning involves somatic cell nuclear transfer, and therapeutic cloning with a differentiated cell from an adult, whose traits are already known, is more difficult.

Suggestions for Presenting the Material

♦ This chapter amplifies the information on nucleic acids presented at the close of Chapter 3. Depending on the amount of information you presented in your lectures at that time, some of this chapter could be repetitious.

♦ For best success in presenting this chapter, use diagrams and models when discussing the structure and replication of DNA.

♦ Use the animations on the PowerLecture to help students visualize DNA structure and replication.

♦ Students find it hard to understand and identify the components of DNA, so begin this section of the text by making sure that they understand what deoxyribose (the five-carbon sugar in DNA), phosphate groups, and the four nitrogen-containing bases each look like. Briefly show the molecular structures of each of these three major players, and then introduce the term nucleotide.

♦ Ask students to think about the benefits and drawbacks of DNA as a genetic material.

♦ Check with some of the companies that supply biochemistry and cell biology texts about the availability of computer software that literally allows the user to build and manipulate DNA models on the screen.

♦ **Common Student Misconceptions:**
   o Remind students that all organisms, including prokaryotes, have DNA.
   o Also, they may have a hard time grasping that all organisms have the same type of blueprint for life.

Classroom and Laboratory Enrichment

♦ Use large three-dimensional models to show DNA structure.

♦ Ask students to work in teams of two. Give each student a set of labeled paper shapes representing the sugars, phosphate groups, and each of the four bases present in DNA. Ask each student to construct a short segment of a DNA strand while his or her partner builds the complementary strand of the DNA double helix. Then ask students to demonstrate the semiconservative replication of DNA.

♦ Use a video to demonstrate the semiconservative nature of DNA replication.

♦ DNA is described as a "double helix" or "twisted ladder." An inexpensive device that can show this structure very well is a plastic parakeet ladder that is flexible enough to be twisted from "ladder" configuration to "helix."

♦ Prepare a chronological listing of the dates, people, and significant contributions to the discovery of the structure of DNA.

A Hero Dog's Golden Clones (revisited)

♦ Why are so many somatic cell nuclear transfers in cloning experiments not successful?

♦ Why do you think the many health issues that Dolly suffered occurred?

♦ Is cloning necessary? Is it desirable? Is it unethical? Is it just "cool"?

Additional Ideas for Classroom Discussion

♦ What are some reasons why DNA might be double stranded instead of single stranded?

♦ When during the cell cycle does DNA replication occur?

♦ What are some advantages of semiconservative replication?

♦ What experiments done before the structure of DNA was known showed that nucleic acid was the carrier of heredity?

♦ How did the Hershey and Chase experiment settle the question of which molecule—DNA or protein—carries heredity?

♦ Why should the term *DNA relative* replace the more popular term *blood relative* when referring to human kinship?

♦ Which of the following is a more likely source of altered DNA sequences?

  a. New copy has error made during replication from correct original.

  b. New copy has error faithfully copied from incorrect original.

♦ A casual reading of any one of a number of biology texts would imply that Fred Griffith was a pioneer in DNA research. Is this an accurate assessment?

♦ Discuss fun facts about DNA—how many base pairs does the human genome have? If the DNA in each cell was unwound, how long would it be? (Each cell has approximately two meters; the entire human body has approximately 20 billion kilometers!)

How Would You Vote? Classroom Discussion Ideas

♦ Monitor the voting for the online question. Have the students explore the ramifications of banning research on animal cloning. Can the ban be enforced by a new "cloning police"? How would scientists get around the ban?

♦ Do you think that in the future those who support cloning will be viewed as visionaries or villains? For a comparison, imagine the first people to try transferring blood between people and imagine the results.

Term Paper Topics, Library Activities, and Special Projects

♦ What happens if DNA is damaged? How does a cell "recognize" an error in base pairing? Does an organism have ways of repairing such damage?

♦ Describe the research tools (such as radioactive labeling) that have been used in the past, and are being used today, to learn about DNA structure and function.

♦ Describe how the semiconservative nature of DNA replication was discovered.

♦ Learn more about the collaborative nature of scientific discovery, using the discovery of DNA as an example. Could such a discovery have been made at the time by only one individual working alone?

♦ The shape and structure of bacteriophages is reminiscent of a piece of hardware designed for outer-space exploration. To make it more visually appealing, construct a model from inexpensive materials.

♦ Prepare a synopsis of James Watson's account of the discovery of DNA as recorded in the book *The Double Helix*, published by Atheneum.

♦ Rosalind Franklin collected data critical to the elucidation of DNA structure. However, she is hardly mentioned in textbook accounts. Locate a biography of her, and speculate on why she is lesser known than her collaborators. Similarly, why was she not awarded a Nobel prize?

♦ Using the diagram in Figure 8.11 as a starting point, show how copies of DNA from your great-grandparents are present in you.

♦ Explain in simple language how animals can be cloned.

Responses to *Data Analysis Activities*

1. Before blending, 0% of the ^{35}S was outside of the bacteria, and 100% was inside the bacteria. With regard to ^{32}P, roughly 17% was outside the bacteria while the remaining 83% was inside the bacteria.

2. After four minutes of blending, approximately 78% of the ^{35}S was outside the cell, and the remaining 22% was inside. At the same time point, approximately 33% of the ^{32}P was outside the cell, while the remaining 67% was inside the cell.

3. The researchers knew that the liberated radioisotopes did not come from ruptured bacteria as fewer than 10% of the bacteria were ruptured by blending.

4. The concentration of ^{35}S increased most dramatically after blending. These results suggest that viruses inject DNA, as the great increase in extracellular ^{35}S came from the viral coats knocked off the cells surface by blending. The small increase in extracellular ^{32}P came from the small number of cells that ruptured during blending.

Possible Responses to *Critical Thinking* Questions

1. While it is true that cells have repair mechanisms to fix structurally altered or discontinuous DNA, these may not be 100 percent foolproof. Perhaps the repair enzymes might come upon a mistake that they have not encountered before, and therefore have no workable repair mechanism. Or perhaps the repair enzymes themselves have been produced from mutated genes and are therefore mutants.

2. The pros of cloning an extinct animal are that we would have the chance to study an animal that was unavailable to science previously, and that could potentially benefit mankind. However, the cons are very ominous. Introducing a previously absent species to an ecosystem could be extremely deleterious to existing species, and it is possible that the resurrected species could harbor a disease or impact existing organisms in some other fashion.

9

FROM DNA TO PROTEINS

Chapter Outline

9.1 RICIN AND YOUR RIBOSOMES

9.2 THE NATURE OF GENETIC INFORMATION
  Converting a Gene to an RNA
  Converting mRNA to Protein

9.3 TRANSCRIPTION
  Post-Transcriptional Modification

9.4 RNA AND THE GENETIC CODE
  rRNA and tRNA – The Translators

9.5 TRANSLATING THE CODE: RNA TO PROTEIN

9.6 MUTATED GENES AND THEIR PROTEIN PRODUCTS
  What Causes Mutations?

RICIN AND YOUR RIBOSOMES (REVISITED)

SUMMARY

DATA ANALYSIS ACTIVITIES

SELF-QUIZ

CRITICAL THINKING

Objectives

1. Recognize the nucleotide sequence of a gene determines the amino acid sequence of a protein.
2. Understand how DNA is converted to mRNA via transcription.
3. Describe the three types of RNA and the role each serves in transcription and translation.
4. Understand how mRNA is converted to a polypeptide chain via translation.
5. Understand the nature of mutations and their role in genetic variation.

Key Terms

genes	translation	alternative splicing
transcription	gene expression	genetic code
ribosomal RNA (rRNA)	RNA polymerase	deletion
transfer RNA (rRNA)	promoter	insertion
messenger RNA (mRNA)	introns	base-pair substitution
	exons	transposable elements

Lecture Outline

9.1 Ricin and Your Ribosomes

  A. Ricin could be a biochemical weapon

    1. It is most concentrated in the seeds of the castor oil plant.

    2. It is very poisonous and is a product of castor oil production.

    3. Ricin inactivates ribosomes.

      a. It takes adenine bases off the RNA on the ribosome.

      b. The ribosome "workbenches" are destroyed and protein synthesis stops; death!

9.2 The Nature of Genetic Information

  A. DNA is like a book of instructions in each cell

    1. The instructions are written in the alphabet of A, T, G, and C. But merely knowing the letters does not tell us how the genes work.

  B. Converting a Gene to an RNA

    1. The path from genes to proteins has two steps.

      a. In *transcription,* molecules of RNA are produced on the DNA templates in the nucleus.

      b. RNA is similar to DNA, but contains uracil instead of thymine, is single-stranded, and has ribose as a sugar instead of deoxyribose.

      c. There are three types of RNA

        - Messenger RNA (mRNA) carries the "blueprint" to the ribosome.

        - Ribosomal RNA (rRNA) combines with proteins to form ribosomes upon which polypeptides are assembled.

        - Transfer RNA (tRNA) brings the correct amino acid to the ribosome and pairs up with an mRNA code for that amino acid.

  C. Converting mRNA to Protein

      a. In translation, RNA molecules shipped from the nucleus to the cytoplasm are used as templates for polypeptide assembly.

      b. The overall process of gene expression may be expressed as: DNA → RNA → protein.

9.3 Transcription

  A. The Nature of Transcription

    1. Transcription differs from DNA replication in three ways.

      a. Only *one* region of *one* DNA strand is used as a template.

      b. RNA polymerase is used instead of DNA polymerase.

      c. The result of transcription is a single-stranded RNA.

    2. Transcription begins when RNA polymerase binds to a promoter (a base sequence region at the start of a gene) and then moves along to the end of a gene; an RNA transcript is the result.

    3. RNA polymerase incorporates complementary RNA nucleotides along the length of the gene.

  B. Post-Transcriptional Modifications

    1. Newly formed mRNA is an unfinished molecule, not yet ready for use.

    2. mRNA transcripts are modified before leaving the nucleus.

      a. Noncoding portions (*introns*) are snipped out, and actual coding regions (*exons*) are spliced together to produce the mature transcript.

      b. The 5′ end is *capped* with a special nucleotide that serves as a "start" signal for translation.

      c. A "poly-A tail" of about 100–200 molecules of adenylic acid is added to the 3′ end.

From DNA to Proteins   **69**

9.4   RNA and the Genetic Code

A. mRNA transcripts are the protein-building "words"

B. Both DNA and its RNA transcript are linear sequences of nucleotides carrying the hereditary code

C. Every three bases (a triplet) specifies an amino acid to be included into a growing polypeptide chain; the complete set of triplets is called the *genetic code*
    1. Each base triplet in RNA is called a *codon*.
    2. The genetic code consists of 61 triplets that specify amino acids and three that serve to stop protein synthesis.
    3. While each codon requesting an amino acid is specific, there is redundancy in the code (i.e. multiple codons may ask for the same amino acid).
    4. With few exceptions, the genetic code is universal for all forms of life.

D. rRNA and tRNA – The Translators
    1.   rRNAs and tRNAs interact to translate mRNA codons into polypeptide chains.
    2.   Ribosomes have two subunits that perform together only during translation. Each subunit consists of rRNA and structural proteins.
    3.   After the mRNA arrives in the cytoplasm, an anticodon on a tRNA bonds to the codon on the mRNA, and thus a correct amino acid is brought into place.
        a.   Each kind of tRNA has an *anticodon* that is complementary to an mRNA codon; each tRNA also carries one specific amino acid.

9.5   Translating the Code: RNA to Protein

A. Translation, the second step in protein synthesis, proceeds through three stages in the cytoplasm.
    1. In *initiation,* a complex forms in this sequence: initiator tRNA + small ribosomal subunit + mRNA + large ribosomal subunit.
    2. In *elongation,* a start codon on mRNA defines the reading frame; a series of tRNAs deliver amino acids in sequence by codon-anticodon matching; a peptide bond joins each amino acid to the next in sequence.
    3. In *termination,* a stop codon is reached and the polypeptide chain is released into the cytoplasm or enters the cytomembrane system for further processing.
    4. The three steps just outlined can be repeated many times on the same mRNA because several ribosomes may be moving along the mRNA at the same time (polysome).

B. What happens to the new polypeptides?
    1. Some polypeptides join the cytoplasm's pool of free proteins; others enter the rough ER of the cytomembrane system to take on their final form.

9.6   Mutated Genes and Their Protein Products

A. A gene mutation is a permanent change in one to several bases in the nucleotide sequence of DNA, which can result in a change in the protein synthesized.

B. Common Mutations
    1. In a "frameshift mutation," there may be an insertion or deletion of several base pairs, causing a misreading of the mRNA during translation.
    2. Spontaneous mutation can cause sickle-cell anemia, which is the result of a single "base pair substitution," which places valine as the sixth amino acid in the hemoglobin chain instead of glutamate.

C. What Causes Mutations?
    1. Mutations are often caused by transposable elements, which are regions of DNA that "jump" to new locations in DNA.

1. Mutations may occur due to errors in DNA replication.
2. Mutations can be caused by mutagens such as ionizing radiation (gamma and X-rays), nonionizing radiation (ultraviolet radiation), and chemicals (natural and synthetic), which act as carcinogens.

Suggestions for Presenting the Material

♦ The subject of protein synthesis is difficult for students. Students should be able to achieve a good understanding of protein synthesis if they begin by visualizing it as two major steps, transcription and translation, rather than getting lost in complex details. The events of protein synthesis can be effectively presented with one of the available videos or animations as visual aids. Students need to have some kind of mental picture in order to understand what happens during the making of a protein. For complex subjects, it is useful to open with a visual aid and conclude by once again reviewing this visual aid.

♦ You may also want to review protein structure (Chapter 3).

♦ Stress the role that mutations play in producing "new" genes and "new" proteins.

♦ **Common Student Misconception:**

  o Be sure to emphasize that mutations are part of the evolutionary arena. Some mutations are beneficial, some are neutral, and some are bad. Students may just assume all mutations are bad, when that is not the case.

  o Students believe that since all organisms have the same universal genetic code, therefore they have the same DNA sequences. Be sure they understand that the actual DNA sequences of that code differ between individuals and that this is what makes each organism different.

Classroom and Laboratory Enrichment

♦ Use models, videos, and animations to show protein synthesis. Refer to the PowerLecture for available animations.

♦ Give students a "dictionary" of the genetic code (Figure 9.7) and ask them to identify the codons within a linear stretch of mRNA and tell what amino acid each codon will specify.

♦ Using Figure 9.4, 9.6 or 9.11 cover several of the labels and ask students to review the steps of protein synthesis aloud in class.

♦ The following items may help your students remember the difference between "transcription" and "translation."

  a. *Transcription* involves the transfer of information from one form to another *in the same* language, for example, an office memo in shorthand is transcribed into typed copy, but both in English; likewise, a section of genetic code in DNA is copied to RNA (both nucleic acids).

  b. *Translation* is the transfer of information in *one language* to *another language*, for example, a story in French is translated to English; likewise, genetic code in RNA is transferred to amino acids (nucleic acid to protein).

♦ As another aid, think of this process like cooking. DNA is a cookbook that you want to protect. Therefore, you make a copy, or transcript, of the recipe you wish to work with. The copied recipe is the RNA, and both the cookbook (DNA) and the recipe (RNA) are the same 'language' = words on paper. To make food, you need to translate the recipe (RNA) to a new 'language' = food. The food is the protein.

◆ As an aid to the understanding of protein synthesis, the following analogy in which the process is compared to the construction of a building may be useful.

a. DNA "sealed" in the nucleus leave .... a. Master blueprints that never the architect's office

b. mRNA that leaves nucleus to go to ribosome .... b. Blueprint copies that are taken to the job site

c. Ribosomes and rRNA .... c. The construction site

d. Enzymes .... d. Construction workers

e. tRNA carrying amino acids .... e. Trucks carrying materials

f. Amino acids .... f. Building materials

◆ Take the opportunity to discuss skin cancer, which is often a result of mutation from UV radiation. This is a topic that will grab your students' attention while educating them on prevention of a common disease.

Ricin and Your Ribosomes (revisited)

◆ Why are ribosomes essential to protein synthesis?

◆ How can one molecule of ricin impact so many ribosomes?

◆ Using 'targeted-ricin' could be useful in fighting cancer cells. Could this process be extended to pathogenic disorders?

Additional Ideas for Classroom Discussion

◆ Ask students to compare and contrast: transcription and translation; codons and anticodons; and rRNA, mRNA, and tRNA.

◆ Why is transcription necessary? Why don't cells use their DNA as a direct model for protein synthesis?

◆ Have students describe the three stages of translation.

◆ In what ways are the instructions encoded in DNA sometimes altered?

◆ In most species, mutation is usually not considered an important evolutionary force. Why?

◆ Demonstrate how gene mutations such as a base substitution or a transposition will produce abnormal proteins.

◆ In what ways does RNA differ from DNA?

◆ Which of the RNAs is "reusable"?

◆ Why do you think DNA has *introns*, which are transcribed but removed before translation begins?

◆ If all DNA is made of the same basic building units (sugar, phosphate, and nitrogenous bases), then how can DNA differ in, say, a human and a bacterium?

◆ This chapter refers to the participants and process involved in protein synthesis as if they have been *seen* doing their work; have they? How then do we know all of this information is accurate?

♦ How can you explain the occurrence of birth defects (caused by altered genes) in children and grandchildren of the victims of the atomic bombs that destroyed Hiroshima and Nagasaki, Japan, when the victims themselves were only mildly affected?

How Would You Vote? Classroom Discussion Ideas

♦ Monitor the voting for the online question. Invite your students to consider the value of mass immunization versus the risks. Remind them that even with a long history of successful immunization for such common diseases as measles, there are still minimal risks. What greater challenges face programs that do not have such a long history? Should the general public be vaccinated for something they are not likely to encounter, like ricin or even anthrax? Would immunizing everyone make the threat less likely?

Term Paper Topics, Library Activities, and Special Projects

♦ Describe experiments performed by Khorana, Nirenberg, Ochoa, Holley, and others to decipher the genetic code.

♦ Discover why repeated applications of a single drug or pesticide can result in resistance among bacterial strains and species of insects. Why does this pose a problem? What steps can be taken to avoid resistant strains of pathogenic bacteria and disease-carrying insects?

♦ Learn more about the discovery and treatment of sickle-cell anemia.

♦ What kinds of substances act as chemical mutagens? What are some of the effects mutagenic substances can have? What kinds of mutagenic agents might be found in industrial waste?

♦ Prepare a visual aid chart that graphically depicts the series of errors (in DNA, mRNA, tRNA, and amino acids) that lead to the production of the abnormal hemoglobin in sickle-cell anemia.

♦ The progress in molecular biology has proceeded from deciphering genetic codes to the construction of man-made genes by machine. Report on the construction and use applications of such devices.

♦ Investigate reports of "gene replacement" as a preventative of possible genetic abnormalities. In what organism has it been tried? Was it successful? What are the difficulties of this procedure?

♦ What are some common substances that act as mutagens? How are some of these mutagens known to cause cancer? Are there substances that will block the effects of mutagens?

♦ Learn more about the research of Barbara McClintock.

Responses to Data Analysis Activities

1. The group that sprayed the low-range amount of 2,4-D had the lower frequency of chromosome breaks.

2. The group with the highest frequency of chromosome missing pieces and breaks was the heavy spray group.

3. In total, 22 herbicide-wielding foresters were tested.

Possible Responses to *Critical Thinking* Questions

1. Antisense drugs interact with their intended target based on information in the genetic code. Overproduction or abnormal production of proteins is implicated in cancer and many diseases. Antisense drugs will stop the translation of these proteins by preventing the mRNA coding for them from reaching the ribosome. They do this by binding (hybridizing) to the target mRNA, which is degraded by enzymes and thus not translated.

2. The amino acid carried by this tRNA would be arginine. A mutation that turned the anticodon C to a G would result in the anticodon recognizing the codon normally requesting proline.

3. The minimum number of nucleotides per codon (assuming four total nucleotides) necessary to specify all 20 amino acids would be three. One-nucleotide codons could specify only four amino acids, and two-nucleotide codons could specify only 16 amino acids. Three-nucleotide codons can specify 64 amino acids (ignoring stop codons).

4. GLY-PHE-LEU-LYS-ARG

5. VAL-SER-STOP-ARG (though it would not make it past the stop codon)

6. Perhaps binding of carcinogenic products of cigarette smoke can cause an error in transcription to mRNA. We know that incorrect codons will match with incorrect anticodons of tRNA, leading to an incorrect sequence in the finished protein. Perhaps one or more of these proteins, either structural or enzymatic, could trigger cancerous growth. There is research (targeting the P53 gene) that supports this hypothesis.

10

CONTROLS OVER GENES

Chapter Outline

Objectives

1. Understand that gene control is impacted by cell specialization, and internal and external conditions.
2. Understand how differentiation proceeds by selective gene expression during development.
3. Understand the role of chromosome inactivation in organism development.
4. Understand how operon controls regulate gene expression in prokaryotes.

Key Terms

cancer	repressor	pattern formation	operators
differentiation	transcription factors	X chromosome	operon
activator	homeotic genes	inactivation	
enhancers	master genes	dosage compensation	

Lecture Outline

10.1 Between You and Eternity

    A. There are more than 200,000 new cases of breast cancer each year.

    B. Cancers are very diverse, but several gene mutations predispose individuals to developing certain kinds.

10.2 Gene Expression in Eukaryotic Cells

    A. Differentiation helps determine which genes are expressed in which cell

    B. Control of Transcription

        1. Promoters are short stretches of base sequences in DNA where regulatory proteins control transcription of specific genes.

        2. Enhancers are the binding sites in DNA where regulatory proteins are found, increasing transcription rates.

        3. Activators bind promoters or enhancers, speeding up transcription; repressors bind promoters, slowing or stopping transcription.

        4. Control can be exerted by chemical modification, such as the methylation of DNA, or by and the duplication and rearrangement of DNA sequences (polytene chromosomes).

    C. mRNA Processing

        1. Controls of mRNA modification include splicing, capping, and the modification of poly-A tails.

    D. mRNA Transport

        1. Processing controls also affect mRNA transport.

    E. Translational Control

        1. Most control over eukaryotic gene expression affects translation.

        2. The stability of mRNA, and microRNAs are examples of mechanisms that control translation.

    F. Post-Translational Modification

        1. These may inhibit, activate, or stabilize the molecule.

10.3 There's a Fly in My Research

    A. Drosophila is a favorite for lab experiments because it is so easy to raise and manipulate

    B. Homeotic Genes

        1. Studies of fruit flies, aided by their short life cycle and small genome, have told us a lot about gene controls over embryonic development.

        2. Homeotic genes are master genes that control the formation of specific body parts during embryonic development.

        3. Master genes, which include homeotic genes, produce products that impact the expression of other genes.

        4. Localized expression of homeotic genes in tissues of embryos gives rise to the details of the body plan.

        5. Knockout experiments, in which individual genes are deleted, have identified many genes by the *absence* of function due to the missing gene; for example, *tinman* is necessary for heart development.

        6. Researchers can control the expression of external cues, such as temperature, by adding special promoters to genes.

C. Filling In Details of Body Plans
   1. Regional gene expression during development results in a dynamic three-dimensional map of an embryo.
   2. The emergence of embryonic tissues and organs in predictable patterns is called pattern formation.

10.4 A Few Outcomes of Gene Controls
   A. X Chromosome Inactivation
      1. In mammalian females, the gene products of only one X chromosome are needed; the other is condensed and inactive—called a Barr body.
      2. Because in some cells the paternal X chromosome is inactivated, while in other cells the maternal X chromosome is inactivated, each adult female is a mosaic of X-linked traits called mosaic tissue effect.
      3. This mosaic effect is seen in human females affected by incontinentia pigmenti, in which a mutant gene on one X chromosome results in darker patches of skin. This effect is also seen in calico cats.
      4. Dosage compensation is the name for the process that shuts down one X of the female so that the overall expression of the remaining X of the female is equivalent to the lone X of the male.
   B. Male Sex Determination in Humans
      1. The Y chromosome carries the SRY gene which triggers male sex development.
      2. SRY is a master gene, impacting the expression of numerous other genes.
   C. Gene Control over Flower Formation
      1. Plants have gene controls too.
      2. Studies of plant mutations in *Arabidopsis thaliana* support an ABC model of floral development and specialization.
         a. Three sets of master genes (A, B, C) guide flower development in a predictable pattern.
         b. Cell differentiation in the plant depends upon which genes of the ABC group are activated.

10.5 Gene Control in Bacteria
   A. Bacteria primarily control their gene expression by altering the rate of transcription
   B. The Lactose Operon
      1. *E. coli* bacteria (common in the human digestive tract) can metabolize lactose because of a series of three genes that code for lactose-digesting enzymes.
         a. The three genes are preceded by a promoter and two operators—all together called an operon.
         b. A regulator gene nearby codes for a repressor protein that binds to both operators when lactose concentrations are low and effectively blocks RNA polymerase's access to the promoter.
      2. When milk is consumed, the allolactose binds to the repressor, changing its shape and effectively removing its blockage of the promoter; thus RNA polymerase can now initiate transcription of the genes.
   C. Lactose Intolerance
      1. Lactase digests lactose in food.
      2. If lactase is missing lactose builds up in the colon. Bacteria take advantage of this carbohydrate for fermentation, creating byproducts that cause abdominal pain.

3. A buildup of undigested carbohydrates disrupts the solute-water balance in the colon and result in diarrhea.
4. A mutation in the lactase shutdown gene allows its continued expression into adulthood.

Suggestions for Presenting the Material

♦ This chapter builds upon information that students learned in previous chapters about gene structure and function. Terms such as DNA, mRNA, transcription, and translation must be familiar before beginning this chapter.

♦ Emphasize to the students that the control of gene expression is an extremely complex subject area, one which is best approached by first studying some fairly simple and well-understood examples in prokaryotes.

♦ Give students opportunities to learn and use new words such as promoter, operator, and operon. Gene control among eukaryotes will be easier to understand if students view it as a series of levels.

Classroom and Laboratory Enrichment

♦ Use visual aids and animations to illustrate the lactose operon (Figure 10.10).

♦ Use models to show induction and repression of gene expression in the operon.

♦ Have posters, statistics, and general information available regarding breast and prostate cancer for students to review.

♦ Prepare a summary table that lists the following:

Type of Control	Specific Example	Found In:		
		Prokaryote	Eukaryote	Both
a. transcriptional				
b. transcript processing				
c. translational				
d. post-translation				

Between You and Eternity (revisited)

♦ BRCA1 and BRCA2 are genes noted to predispose individuals to breast cancer. Are there other genes that predispose people to other cancers?

♦ What are the benefits of learning you have a gene that may lead to cancer? What are the disadvantages of receiving such knowledge?

♦ What is the likelihood that there will be a breakthrough cure for cancer in your lifetime?

Additional Ideas for Classroom Discussion

♦ What is the role of gene control in causing cancer? How are some viruses known to be linked to cancer?

♦ Do you think cancer-causing genes could someday be repaired?

- What would be the hypothetical effect on the lactose operon of a modified lactose molecule? Do you think it would still bind to the repressor?
- What is the "economic" advantage to a prokaryotic cell of possessing inducible enzymes?

How Would You Vote? Classroom Discussion Ideas

- Monitor the voting for the online question. The decision by some women to have their breasts removed to prevent developing cancer could be a truly life-altering decision. At first glance, this decision could make sense for those women who are at elevated risk due to genetic or family history factors. But given the societal correlation between breasts and the feminine, this surgery can have major ramifications on how these women are received by society. This surgery is also a major surgery that is not to be taken lightly.

Term Paper Topics, Library Activities, and Special Projects

- Learn more about current research efforts attempting to uncover the mysteries of differentiation.
- Describe the operon and its function.
- Learn more about oncogenes and cancer.
- Discover more about the discovery and diagnostic uses of the Barr body in female mammalian cells.
- What are some common substances that act as mutagens? How are some of these mutagens known to cause cancer? Are there substances that will block the effects of mutagens?
- Learn more about tumor cell lines used to study cancerous cell growth in vitro in the laboratory.
- Locate the original article by Francois Jacob and Jacques Monod proposing the lac operon. How have the details changed?
- Likewise, see if you can locate the original research publications of Murray Barr and Mary Lyon. Notice the dates of these publications. Were they before or after the publication of DNA structure by Watson and Crick in 1953?

Responses to *Data Analysis Activities*

1. According to this study, women who have had two close relatives with breast cancer have an 8.6% chance of dying of breast cancer.
2. If a woman in this study had a mutated BRCA1 gene, she had an 18% chance of dying of breast cancer.
3. According to these results, a BRCA1 gene mutation is much more dangerous.
4. In order to ascertain the effectiveness of preventative mastectomy or oophorectomy, one would need to see the fraction of patients that underwent those procedures that subsequently died of cancer.

Possible Responses to *Critical Thinking* Questions

1. A cell regulates its gene expression because it contains too many genes. The compromise of being multicellular is that every cell contains every gene the organism needs to live. However, , the majority of which are not needed by any specific cell at a specific time.

2. No. Three types of gene controls are: (1) control by histone organization of the DNA, (2) transcriptional control by regulatory proteins in operons, and (3) control of the transport of mRNA out of the nucleus. Those not found in prokaryotes are: (1) because the single, circular DNA of prokaryotes is not organized around histone proteins; and (2) because there is no nucleus in prokaryotes. Of course, (3) is very typical of prokaryotes; the same mechanism is not found in eukaryotes.

3. According to several websites that describe (in detail with photos) how to determine the sex of a guinea pig, the observation must be done very carefully. Some even suggest that novices take the animals to a vet for proper identification. The macroscopic identification involves manipulating the genital area to force the penis outward. This is crucial because the female and male genital areas of guinea pigs are extremely similar. Of course, you could also make a definitive determination by observing the chromosomes using a microscope. This would involve a skillful preparation of the chromosomes, which is beyond the expertise of most persons. The male would have XY and the female XX chromosomes in the karyotype.

4. The mutation in an *E. coli* strain has hampered the capacity of CAP protein to bind near the promoter region of the *lac* operon. This in turn means that the RNA polymerase necessary for the transcription of the genes for lactose-metabolizing enzymes cannot bind. Lactose will therefore not be metabolized if it is present.

   (a) If both lactose and glucose are present, the bacteria will metabolize the glucose by preference due to the non-binding mentioned just above.
   (b) If lactose is available but not glucose, normally the lactose-metabolizing enzymes would kick in, but they are not available due to the non-binding. In this case, the bacterium has an energy source, but it is not usable.
   (c) If both lactose and glucose are absent, the bacterium has no energy source, unless the pathway for another sugar is somehow induced.

11

HOW CELLS REPRODUCE

Chapter Outline

Objectives

1. Understand what is meant by *cell cycle* and explain where mitosis fits into the cell cycle.
2. Be able to describe each phase of mitosis.
3. Explain various mechanisms of cytoplasmic divisions, specifically as it relates to plant and animal cells.
4. Understand some of the implications when the control of cell division is lost.

Key Terms

cell cycle	asexual	telophase	tumor
interphase	reproduction	cytokinesis	oncogene
mitosis	prophase	cleavage furrow	proto-oncogenes
homologous	spindle	cellplate	cancer
chromosomes	metaphase	neoplasm	metastasis
	anaphase	growth factors	

Lecture Outline

11.1   Henrietta's Immortal Cells

    A.   Researchers at Johns Hopkins University cultured a line of immortal cells in 1951

        1.   They are referred to as HeLa cells after their source—a woman named Henrietta Lacks.

        2.   Her cells continue to provide for research around the world.

11.2   Multiplication by Division

    A.   The Life of a Cell

        1.   The control of cell division resides in the subphases of interphase.

            a.   During G_1, cells assemble most of the carbohydrates, lipids, and proteins that are needed by the cell and for export.

            b.   During the S phase the DNA and histones are copied.

            c.   During G_2, further protein synthesis drives the cell toward mitosis.

        2.   Before cells are able to reproduce, there must be a division of the nucleus and it's DNA.

            b.   During mitosis, the homologous chromosomes pair up, and then separate.

        3.   After cell and nuclear division, the entire cycle begins again.

    B.   A Bigger Picture of Cell Division

        1.   Most of a cell's existence (about 90 percent) is spent in interphase; mitosis occupies only a small portion.

            a.   During interphase the cell's mass increases, the cytoplasmic components approximately double in number, *and the DNA is doubled.*

            b.   Some cells are arrested in interphase and usually never divide again (example: brain cells).

  2.   Prokaryotic cells reproduce asexually by an entirely different mechanism called asexual reproduction.

11.3   Mitosis

    A.   Mitosis begins with prophase.

        1.   Chromosomes become visible as rodlike units, each consisting of two sister chromatids.

        2.   Microtubules move one pair of centrioles to opposite poles of the cell.

        3.   The nuclear envelope begins to disintegrate.

        4.   Microtubules of the spindle extend from the centrioles and attach to the centromeres (kinetochore area) of the duplicated chromosomes.

    B.   The transition to metaphase occurs as the chromosomes begin an orderly arrangement.

        1.   Sister chromatids are each attached separately to microtubules from opposite poles.

        2.   When all the chromosomes are aligned at the cell's equator halfway between the poles, the cell is said to be in metaphase.

    C.   During anaphase the chromosomes migrate to opposite poles.

        1.   The kinetochores of sister chromatids separate and move toward opposite poles.

            a.   Microtubules attached to the centromeres shorten and pull the chromosomes toward the poles.

            b.   Other microtubules at the spindle poles ratchet past each other to push the two spindle poles apart.

        2.   Once separated, each chromatid is now an independent chromosome.

    D.   Telophase gets underway when the chromosomes reach the respective poles.

        1.   Each half of the cell now contains two clusters of chromosomes that are identical and equal in number.

2. The chromosomes decondense and return to the threadlike form typical of interphase.

3. The nuclear envelope forms from the fusion of small vesicles; mitosis is complete.

11.4 Cytokinesis: Division of Cytoplasm

A. How Do Animal Cells Divide

1. Cytoplasmic division (cytokinesis) in animals is by means of a cleavage furrow.

  a. The flexible plasma membrane of animal cells can be squeezed in the middle to separate the two daughter cells.

  b. Parallel arrays of microfilaments, called the contractile ring, slide past one another at the cleavage furrow, pulling the plasma membrane inward.

2. Each daughter cell ends up with a nucleus, some cytoplasm (with organelles), and a plasma membrane.

B. How Do Plant Cells Divide

1. Because of the rather rigid cell wall, the cytoplasm of plant cells cannot just be pinched in two.

2. Instead vesicles containing remnants of the microtubular spindle form a disk-like structure, called a cell plate, between the two new cells.

11.5 Controls Over Cell Division

A. The Cell Cycle Revisited

1. The cell cycle has built-in checkpoints where proteins can advance, delay, or block forward progress of the cycle.

2. Certain proteins can signal the end of DNA replication; growth factors signal the start of mitosis.

B. Checkpoint Failure and Tumors

1. When checkpoint mechanisms fail, a cell loses control over its replication cycle.

  a. The result is a neoplasm: a mass of cells that has lost control over growth and division.

  b. Incorrect recognition of growth factors can result, leading to unregulated cell division.

11.6 Cancer: When Control Is Lost

A. Characteristics of Cancer

1. Proto-oncogenes code for proteins that stimulate mitosis; if these are mutated they may become oncogenes.

  a. Neoplasms are abnormal masses of cells that have lost controls over their growth and cell division and may form a cancer.

  b. First, cancer cells grow and divide abnormally.

  c. Second, cancer cells are physically altered, changing both their shape and metabolism; as a result they may move from their intended location.

Suggestions for Presenting the Material

♦ This is the first of two chapters concerning cell reproduction. The present one explains mitosis—division in which the number of chromosomes remains the same in the identical daughter cells. The next chapter explains meiosis, in which the number of chromosomes is reduced during the production of cells destined to become gametes.

♦ Students often have trouble following the number of chromosomes throughout the stages of mitosis. To help them, remind them that each chromosome has one centromere, and that it is

How Cells Reproduce **83**

not until centromeres divide in anaphase that "sister chromatids" are considered "chromosomes." Make certain that students understand where and when mitosis occurs in any organism.

♦ If you emphasize the *number* of chromosomes prior to, and just after, mitosis, it may be less confusing to temporarily ignore the use of *sister chromosome* and *daughter chromosome* and replace with *potential chromosome* and *chromosome*, respectively.

♦ Another approach to explaining the *number* of chromosomes before and after mitosis is to abandon all mention of chromosomes and simply keep track of the number of DNA molecules present at each stage. It would look like this for a human somatic cell: G_1 (46); S (92); G_2 (92); prophase (92); metaphase (92); anaphase (46 moving to each pole); telophase (46 each cell).

♦ Emphasize to the student that the "secret" to preserving the chromosome number in the two daughter cells of mitosis and cutting the chromosome number in half in the four daughter cells of meiosis (next chapter) is the same—DNA duplication during interphase!

♦ **Common Student Misconceptions:**

  o Students have a hard time visualizing the cell cycle as a cycle. Emphasize the cell cycle, stressing that cells are not dividing all of the time. Students should be aware of the fact that the steps of cell division are part of a continuum. Our separation of the process into four stages is an artificial one, and it may be hard to say where one stage ends and the next begins when looking at a dividing cell. You may compare it to the showing of a "game tape" that athletes watch to see the errors committed in the big game.

  o The vocabulary involved in cell division is confusing to the students. When using sister chromatids, homologous chromosomes, chromosome, etc. be sure to emphasize the proper definition so students can follow the explanation.

Classroom and Laboratory Enrichment

♦ Ask students (working individually or in small groups) to use chromosome simulation kits (available from biological supply houses) to demonstrate chromosome replication during the stages of mitosis. If kits are unavailable, make your own chromosomes using a pop-it bead (or bead and cord) for each chromatid and a magnet for each centromere.

♦ View ready-made squashes of mitotic material, such as onion root tip, or an overhead transparency of mitotic material using a microprojector. Ask students to estimate the length of each mitotic phase after counting the number of cells in each phase in several fields of view. Also ask students to identify each phase and to give one or two major events happening in each phase.

♦ Perhaps the following analogy can help students visualize chromosomes during mitosis:

2 chromatids   =   2 nearly matched socks

1 centromere   =   1 clothespin

spindle fiber   =   clothesline

♦ Emphasize an application of cell division to students. Have part of the laboratory session dedicated to exploring cancer and cancer prevention. Use the lab time to interpret graphs and statistics on cancer. Potentially, springboard into the scientific process by discussing clinical trials (how they are set up, what placebo means, why placebos are used, whether it is ethical to use placebos, etc.).

Henrietta's Immortal Cells (revisited)

◆ Loosely speaking, the process of one cell becoming two cells is often referred to as mitosis, but to be completely accurate, what does mitosis *specifically* refer to?

◆ How can the mathematically impossible become the biologically possible—namely, a cell with 46 chromosomes splits to form two cells *each* with 46 chromosomes? This means 46 divided by 2 equals 46 and 46. What event during the cell cycle makes this possible?

◆ How do cancer cells differ from regular cells with regard to their ability to divide in culture? Why does this increase their value as a research tool?

Additional Ideas for Classroom Discussion

◆ Using a generation time of 20 minutes, calculate the size of a bacterial population that has arisen from a single bacterium growing under optimum conditions (for example, *Salmonella* in a bowl of unrefrigerated potato salad at a picnic on a warm summer day) for eight hours.

◆ Many of the drugs used in chemotherapy cause loss of hair in the individual being treated. Ask students if they can figure out why such drugs affect hair growth.

◆ Biologists used to believe that interphase was a "resting period" during the life cycle of the cell. Why did this appear to be so?

◆ How can there be 46 chromosomes in a human cell at metaphase and also 46 chromosomes after the centromere splits in anaphase (see Figure 8.6)? Hint: Focus on the name change of chromatids to daughter chromosomes.

◆ What is there about the composition of an animal cell versus a plant cell that necessitates different methods of cleavage?

How Would You Vote? Classroom Discussion Ideas

◆ Monitor the voting for the online question. The very question of whether a person (or his relatives) should be compensated for being the source of tissue is very much in debate today. Various court cases have decided the issue both for and against. One the one hand, the donor is highly unlikely to possess the skills to study their cells in the manner that could lead to potential treatment to others. On the other hand, researchers are reliant on donor cells, and quite often the donor is in a situation in which financial remuneration for themselves or their family would be most welcome.

◆ In the case of Henrietta Lacks, she most likely donated her cells without knowledge, and this was likely legal at the time. Should drug companies be obligated to compensate family members alive today that likely did not know Henrietta or could justify a great suffering from her loss? Similarly, can the current knowledge of her cell's value be used to assess the compensation for her family (e.g. in 1962, what would have been paid for all future royalties from a band named The Beatles assuming one could not see the future?)

Term Paper Topics, Library Activities, and Special Projects

♦ Much progress in studying human disease has been made using the research technique of tissue culture. Describe techniques of tissue culture, explaining how cells can be induced to grow and divide in vitro.

♦ Explore diseases (such as cancer) that involve cell growth gone wrong. How do such diseases affect the mechanism of cell division? What drugs are used to halt runaway cell growth? How do these drugs work, and what are their side effects?

♦ Why do some cells of the human body (for example, epithelial cells) continue to divide, yet other cells (for example, nerve cells) lose their ability to replicate once they are mature? Describe some of the latest research efforts to induce cell division in nerve cells.

♦ Colchicine is a chemical used to treat dividing plant cells to ensure that chromosomes of cells undergoing mitosis will be visible. How does colchicine achieve this effect? What is the natural source of colchicine?

♦ The 1956 edition of the high school biology text *Modern Biology* by Moon, Mann, and Otto was the last to state the human chromosome number as 48. This was not a misprint. What investigations resulted in assigning the correct number of 46 to humans?

♦ The preparation of a karyotype (picture of chromosomes) is a simple but multi-step procedure. Provide a procedural outline for making such a preparation of chromosomes for publication in a book.

♦ There is some question as to exactly how chromosomes move to opposite ends of the cell in concert with the bipolar mitotic spindle fibers. Investigate the various theories, and report on their strengths and weaknesses.

Responses to *Data Analysis Activities*

1. The chromosome number of this HeLa cell is 82.

2. This cell has 36 more chromosomes than a regular human cell.

3. That this cell came from a female is apparent because there are no Y chromsomes.

Possible Responses to *Critical Thinking* Questions

1. This is a very big question with huge ramifications. On the one hand, that given cell does cease to exist so it could be thought that its life ends. On the other hand, no part of the cell actually is lost in mitosis and thus it could be thought that the cell continues to live. If the latter is the case, and argument could be made that all cells alive today are as old as the first cell!

2. There is a distinct cleavage furrow, and thus it is an animal cell.

3. One way to measure the amount of DNA in the cell is to keep account of the number of DNA molecules at each point in the cell cycle. It would look like this for a human somatic cell: G_1 (46); S (92); G_2 (92); prophase (92); metaphase (92); anaphase (46 moving to each pole); telophase (46 each cell).

12

MEIOSIS AND SEXUAL REPRODUCTION

Chapter Outline

Objectives

1. Contrast asexual and sexual types of reproduction that occur on the cellular and multicellular organism levels.
2. Describe the events that occur in each meiotic phase, and how meiosis reduces the chromosome number.
4. Understand sources of genetic variation as they relate to meiosis.
5. Understand the basic steps in the development of male and female gametes.
6. Describe similarities and differences between mitosis and meiosis.

Key Terms

sexual reproduction	germ cells	zygote	sperm
somatic	gametes	crossing over	egg
alleles	haploid	sporophyte	
meiosis	fertilization	gametophyte	

Lecture Outline

12.1   Why Sex?

    A.   Asexual reproduction is quick and efficient.

        1.   Asexual reproduction does not require the participation of a partner.

        2.   But the offspring are all clones—no variation!

    B.   Sexual reproduction is most costly, but most responsive to changing conditions.

        1.   Male and female partners must find each other and exchange genetic material.

        2.   The variation introduced by sex has selective advantages.

12.2   Sexual Reproduction and Meiosis

    A.   Introducing Alleles.

        1.   Genes for each trait come in slightly different forms called alleles, originally produced by mutations.

        2.   Meiosis shuffles the alleles during gamete formation, and fertilization produces offspring with unique combinations of alleles.

        3.   The variation generated by sexual reproduction is the testing ground for natural selection and is the basis for evolutionary change.

    A.   What Meiosis Does

        1.   Meiosis begins with diploid ($2n = 46$) germ cells and produces haploid gametes ($n = 23$).

            a.   In $2n$ cells, there are two chromosomes of each type, called homologous chromosomes.

            b.   Homologous chromosomes line up (even unequally matched sex chromosomes!) during meiosis.

        2.   Each gamete produced by meiosis has *one of each pair* of homologous chromosomes, all the nuclei are haploid.

12.3 The Process of Meiosis

    A.   Unlike mitosis, meiosis has two series of divisions—meiosis I and II.

        1.   Meoisis 1

            a.   During prophase I of, homologous chromosomes pair.

            b.   During metaphase I, the chromosomes line up.

            c.   During anaphase I, the microtubules separate the homologous chromosomes.

            d.   During Telophase I, the two new nuclei form; after this the cytoplasm may separate.

        2.   Meiosis II

            a.   The sister chromatids of each chromosome separate; the cytoplasm divides again, resulting in four haploid cells.

12.4   How Meiosis Introduces Variation in Traits

    A.   Crossing Over in Prophase I

        1.   Homologous chromosomes pair up.

            a.   Nonsister chromatids exchange segments in a process called crossing over.

            b.   Because alleles for the same trait can vary, new combinations of genes in each chromosome can result; this is one source of genetic variation.

        2.   Crossing over leads to genetic recombination.

        3.   Crossing over is a common event. In humans between 46 and 95 crossovers occur in each cycle of meiosis. The crossover rate varies among species and chromosomes.

B. Segregation of Chromosomes Into Gametes
1. During metaphase I, homologous chromosomes randomly line up at the spindle equator.
2. During anaphase I, homologous chromosomes (still duplicated) separate into two haploid cells, each of which has a *random* mix of maternal and paternal chromosomes.
3. This alignment is another source of genetic variation for each new generation.
4. Ignoring crossing over, this creates 2^{23} possible gametes for each round of meiosis.

12.5 From Gametes to Offspring
A. Gamete Formation in Plants
1. Sporophytes are usually diploid and produce spores that are haploid cells that undergo mitosis and give rise to multi-celled haploid gametophytes.
2. Haploid spores germinate into haploid gamete-producing bodies in gametophytes.
3. Gamete-producing bodies and spore-producing bodies develop during the life cycle of plants.
B. Gamete Formation in Animals
1. In males, meiosis and gamete formation are called spermatogenesis.
   a. Germ cell ($2n$) → primary spermatocyte ($2n$) → MEIOSIS I → two secondary spermatocytes (n) → MEIOSIS II → four spermatids (n).
   b. Each spermatid develops a tail to become a mature sperm.
2. In females, meiosis and gamete formation are called oogenesis.
   a. Germ cell ($2n$) → primary oocyte ($2n$) → MEIOSIS I → secondary oocyte (n, and large in size) plus polar body (n, and small in size) → MEIOSIS II → one large ovum (n) plus three polar bodies (n, small).
   b. The single ovum is the only cell capable of being fertilized by a sperm; the polar bodies wither and die.
C. Fertilization
1. The diploid chromosome number is restored at fertilization when two very different gamete nuclei fuse to form the zygote.
D. Variation present at fertilization is from three sources:
1. Crossing over during prophase I.
2. Random alignments at metaphase I lead to millions of combinations of maternal and paternal chromosomes in each gamete.
3. Of all the genetically diverse gametes produced, chance will determine which two will meet at fertilization.

12.6 Mitosis and Meiosis—An Ancestral Connection
A. Mitosis results in clones and occurs in single celled eukaryotes as a means of asexual reproduction. All eukaryotes engage in mitosis for growth and tissue repair.
B. Meiosis occurs in immature reproductive cells giving rise to gametes.
C. Both processes of meiosis and fertilization give rise to genetic variation.
D. Despite the differences, there are similarities in the steps of mitosis and meiosis. The molecular machinery of mitosis may have been recruited for meiosis (sexual reproduction).
1. Proteins that recognize and repair breaks in DNA are used in mitosis and meiosis.
2. If the separation in anaphase of mitosis did not occur properly the result would be that of anaphase I in meiosis.
3. Did sexual reproduction result through mutations in the proteins that fix mistakes in mitosis?

Suggestions for Presenting the Material

♦ Before beginning this chapter, use mitosis as a review. Ask questions about the vocabulary, purpose, and phases of mitosis.

♦ The events of meiosis can be confusing. Emphasize that meiosis makes it possible for organisms to undergo sexual reproduction. Remind students of the benefits of sexual reproduction; this helps them to understand why a process as complex as meiosis has evolved.

♦ Students often find it hard to understand when and how the chromosome number changes during meiosis, so be sure they understand that the two chromatids of one chromosome are each considered a chromosome in their own right after the centromere splits during meiotic anaphase II.

♦ Meiosis will be easier to grasp if students can become thoroughly acquainted with a typical animal life cycle (use the human life cycle as a familiar example). Before finishing with this chapter, question the students about the events of meiosis and its consequences to the organism. Use Figure 12.8 and 12.9 and the related animations to help the students visualize these concepts.

♦ Review the comparison of mitosis and meiosis in Figure 12.11.

♦ **Common Student Misconceptions:**

   o Since students have been taught meiosis all through middle school and high school, they often think they understand the concepts; thus they do not pay attention as they should. Quiz them at the beginning of the chapter to recall what they remember. Ask them to draw the phases, make comparisons between mitosis and meiosis, recall in what organisms meiosis occurs and where in those organisms, etc. This quiz will challenge them to be more receptive to the content presentation.

   o Many students do not view plants as sexual organisms. Briefly review this concept with them before starting.

Classroom and Laboratory Enrichment

♦ Demonstrate the phases of meiosis, using a series of progressive transparencies or a video.

♦ Show students an overhead transparency of a karyotype of a normal man or woman to introduce the concept of homologous pairs.

♦ Compare a human karyotype to that of another organism.

♦ Ask students (working individually or in small groups) to use chromosome simulation kits (available from biological supply houses) to demonstrate chromosome replication and reduction of chromosome number during the stages of meiosis. If kits are unavailable, make your own chromosomes using a pop-it bead (or bead and cord) for each chromatid and a magnet for each centromere.

♦ Show adult plants or animals, and ask students where meiosis occurs in each organism.

♦ Place Figure 12.5 on the screen and have students indicate the number of *human* chromosomes present at each stage (note how conveniently the *four* chromosomes in the diagram convert to *forty-six* human ones). Use the centromere hint in the Discussion section below.

- If you can locate a segment of video depicting the union of gametes and subsequent cleavage, it will provide visual presentation of what mitosis and meiosis accomplish in a living cell.

Why Sex? (revisited)

- Why do cells undergoing mitosis require one set of divisions but cells undergoing meiosis need two sets of divisions?

- All but the most primitive species of organisms have the ability to reproduce sexually. Can you explain why sexual reproduction is considered a hallmark of evolutionary advancement? What are the advantages over asexual reproduction?

- What would be an advantage of parthenogenesis – the development of unfertilized eggs into offspring?

Additional Ideas for Classroom Discussion

- Do more advanced organisms have more chromosomes than primitive organisms? Review chromosome numbers of some common plants and animals.

- Division of the cell cytoplasm is equal during spermatogenesis but unequal during oogenesis. Can you think of at least one reason why?

- An old-fashioned name for meiosis is "reduction division." Why?

- What would happen in the formation of the zygote if meiosis did not halve the chromosome number?

- Why does crossing over occur in prophase of *meiosis* and not *mitosis*?

- One of the meiotic series is very much like mitosis. Is it meiosis I or II?

- Does the reduction in chromosome number occur in meiosis I or II? Hint: To conveniently count the number of chromosomes, whether doubled as chromatids or newly formed daughter chromosomes, simply count the number of centromeres (or portions thereof) present in any particular stage.

- When do the processes of human spermatogenesis and oogenesis begin? Are they the same in males and females?

- What is the derivation of the prefix *chrom-* as used in describing the threadlike bearers of hereditary instructions?

How Would You Vote? Classroom Discussion Ideas

- Monitor the voting for the online question. The type of research described here in which an all-female DNA zygote was produced is certainly not routine (600 attempts). So there is little worry at this time that it will become commonplace. Nevertheless, many people are concerned that this type of research is dabbling in a "forbidden" zone due to ethical issues. Two questions might be asked: (1) does this type of research have a goal that will lead to some advance in medicine beneficial to humankind, or (2) is it being done just to say, "We did it"?

Term Paper Topics, Library Activities, and Special Projects

♦ How are human karyotypes prepared? Discover the laboratory steps required in this procedure.

♦ Use the karyotypes of related species (for example, primates) to describe evolutionary relationships, if any, between the species.

♦ Meiosis precisely reduces the chromosome number so that union of several gametes restores the diploid number. How many extra or fewer chromosomes can a human body cell have and survive? Are there consequences? Does the same hold true for plants?

♦ What are the latest theories and evidence relative to the blockage of entry into the egg of all sperm subsequent to the first one?

♦ NOVA (PBS) has a segment titled "Life's Greatest Miracle" that reviews cell division and compares mitosis and meiosis. This segment and animation are a nice summary of cell division. The animation can be viewed online through the NOVA Online website at: http://www.pbs.org/wgbh/nova/miracle/divide.html#.

Responses to *Data Analysis Activities*

1. 12.1% of the mice not exposed to damaged caging (Control and Damaged Bottle groups) displayed abnormalities.

2. The group exposed to damaged caging and damaged bottles showed the highest incidence of abnormalities: 41.4%.

3. In figure 12.12B, the chromosomes are not lined up on the cell plate. In figure 12.12C, there is a single chromosome far out of alignment. In figure 12.12D, the chromosomes seem to have clustered into four groups.

Possible Responses to *Critical Thinking* Questions

1. Meiosis produces recombination of genes leading to genetic differences by: (1) crossing over during prophase I, and (2) independent assortment of the chromosomes during metaphase I. In addition, random fertilization creates a limitless possibility of combinations resulting from the mating.

2.

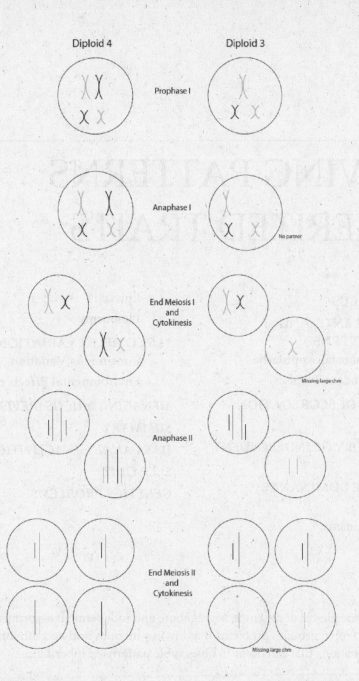

3. For the first generation, the frogs would have the usual 26 chromosomes in the diploid stage. The second generation would have twice this many – 52 chromosomes – if meiosis did not reduce the gamete number before chromosome number. Assuming two second generation frogs mated together, the third generation would have 104 chromosomes. You can see how this rapidly spirals out of control!

13

OBSERVING PATTERNS IN INHERITED TRAITS

Chapter Outline

Objectives

1. Know Mendel's principles of dominance, segregation, and independent assortment.
2. Understand how to solve genetics problems that involve monohybrid and dihybrid crosses.
3. Understand the variations that can occur in observable patterns of inheritance.

Key Terms

locus	dominant	dihybrid cross	incomplete dominance
homozygous	recessive	law of independent	epistasis
genotype	Punnett square	assortment	pleiotropic
phenotype	test cross	linkage group	continuous variation
hybrids	monohybrid cross	codominance	bell curve
heterozygous	law of segregation	multiple allele systems	

Lecture Outline

13.1 Menacing Mucus

A. Cystic fibrosis is the most common fatal genetic disorder in the United States
   1. It results from the deletion of a single chromosome in the CFTR gene.
   2. The impact is impaired chloride ion transport, ultimately leading to heavy mucus on the cell surfaces.
   3. Individuals usually die of lung failure – there is no cure.

B. The cystic fibrosis mutation in the CFTR gene is recessive
   1. As a result, there are over 10 million carriers, but afflicted individuals only occur if in 25% of heterozygous carrier matings.

13.2 Mendel, Pea Plants, and Inheritance Patterns

A. Introduction
   1. By the late nineteenth century, natural selection suggested that a population could evolve if members show variation in heritable traits. Variations that improved survival chances would be more common in each generation—in time, the population would change or evolve.
   2. The theory of natural selection did not fit with the prevailing view of inheritance—blending.
      a. Blending would produce uniform populations; such populations could not evolve.
      b. Many observations did not fit blending—for example, a white horse and a black horse did not produce only gray ones.
   3. Gregor Mendel used experiments in plant breeding and his knowledge of mathematics to form his hypotheses.

B. Mendel's Experimental Approach
   1. Mendel used the garden pea in his experiments to learn how traits are inherited.
      a. This plant can fertilize itself; true-breeding varieties were available to Mendel.
      b. Peas can also be cross-fertilized by human manipulation of the pollen.
   2. Mendel cross-fertilized true-breeding garden pea plants having clearly contrasting traits (example: white vs. purple flowers).

C. Inheritance in Modern Terms
   1. Genes are units of information about specific traits, each located at a particular locus on a chromosome.
   2. Diploid cells have two genes (a gene pair) for each trait—each on a homologous chromosome.
   3. Mutation alters a gene's molecular structure; alleles are various molecular forms of a gene for the same trait.
   4. True-breeding lineage occurs when offspring inherit identical alleles, generation after generation; non-identical alleles produce hybrids.
   5. When both alleles are the same, the condition is called the homozygous condition; if the alleles differ, then it is the heterozygous condition.
   6. When heterozygous, one allele is dominant (A), and the other is recessive (a).
   7. Homozygous dominant = AA; homozygous recessive = aa; and heterozygous = Aa.
   8. Gene expression is the process in which the gene's information is converted to its function. Expressed genes determine traits.
   9. Genotype is the alleles of an individual (the gene make up), and phenotype is how the genes are expressed (the traits that are observed).

13.3   Mendel's Law of Segregation

A. Monohybrid Experiments
1. Mendel suspected that every plant inherits two "units" (genes) of information for a trait, one from each parent.
2. Mendel's first experiments were monohybrid crosses.
    a. Monohybrid crosses have two parents that are true-breeding for contrasting forms of a trait (white vs. purple flowers).
    b. One form of the trait (white) disappears in the first generation offspring (F_1), only to show up in the second generation (F_2).
    c. We now know that all members of the F_1 offspring are heterozygous (Aa) because one parent could produce only an A gamete and the other could produce only an a gamete.
3. In the F_2 generation, the white flowers reappeared.
    a. The numerical ratios of crosses suggested that genes do not blend.
    b. For example, the F_2 offspring showed a 3:1 phenotypic ratio of purple to white.
    c. Mendel assumed that each sperm has an equal probability of fertilizing an egg. This can be seen most easily by using the Punnett square.
    d. Thus, each new plant has three chances in four of having at least one dominant allele.

B. Testcrosses
1. To support his concept of segregation, Mendel crossed F_1 plants with homozygous recessive individuals.
2. A 1:1 ratio of recessive and dominant phenotypes supports his hypothesis.
3. The Mendelian theory of segregation states that diploid organisms inherit two genes per trait on pairs of chromosomes. Each gene segregates from the other during meiosis such that each gamete will receive only one gene per trait.

13.4   Mendel's Theory of Independent Assortment

A. Dihybrids are the offspring of parents that breed true for different versions to two traits.
1. Mendel also performed experiments involving two traits—a dihybrid cross.
    a. Mendel correctly predicted that all F_1 plants would show both of the dominant alleles (example: all purple flowers and all tall plants).
    b. Mendel wondered if the genes for flower color and plant height would travel together when two F_1 plants were crossed.
2. The F_2 results showed 9/16 were tall and purple-flowered and 1/16 were dwarf and white-flowered—as were the original parents; however, there were 3/16 each of two new combinations: dwarf purple-flowered and tall white-flowered.
    a. The overall ratio revealed here is 9:3:3:1.
    b. This revealed that each trait was transmitting independently – the genes were not linked.

B. The Contribution of Crossovers
1. Even genes on the same chromosome assort independently due to crossovers.
2. Genes so close together that crossovers between them are less likely are said to be linked they do not exhibit independent assortment.

13.5   Beyond Simple Dominance

A. Codominance
1. In codominance, nonidentical alleles for a gene are fully expressed in heterozygotes.

2. Blood type is determined by markers produced by three genes—a multiple allele system.
    a. *A* and *B* are each dominant to *O*, but are codominant to each other.
    b. Therefore, some persons can express both genes and have AB blood.
    c. Blood typing is used to ensure incompatible blood types are not received during blood transfusions.
B. Incomplete Dominance
    1. In *incomplete dominance,* a dominant allele cannot completely mask the expression of another. One allele of a pair is not fully dominant over its partner.
    2. For example, a true-breeding red-flowered snapdragon crossed with a white-flowered snapdragon will produce *pink* flowers because there is not enough red pigment (produced by the dominant allele) to completely mask the effects of the white allele.
C. Epistasis
    1. Traits are expressed through epistasis—interactions among products from two or more gene pairs.
    2. Variations in human skin color and Labrador retriever coat colors are examples of epistasis.
D. Pleiotropy
    1. The impact of one allele on multiple traits is termed pleiotropy.
    2. Marfan syndrome, and example of pleiotropy, is characterized by these effects: lanky skeleton, leaky heart valves, weakened blood vessels, deformed air sacs in lungs, pain, and lens displacement in the eyes.
13.6   Complex Variation in Traits
A. Continuous Variation in Populations
    1. A given phenotype can vary, by different degrees, from one individual to the next in a population.
        a. This is the result of interactions with other genes, and environmental influences.
        b. In humans, eye color and height are examples.
    2. Bell curves are typical of traits that show continuous variation.
B. Genes and the Environment
    1. Fur on the extremities of certain animals will be darker because the enzyme for melanin production operates at cooler temperatures but is sensitive to heat on the rest of the body.
    2. The color of the floral clusters on yarrow plants will vary depending on the elevation of their habitat.
    3. Some persons tolerate stress better than others, perhaps due to differences in the gene for a serotonin-transporting protein.

Suggestions for Presenting the Material

♦   Students should be curious and interested in genetics. Start first with the simple examples of Mendel's monohybrid and dihybrid crosses before fielding questions on human traits such as height or eye color. Emphasize the remarkable nature of Mendel's work; remind the students that he knew nothing of chromosomes and that the term *gene* did not exist until several years after his death.

♦   Use Mendel's experiments and his conclusions as real-life examples of the scientific method at work. Ask questions to make sure students understand monohybrid and dihybrid crosses and testcrosses. Emphasize the genetic terms and the figures that make use of these terms.

- Students should be able to relate the events of meiosis to the concepts of segregation and independent assortment; if their understanding of meiosis is weak, they will have trouble doing this.

- Beginning with this chapter, students will be quick to ask questions about human traits, many of which are governed by mechanisms more complex than those postulated by Mendel. Answer questions in this area during (or after) the discussions of variations on Mendel's themes presented in the second half of this chapter.

Classroom and Laboratory Enrichment

- Ask groups of students to conduct coin tosses. Demonstrate the importance of large sample size by having the students vary the number of tosses before calculating variation from expected ratios.

- Distribute PTC tasting paper to your students, and calculate the number of tasters and nontasters in the classroom. Students are also excited to use physical traits such as tongue rolling or earlobe attachment.

- Expand the biographical sketch of Mendel, including his education and practice as a clergyman. Enliven your presentation with as many slides of photos as you can find.

- Hand out a partially completed pedigree, and show students how to assign squares and circles for their family. Then ask them to select a trait and complete the pedigree after surveying the family members for presence/absence of the trait.

- Select a portion of the class to reenact the photo in Figure 13.13. If the quantity of students chosen does not provide a bell-shaped curve, use this as an illustration of how the greater number of trials/subjects/experiments tends to increase probability.

- Prepare photos of the examples of "variations on Mendel's themes." This will remove some of the abstractness of these topics.

- Show a video on genetics.

- To dramatize independent assortment, use the following simulation of a cocktail party. Have several students pair off and line up as couples. Next, allow all participants to intermingle, but ask a few couples to switch partners and form new couples. (Explanatory comments: Those couples that did not switch but remained together represent genes linked together on the same chromosome; they travel together. Those that did switch were not linked and could independently assort themselves.)

Menacing Mucus (revisited)

- Given the lethality of cystic fibrosis, why is the recessive gene that results in the disorder so prevalent?

- Compare the prevalence of the cystic fibrosis gene in a historical population to prevalence of typhoid fever in the geographical area. Does a correlation exist?

- Are there other genetic disorders that are deleterious in the homozygous recessive condition that convey a benefit in the heterozygous condition?

Additional Ideas for Classroom Discussion

♦ Describe the behavior of one trait with regard to its inheritance in a particular cross; then ask students to identify the genetic mechanism at work (simple dominance/recessiveness, incomplete dominance, codominance, epistasis, pleiotropy, continuous variation).

♦ List some human traits that you would guess are each governed by a single gene.

♦ Give several reasons why Mendel's pea plants were a good choice for an experimental organism in genetics. Give an example of an organism that would be a poor choice for genetic research, and explain your choice.

♦ Describe several different crosses using organisms such as Mendel's pea plants. Then ask students to calculate phenotypic and genotypic ratios for each cross.

♦ Discuss the significance of Mendel's use of mathematical analysis in his research.

♦ Why do you think Mendel was not immediately recognized as the discoverer of a new area of biology—genetics?

♦ What conclusions would Mendel have come to if he had chosen *snapdragons* instead of *peas* for his study material?

♦ Why are the traits of (a) human skin color and (b) human height not suitable for explaining the concept of simple dominance?

♦ There are four possible blood types in the ABO system. But how many *different* alleles are in the human population for this marker?

♦ What is the subtle difference between *incomplete dominance* and *codominance*?

♦ What is the significance of using upper- and lowercase versions of the same letter (for example, A and a) for the dominant and recessive trait, respectively, rather than a capital A for dominant and a B (or b) for recessive?

How Would You Vote? Classroom Discussion Ideas

♦ Monitor the voting for the online question. As more options become available for parents to select the genetic makeup of their offspring, it is inevitable that many will choose to do so. Whether this is "right" or ethical will be debated even as the selection process proceeds. Some persons say that we should be allowed to be as selective of our children as we are about fruit at the grocery. Others draw the line and prefer to let nature or God be in control. What does your class say?

Term Paper Topics, Library Activities, and Special Projects

♦ What organisms are used most frequently in modern genetic research, and why?

♦ Describe the legal role now played by blood type evidence in paternity cases. Are other aspects of blood genetics (besides the ABO series) now used in deciding such cases?

♦ How do you think Charles Darwin's writings on his theory of evolution might have changed had he known of Mendel's work?

♦ Describe examples of how modern knowledge of genetics has led to improved agricultural strains of plants and animals.

- Discuss genetically modified crops and the positive and negative impacts they have. Include why they are controversial and why GMOs are banned in some countries.

- Search for details of Mendel's life and work. Seek answers to the allegations that his results may have been "too good."

- When studying genetics, it is easy to discover variations in plants and animals that result in organisms that, even though related, are very different in appearance. How does a researcher determine whether or not the variants are/are not the "same species"?

- Prepare an update on the extent of sickle-cell anemia in the United States and the world. Include in your report the consequences to those persons who are recessive and those who are carriers.

- Sickle-cell anemia results from an abnormal hemoglobin in which valine is substituted for glutamate. Is this substitution random, or does it occur under the direction of the molecules that direct protein synthesis? Explain the mechanism.

- Research recent evidence that scientists may be able to reactivate the production of fetal hemoglobin to offset the effects of sickle-cell anemia.

- Research the genetic counseling and the new technologies that are used to help determine genetic inheritance of fetuses.

Responses to *Data Analysis Activities*

1. Well over five times as many bacteria were able to enter cells expressing an unmutated CFTR in comparison to those with a ΔF508 mutation in the CFTR gene.
2. Ty2 entered the normal epithelial cells most easily.
3. The 167 strain had cell entry most inhibited by the ΔF508 mutation.

14

HUMAN INHERITANCE

Chapter Outline

Objectives

1. Understand how inheritance of genetic traits can be tracked through family trees.
2. Recognize the patterns characteristic to autosomal inheritance.
3. Recognize the patterns characteristic to sex-linked inheritance.
4. Recognize how changes in chromosome structure or number can result in a genetic disorder.
5. Explain how modern methods of genetic screening are used as diagnostic procedures and how they can minimize potentially tragic events.

Key Terms

pedigrees	deletion	translocation	aneuploidy
duplication	inversion	nondisjunction	

Lecture Outline

14.1 Shades of Skin

  A. Human Skin Color

    1. The is largely determined by the type of melanin present in the melanosomes.

    2. The type and amount of melanin showed an evolutionary balance.

      a. Enough to protect against dangerous UV radiation.

      b. Not so much as to inhibit vitamin D conversion.

    3. Individuals of mixed ethnicity may be heterozygous at the alleles responsible for melanin type and amount.

14.2 Human Genetic Analysis

  A. Pedigrees

    1. Unlike laboratory test organism, human breeding cannot be regulated.

    2. Pedigrees can be used to track the appearance of a genetic trait through a family tree.

  B. Types of Genetic Variation

    1. Some traits show the simple inheritance pattern observed in Mendel's peas.

      a. In these traits, a single trait is governed by a gene with a recessive and dominant allele.

      b. Approximately 6000 genes are regulated in this fashion

    2. These traits are usually regulated by single genes.

      a. The focus of this chapter is human genetic disorders, which collectively affect 1 in 200 people.

14.3 Examples of Human Inheritance Patterns

  A. The Autosomal Dominant Pattern

    1. The dominant allele is nearly always expressed even in heterozygotes.

    2. If one parent is heterozygous and the other homozygous recessive, there is a 50 percent chance that any child will be heterozygous.

    3. If the gene (and its resulting disorder) reduces the chance of surviving or reproducing, its frequency should decrease, but may not due to mutations, nonreproductive effects, and postreproductive onset.

      a. *Achondroplasia* (dwarfism) is a benign abnormality that does not affect persons to the point that reproduction is impossible, so the gene is passed on.

      b. Huntington disease is a serious degeneration of the nervous system with an onset from age 40 onward, by which time the gene has (usually) been passed from parent to offspring unknowingly.

  B. The Autosomal Recessive Pattern

    1. Characteristics of this condition:

      a. Either parent can carry the recessive allele on an autosome.

      b. Heterozygotes are symptom-free; homozygotes are affected.

      c. Two heterozygous parents have a 50 percent chance of producing heterozygous children and a 25 percent chance of producing a homozygous-recessive child. When both parents are homozygous, all children can be affected.

    2. *Albinism* (a lack of melanin) is an example of autosomal recessive inheritance in which a single gene mutation prevents the proper synthesis of melanin.

    3. Tay-Sachs is also an autosomal recessive disorder in which ganglioside breakdown is impaired leading to damage to nerve cells

14.4 X-Linked Inheritance Patterns

    A. Characteristics of X-Linked Inheritance

        1. The mutated gene occurs only on the X chromosome.

        2. Heterozygous females are phenotypically normal; males are more often affected because the single recessive allele (on the X chromosome) is not masked by a dominant gene on any other chromosome.

        3. A normal male mated with a female heterozygote has a 50 percent chance of producing carrier daughters and a 50 percent chance of producing affected sons. In the case of a homozygous recessive female and a normal male, all daughters will be carriers and all sons affected.

        4. Approximately 2000 genes are located on the X chromosome.

    B. Red-Green Color Blindness

        1. Color blindness is the inability to distinguish colors, in which mutated genes change the light-absorbing capacity of sensory receptors of the eyes.

        2. Normal people can distinguish among 150 colors. Those with color blindness can only see 25 colors.

    C. Hemophilia A

        1. Hemophilia is a serious X-linked recessive condition that prevents blood from clotting properly.

        2. The blood cannot clot because the genes do not code for the necessary clotting agent(s).

        3. Today hemophilia affects about 1 in 7500 people. This number may be on the rise since hemophilia is treatable.

    D. Duchenne Muscular Dystrophy

        1. Duchenne Muscular Dystrophy (DMD) affects about 1 in 3500 boys and is characterized by a rapid degeneration of muscles.

        2. A recessive allele encodes for dystrophin. Abnormal or absent dystrophin causes the muscle degeneration.

14.5 Heritable Changes in Chromosome Structure

    A. The Main Categories of Structural Change

        1. Duplication occurs when a gene sequence is repeated two or more times.

        2. A deletion is the loss of a chromosome segment. An example is the loss of a portion of chromosome 5, causing a disorder called cri-du-chat with its symptoms of crying and mental retardation.

        3. An inversion alters the position and sequence of the genes so that gene order is reversed. Inversions may affect an individual's fertility.

        4. A translocation occurs when a part of one chromosome is transferred to a nonhomologous chromosome. Most translocations are reciprocal or balanced. Translocations may also result in an individual's fertility.

    B. Chromosome Changes in Evolution

        1. Changes in chromosome structure tend to be selected against rather than conserved over evolutionary time.

        2. However, gene regions for the polypeptide chains of globin have duplicated to produce different globins with different oxygen-transporting efficiencies.

        3. The X and Y chromosomes were once homologous – a mutation occurring ~350 million years ago lead to the slow accumulation of differences that is today so striking.

14.6 Heritable Changes in the Chromosome Number

    A. Abnormal events occur before or during cell division, causing a change in the chromosome number.

1. *Nondisjunction* at anaphase I or anaphase II frequently results in a change in chromosome number.
   a. If a gamete with an extra chromosome ($n + 1$) joins a normal gamete at fertilization, the diploid cell will be $2n + 1$; this condition is called *trisomy*.
   b. If an abnormal gamete is missing a chromosome, the zygote will be $2n - 1$; this is monosomy.
2. Aneuploidy is a condition in which the gametes or cells of an affected individual end up with *one extra* or *one less* chromosome than is normal.
3. Polyploidy is the presence of *three or more* of each type of chromosome in gametes or cells. If cytoplasmic division does *not* follow normal processes, the chromosome number can change during mitotic or meiotic cell division. Polyploidy also can occur during the fertilization process. It is common in plants and some animals but fatal in humans.

B. Autosomal Change and Down Syndrome
   1. Down syndrome results from trisomy 21; 1 in 800–1,000 live newborns in North America are affected.
   2. Most children with Down syndrome show mental retardation, and 40 percent have heart defects.
   3. Down syndrome occurs more frequently in children born to older women.

C. Change in the Sex Chromosome Number
   1. Female Sex Chromosome Abnormalities
      a. *Turner syndrome* involves females whose cells have only one X chromosome (designated XO).
         I) Affected individuals (1/2,500 to 10,000 newborn girls) are infertile and have other phenotypic problems such as premature aging and shorter life expectancy.
         II) About 75 percent of the cases are due to nondisjunction in the father; furthermore, about 98 percent of all XO zygotes spontaneously abort.
      b. The XXX condition is an inheritance of multiple X chromosomes.
         I) About 1 in 1,000 females inherits 3, 4, or 5 X chromosomes.
         II) Most of these girls are taller and slimmer than average, but are fertile and fall within the normal range of appearance and social behavior.
   2. Male Sex Chromosome Abnormalities
      a. Klinefelter syndrome is caused by a nondisjunction, which results in an extra X chromosome in the cells (XXY) of affected males (1 in 500 affected). Sterility, slight mental retardation, and body feminization are symptoms.
      b. In the XYY condition the extra Y chromosome in males (1/1,000) does not affect fertility, but they are taller than average and are slightly mentally retarded.

14.7 Genetic Screening
   A. Data on human inheritance is displayed in pedigrees.
      1. A pedigree is a chart that shows genetic connections among individuals.
      2. The analysis of family pedigrees provides data on inheritance patterns through several generations.
      3. Knowledge of probability and Mendelian inheritance patterns is used in analysis of pedigrees to yield clues to a trait's genetic basis.
   B. Some traits are deviations from the average.
      1. Genetic abnormality is a term applied to a genetic condition that is a deviation from the usual, or average, and is not life-threatening.
      2. Genetic disorder is more appropriately used to describe conditions that cause medical problems.
      3. Syndrome is a recognized set of symptoms that characterize an abnormality or disorder.

4. Genetic disease might be an appropriate term only when factors alter previously workable genes in a way that disrupts body functions.

C. Prenatal Diagnosis
   1. Amniocentesis is a procedure in which small amounts of fluid from inside the amnion sac are removed and analyzed for the presence of abnormal cells that have been shed from the fetus.
   2. Chorionic villi sampling (CVS) is also a sampling of cells from the fetus, but in this case from the chorion; it can be done weeks earlier than amniocentesis.
   3. Fetoscopy uses a fiber-optic device with pulsed sound waves that scans the contents of the uterus.

D. Preimplantation Diagnosis
   1. Relying on in vitro fertilization for conception, couples may ask for an analysis to be done on the embryos before insertion into the female for implantation.
   2. Embryos with no detectable genetic defects are implanted; those with defects are discarded; again some may consider this a type of abortion.

Suggestions for Presenting the Material

♦ Students should be well grounded in their understanding of chromosomal structure and meiosis before attempting to tackle the material in this chapter. A review will greatly assist in making this material as clear as possible.

♦ Remind students that crossing over and genetic recombination create variability among sexually reproducing organisms; encourage students to think about the role this plays in evolution.

♦ To reduce the difficulty that students often have when learning about sex-linked genes, remind them that more precise terms are X-linked or Y-linked. Describe the steps of Thomas Hunt Morgan's work to show how sex-linkage was discovered. Ask students to solve the genetics problems that deal with sex-linked genes at the end of the chapter. To assess how well students understand this material, work on as many of these problems together in class as time allows.

♦ Explain how karyotypes are prepared before showing a human karyotype; otherwise, students might think that human chromosomes naturally occur paired-up as shown.

♦ Students need practice to learn how the different types of inheritance (autosomal recessive, autosomal dominant, and X-linked recessive) actually influence the inheritance of a trait in real-life examples. Review, if necessary, basic genetic terms such as *homozygous, heterozygous, dominant*, and *recessive*. To see how well students understand these types of inheritance, begin by working through some simple examples (as shown in Figures 14.3 and 14.5) of autosomal dominant inheritance, autosomal recessive inheritance, and X-linked recessive inheritance at the blackboard; ask students to predict the possible phenotypic outcomes in each example.

♦ During lectures, use the genetics problems at the end of the chapter as they apply, working through one or two examples at the blackboard with your class as a whole and then asking students to complete the rest in class (possibly as part of a quiz) or on their own time. Students will enjoy the puzzle-solving aspects while at the same time measuring their level of understanding of the different types of inheritance.

- Many of the genetic disorders and abnormalities mentioned in this chapter are ones whose names students have heard but whose mechanisms of inheritance were unknown to them before reading this chapter. To lend more meaning to the conditions described here, ask students to think about the social and ethical problems associated with some of the diseases mentioned in this chapter.

Classroom and Laboratory Enrichment

- Show karyotypes of males and females of different species without revealing the sex of the individual. Ask students to identify the sex.

- Use karyotypes to enhance problem solving/data analysis skills in lab or in a discussion session. The University of Arizona has a great interactive site for karyotyping. Search for Arizona State, Biology Project, and karyotyping to find this internet activity.

- Discuss gene mapping in humans using examples showing some of the known locations of particular genes.

- Ask a local health unit or testing lab if you can copy (anonymously, of course) some karyotypes that show chromosomal defects. Show these to the class, and ask if the students can spot the defect before it is revealed to them.

- Prepare unlabeled overhead transparencies of normal individuals and individuals with chromosomal abnormalities such as Turner syndrome, Klinefelter syndrome, or Down syndrome. Ask students if the karyotype appears normal; if not, what is wrong?

- Ask a genetic counselor to speak to your class about his/her job.

- Draw a pedigree for an unnamed genetic condition. Ask students if the disorder is autosomal dominant, autosomal recessive, sex-linked dominant, or sex-linked recessive.

- Obtain from your local health unit several brochures that explain the various genetic problems that can be inherited. Share these with the class for their evaluation and information.

- From the same source mentioned above, you may be able to obtain a list of those genetic "diseases" for which there is mandatory testing (usually of newborns) in your state. What voluntary testing programs are available?

Shades of Skin (revisited)

- What can the evidence of the difference in melanin alleles between European and Chinese populations tell us about evolution and early human migration?

- Is it likely that a novel change in a melanin allele could spread to impact only a specific geographic population today? Why or why not?

Additional Ideas for Classroom Discussion

- If it becomes possible to easily and inexpensively choose the sex of your child, how will this change the male to female ratio among newborns? Do you think it is ethically correct to select the sex of your children?

- If male and female offspring occur at a ratio of approximately 50:50, why do some couples have only boys or only girls?

- What is the distinction between the terms *gene* and *allele*?

- Why do individual chromosomes present at the conclusion of meiosis not have the same genetic constituency as they did before meiosis?

- If one sex of offspring tends to exhibit a trait more frequently than the other sex, this is an indication of what?

- What is the physical relationship of *genes* to *chromosomes* to *DNA*?

- What is the difference between a *translocation* of chromosomal segments and *crossing over*?

- Discuss the risks and benefits of amniocentesis. Would you elect to undergo this procedure (or urge your spouse to do so) if you had a history of genetic abnormalities in your family, or you or your spouse were over 35? Why or why not?

- Why is hemophilia more threatening to the life of a female victim than to a male victim?

- Why do so many people insist that girls cannot be red-green color blind?

How Would You Vote? Classroom Discussion Ideas

- Monitor the voting for the online question. While skin color may be a convenient means of differentiating races, it is clearly not perfect. Our modern understanding of genetics may suggest that we need to either abandon the idea of races in human beings as simply stereotypes of phenotypic extremes, or we need to find some significant allelic difference between populations to quantitatively separate them as distinct races.

Term Paper Topics, Library Activities, and Special Projects

- How do the sex chromosomes actually determine the sex of the individual? What are some of the characteristics governed by genes of the X and Y chromosomes?

- Because the sex of an individual is determined by the sperm at the moment of conception, is it possible to select the sex of a child by separating sperm with X chromosomes from those with Y chromosomes? Discuss recent experimental techniques that attempt to do this.

- How are human karyotypes prepared? Discover the laboratory steps required in this procedure.

- Find specific examples of how irradiation, chemical action, or viral attack can cause chromosome breakage.

- Are any human traits Y-linked?

- Describe how (and why) artificially induced changes in chromosome number have been used to create new varieties of fruits and vegetables.

- The predicted ratio of newborns should show a 50:50 sex ratio. Ask a local hospital to provide statistics on the sex ratio in order to confirm or deny this prediction.

- Report on the progress being made on the human chromosome-mapping project. What is the value of chromosome mapping?

- Prepare a protocol for rearing *Drosophila* in the lab and making simple crosses.

- Construct a pedigree for your own family using a trait governed by simple Mendelian inheritance.

- Describe the history of the discovery and treatment of any one of the human genetic abnormalities or disorders described in your text.

- Discover information about some of the tests now available for some genetic diseases (for example, Huntington disorder) to determine if one is a carrier for that disease. What are some of the ethical questions raised by such tests?

- Learn more about hemophilia: Discuss its history, its role in the downfall of the Russian monarchy, and modern treatments for the disease.

- Contact your local health unit for statistics on the incidence of Down syndrome and other genetic disorders whose causes are known.

- Research the current treatment for hemophilia. Is there a difference in the regimen for males and females?

- Research the objections that have been raised to genetic screening programs. Helpful sources include medical ethical textbooks and the internet.

Responses to *Data Analysis Activities*

1. Kenya receives the most UV radiation at 354.21 UVMED.

2. People native to Australia have the darkest skin at a 19.30 measure of skin reflectance.

3. While the correlation is not perfect, there is a strong general correlation between decreasing UVMED and decreasing skin reflectance. This is agreement with less UV radiation requiring less protection and necessitating less reflectance to allow for vitamin D conversion.

15

BIOTECHNOLOGY

Chapter Outline

15.1 PERSONAL DNA TESTING

15.2 CLONING DNA
   cDNA Cloning

15.3 FROM HAYSTACKS TO NEEDLES
   Isolating Genes
   PCR

15.4 DNA SEQUENCING
   The Human Genome Project

15.5 GENOMICS
   DNA Profiling

15.6 GENETIC ENGINEERING

15.7 DESIGNER PLANTS

15.8 BIOTECH BARNYARDS

Knockout Cells and Organ Factories

15.9 SAFETY ISSUES

15.10 GENETICALLY MODIFIED HUMANS?
   Getting Better
   Getting Worse
   Getting Perfect
   Getting There

PERSONAL DNA TESTING (REVISITED)

SUMMARY

DATA ANALYSIS ACTIVITIES

SELF-QUIZ

CRITICAL THINKING

Objectives

1. Describe how DNA cloning technologies are used in making recombinant DNA.
2. Understand the role of PCR in magnifying specific portions of the genome for further study.
3. Understand how DNA sequencing can be used to analyze and compare genomes.
4. Understand how genetic engineering is being used to move genes between organisms.
5. Understand the possibilities and problems that gene therapy presents.

Key Terms

restriction enzymes
recombinant DNA
DNA cloning
plasmids
cloning vectors
reverse transcriptase
genome

DNA libraries
probe
nucleic acid
   hybridization
polymerase chain
   reaction (PCR)
primers

DNA sequencing
electrophoresis
genomics
DNA profiling
short tandem repeats
genetic engineering
transgenic

genetically modified
   organism (GMO)
xenotransplantation
gene therapy
eugenics

Lecture Outline

15.1   Personal DNA Testing
   A. Valuable Differences
     1. All humans have about 99% the same DNA.
     2. It is the remaining differences, about 30 million, that differentiate us.
        a. The allelic variability is what causes us to have different phenotypes.
        b. Most of the variability comes in the form of single nucleotide polymorphisms (SNPs).
        c. Different SNP's impacts range from nominal to deadly.
     3. It may soon be possible to identify a large number of SNPs very quickly, allowing for very rapid genetic assessment of an individual.

15.2   Cloning DNA
   A. Isolating and Copying DNA
     1. Restriction enzymes are bacterial enzymes that cut DNA as specific nucleotide sequences.
     2. Two pieces of DNA cut with the same restriction enzyme bind to each other. If the DNA pieces are from different sources, the result is recombinant DNA
   B. Plasmids
     1. Plasmids are small, extra-chromosomal circles of DNA found in bacteria.
     2. By using them as cloning vectors (binding the DNA of interest to them as recombinant DNA), the DNA of interest can be copied as the host bacteria replicates.
   C. cDNA Cloning
     1. Even after a desired gene has been isolated and amplified, it may not be translated into functional protein by the bacteria because introns (noncoding regions) are still present.
     2. Researchers minimize this problem by using cDNA, which is made from mRNA transcripts.
        a. The cDNA is made from mRNA by reverse transcriptase.
        b. The cDNA can be inserted into a plasmid for amplification.

15.3   From Haystacks to Needles
   A. Isolating Genes
     1. A *gene library* is a collection of bacteria that house different cloned DNA fragments, one of which is of interest; it may be the entire genome or of *cDNA*, which is free of introns.
     2. A particular gene of interest can be isolated from other genes by use of probes.
        a. DNA probes, short DNA sequences assembled from radioactive nucleotides, can pair with parts of the gene to be studied.
        b. This nucleic acid hybridization technique can be used with other procedures to select cells and their DNA, which may be of interest to the researcher.
   B. PCR
     1. The polymerase chain reaction (PCR) can be used to make millions of copies of DNA.
     2. How does the amplification of the reaction occur?
        a. Primers are synthetic single strands of DNA that are designed to base-pair with the ends of the target DNA that is to be amplified.
        b. Researchers mix primers, DNA polymerase, target DNA from an organism (the DNA to be amplified), and free nucleotides.
        c. Precise temperature cycles cause the DNA strands to separate, exposing the bases.

d. Primers become positioned on the exposed nucleotides to form new copies of the original DNA.

e. Each round of reactions doubles the number of DNA molecules to eventually produce billions of molecules from very tiny amounts of original DNA.

15.4 DNA Sequencing

A. DNA sequencing is used to determine the unknown sequence of bases in a DNA sample.

1. DNA strands are built on a machine using eight kinds of bases: four normal and four that are modified with a colored pigment (it fluoresces).

2. When a modified base is incorporated, DNA synthesis is halted producing tagged fragments of different lengths.

B. The fragments are next sorted by gel electrophoresis.

1. The DNA fragments move through the gels at different rates, according to their size.

2. A computer detects and records the information from all the nucleotides in the sample to reveal the entire DNA sequence.

C. The Human Genome Project

1. Comparing the human genome to other organisms provides insights on how the body works.

2. Beginning in 1988, NIH directed the public effort in many laboratories to sequence the human genome.

3. In the late 1990s, Craig Venter launched his effort at genome sequencing using powerful automated sequencing machines.

4. Sequencing of the human genome was officially completed in 2003. The next step is to decipher which each sequence encodes.

D. A DNA fingerprint is a unique array of base sequences in each organism that is slightly different from the DNA in other organisms—even close relatives. Ninety-nine percent of our DNA is the same, but 1 percent differs between individuals.

1. The technique focuses on short tandem repeats, copies of the same short DNA sequences that are highly variable from one person to the next.

2. The differences can be detected by gel electrophoresis, a technique that pulls molecules through a gel matrix by electric current; different size molecules travel at different speeds.

3. The banding patterns of genomic DNA fragments are unique to each individual.

E. DNA fingerprinting is now a widely accepted and valuable tool to identify criminals, remains, and genetic relationships.

15.5 Genomics

A. Genomics

1. The new field of genomics focuses on mapping and sequencing the genomes as well as elucidating the possible evolutionary relationships of groups of organisms.

a. Structural genomics deals with the actual mapping and sequencing of genomes of individuals.

b. Comparative genomics is concerned with finding evolutionary relationships among groups of organisms.

2. Comparing the human genome to other genomes, such as the mouse, allows researches to learn more about the function of particular genes.

B. DNA Profiling
   1. DNA profiling is identifying an individual by their DNA sequence – especially the polymorphisms.
      a. Single nucleotide polymorphisms can be identified on a DNA chip.
      b. Variations in the length of short tandem repeats can also be used. These are currently the more commonly employed, and are more likely to be employed in criminal cases and paternity tests.

15.6   Genetic Engineering
   A. Genetic engineering is a laboratory process where genes (intact or modified) of one species are transferred into another organism
      1. The result is a transgenic organism, or a genetically modified organism (GMO).
   B. Plasmid-taking bacteria are now widely used in basic research, agriculture, medicine, and industry
      1. Genetically engineered bacteria make useful amounts of synthetic insulin for humans, in addition to other important proteins used for other drugs and vaccines.
      2. Engineered microbes are used in the food industry to make cheese, beer, fruit juice, bread, and modified fats.
      3. Environmental remediation uses modified bacteria to clean up environmental messes, such as oil spills, heavy metals, or even radioactive wastes.

15.7   Designer Plants
   A. How Plants Get Engineered
      1. *Agrobacterium tumefaciens* infects many plants.
      2. A plasmid from *A. tumefaciens* is used as a vector to transfer foreign or modified genes into plants.
      3. Other techniques of making genetically modified organisms include electrical shock, the use of chemicals or blasts of DNA-coated bullets.
   B. Genetically Engineered Plants
      1. There is worldwide pressure to produce more food at lower cost and with less damage to the environment.
      2. Some farmers rely on genetically engineered crop plants for improved yields.
      3. Plants are engineered to have an insecticide gene that kills only the insects that feed on them; others are more resistant to herbicides or droughts.
      4. There is controversy regarding the used of GMOs since they may increase resistance to specific chemicals, and the transgenic genes may escape the transgenic plant and spread to wild plants.

15.8.   Biotech Barnyards
   A. From the Lab to the Farm
      1. Mice were the first genetically modified organisms, and they were used for research purposes.
      2. Genetically modified animals in the farm yard are more commonly used as sources of pharmaceuticals.
         a. Goats have been modified to make milk use to treat cystic fibrosis, heart attacks, and other conditions.
         b. Rabbits produce interleukin-2, which stimulates divisions of immune cells.
      3. Genetic engineering could be viewed as a means to improve our livestock, just as natural breeding practices have for thousands of years.

B. Knockoutsand Organ Factories
   1. Xenotransplantation is the transferring of an organ from one species to another.
   2. Pigs can be engineered to lack certain genes that would cause rejection problems when their organs are transplanted to humans.
   3. This issue is highly controversial.

15.9 Safety Issues

A. There is an ongoing debate about potential dangers of transgenic organisms entering the environment before rigorous testing.

B. Scientists reached a consensus on the safety guidelines for DNA research, which was adopted by NIH (National Institutes of Health).

C. Pathogenic or toxic organisms cannot be used for recombinant experiments without proper containment facilities.

D. Testing, improving, and importing genetically modified organisms is regulated by the USDA.

15.10 Modified Humans?

A. Getting Better
   1. There are more than 15 000 genetic disorders, all of which could be potentially be treated with gene therapy.
   2. Gene therapy was initially successful in a trial against SCID-X1 (severe immune deficiency) in which 10 of 11 patients were benefited.

B. Getting Worse
   1. The impact of inserting a gene is hard to predict, primarily due to impacts with disruptions caused by the gene insertion.
   2. Three of the group later developed leukemia, which has raised questions about future treatments.

C. Getting Perfect
   1. Eugenic engineering is the idea of being able to select desirable human traits, including behaviors.
   2. Who decides what is "desirable"? Forty percent of surveyed persons said it would be all right to use gene therapy to make people smarter and better looking.

D. Getting There
   1. The question of when we have sufficiently mastered genetic engineering to safely employ it is difficult to answer.

Suggestions for Presenting the Material

♦ Help students to see the relevance of this subject by telling them about some of the products (such as insulin and human growth hormone) that are produced as a result of genetic engineering.

♦ Point out to your students that many of today's popular TV shows use modern forensics to identify criminals using the techniques outlined in this chapter.

♦ Remind students that genetic recombination occurs naturally in all organisms during meiosis. Emphasize that even though examples of genetic research in bacteria may seem obscure and of little relationship to more complex eukaryotic genomes, such experimentation yields results of great value to humans.

- **Common Student Misconceptions:**
  - o Students may think of cloning as cloning entire organisms. Be sure they understand that this chapter is referring to gene cloning.
  - o There are ethical concerns regarding GMOs and enhancing humans. Save time to address student concerns and to debate the risks versus benefits.

Classroom and Laboratory Enrichment

- There are a number of biotechnology labs available. Consider manipulating DNA as a lab activity so that your students have hands-on experience with this subject matter.
- Demonstrate the transfer of a plasmid for antibiotic resistance from one strain of bacteria to another using selected strains of *E. coli.* (Laboratory kits containing all necessary materials are available.)
- Illustrate some of the techniques presented in this chapter via animations, videos, or interactive activities.
- Prepare a summary table of the recombination methods listed in this chapter. Include the following information:
  a. Natural versus manmade
  b. Examples of organisms
  c. Usefulness
- Ask two groups of students to prepare brief arguments *for* and *against* the continuation of genetic engineering research and development.
- Arrange for a classroom presentation on the use of DNA fingerprinting.

Personal DNA Testing (revisited)

- The major issue with using SNPs to predict future diseases is that the generally indicate only an increased likelihood of developing a disorder. How does one deal with an increased chance of contracting something?
- Do you think we could ever completely predict the development of a disease?
- Discuss the benefits of genetic engineering versus potential risks.

Additional Ideas for Classroom Discussion

- Why are restriction enzymes useful tools for genetic engineering? How is DNA ligase used in genetic engineering?
- Do you think that new genomes resulting from genetic engineering should be patented? Who should receive monetary benefits from such discoveries—the research scientists performing the work or their academic institutions?
- What advantages would insulin produced by genetic engineering have over preparations from animal sources in the treatment of human diabetes mellitus?

- Is genetic engineering a new concept in nature or just the human application of a natural mechanism already in operation? Explain with examples.

How Would You Vote? Classroom Discussion Ideas

- Monitor the voting for the online question. Our understanding of the impact of genes on developing diseases is very early, and creates a number of ethical issues. On one hand, you could argue that it is unfair to inform clients (or employers? Insurance companies?) of having an increased risk of developing an untreatable condition. On the other hand, is not using a high cholesterol level as a warning sign the same thing as it represents only a statistical likelihood?

Term Paper Topics, Library Activities, and Special Projects

- Compile a history of research efforts in genetic engineering.
- Describe problems that have resulted from the standard prophylactic use of antibiotics among farm animals such as poultry, pigs, and cattle.
- Describe the safeguards currently followed in labs doing work in genetic engineering.
- List and describe companies currently doing research in genetic engineering. Investigate the current financial worth of some of these companies.
- Discuss the growing problem of antibiotic resistance among the different species of bacteria responsible for causing diseases such as gonorrhea, typhoid, and meningitis.
- Trace the history of the development and production of interferon, insulin, or any other substance produced using techniques of genetic engineering.
- In the early days of genetic recombination research, fears of creating "monster" bacteria that could run amok in the human population were quite real. However, after careful evaluation of all laboratory procedures used in thousands of experiments, these fears seem exaggerated. Why do *you* feel this thinking has changed?
- It is known that the HIV virus that causes AIDS can delay its deadly effects for some time. Search the literature to find out if this is an instance of the virus entering a latent state before resuming its attack.
- Research the pros and cons of GMO as food sources. Present an argument to either incorporate or avoid these foods in your diet.
- Investigate why other nations ban GMOs as food products.

Responses to *Data Analysis Activities*

1. In the first test, unmodified mice needed just over five days of training to find the platform in ten seconds.
2. The modified mice learned the location of the platform faster on the first test.
3. The modified mice also learned the location of the platform faster on the second test.
4. On a percentage basis, the modified mice showed the greater improvement between the first and second test.

Possible Responses to *Critical Thinking* Questions

1. Restriction enzymes cut only a specific sequence of DNA. To protect themselves, bacteria do not have a sequence of DNA that matches the sequence to which their restriction enzymes respond.

2. Inserting genes governing human traits, such as speech, into chimpanzees may help us understand the mechanism of speech better. If we can change a monkey to speak, then maybe we could use this therapeutic treatment to restore speech to a person who has lost the ability to speak.

    However, these types of manipulations make people uncomfortable. Where is the line crossed? Would we also transfer foreign genes into human embryos—for good or evil intent? The technology is there. Xenotransplants are on the cutting edge of medical science, and some scientists think they hold the key, not only to replacing organs, but to curing other deadly diseases as well. The question becomes: "Just because we *can* do something, does that mean we *should*?" The general public will be concerned about this idea until they can see positive benefits for cures of genetic defects and diseases that presently are incurable. Some will still say it is wrong to "tamper" with nature, and that we should just let the natural processes of life take precedence. Of course, those in the scientific community would be more sympathetic to such transfers if they were based on a reasonably plausible prospect of affecting a cure for some genetic malady or conferring immunity against some devastating disease like AIDS. The legal ethics of such procedures is not yet in place, but our policy makers need to be ready.

16

EVIDENCE OF EVOLUTION

Chapter Outline

Objectives

1. Understand the development of evolutionary theory and the struggle to overcome early beliefs.
2. Explain the origin and eventual articulation of the views Darwin had on evolution.
3. Understand how fossils can be used to visualize past changes in organisms.
4. Recognize how geological events have impacted evolution.
5. Understand that possessing similar body parts is often indicative of a shared ancestor.

Key Terms

mass extinction
naturalists
biogeography
comparative
  morphology
fossil
catastrophism
evolution

lineage
theory of
  uniformity
artificial selection
fitness
adaptation
adaptive trait
natural selection

half-life
radiometric dating
geologic time scale
Pangea
plate techtonics
Gondwana
homologous
  structures

morphological
  divergence
analogous
  structures
morphological
  convergence

Lecture Outline

16.1 Reflections of a Distant Past

    A. Understanding the distant past and large blocks of time requires an intellectual leap from the familiar to the unknown

    B. Millions of large asteroids orbit our sun between Mars and Jupiter

        1. 50,000 years ago a 330,000 tone asteroid slammed into earth creating the Barringer Crater in Arizona.

        2. Geologists examine tons of meteorites and other physical evidence to establish cause and effect for events in the past before humans were present.

        3. Large impacts like these influence the history of life on Earth in a major way.

            a. Fossil evidence from the K-T boundary 65 million years ago points to some global disturbance related to the extinction of dinosaurs.

            b. Asteroid impacts 5 million years ago may have influenced human evolution.

    C. Natural phenomena that occurred in the past can be explained by physical, chemical, and biological processes that operate today

16.2 Early Beliefs, Confounding Discoveries

    A. Early naturalists observed life from a scientific perspective

        1. By the fourteenth century, the ancient view of gradual levels of organization from lifeless matter to the most complex organisms had been formalized into the great Chain of Being.

            a. The chain extended from lowest forms to spiritual beings.

            b. Each being (*species*) had its fixed place in the divine order—unchanged and unchanging since creation.

        2. Explorations of distant lands discovered new species and new links in the chain of being.

            a. The study of the impact of location on life is biogeography.

            b. Some patterns are very intriguing, such as isolated species resembling each other.

            c. Examples include large flightless birds isolated on different continents, all occupying similar habitats and having similar behaviors. Similar patterns can be found in the plant kingdom.

    B. Comparative Morphology Revealed Hidden Relations

        1. Studies of the comparative morphology of seemingly unrelated animals led to questions of why certain structures should be so similar, for example, bones in a human arm and a porpoise flipper.

    C. Fossils Revealed Transition of Form

        1. Geologic studies identified identical sequences of rock layers in different parts of the world. This added to the confusion. Fossils from rock layers were recognized as evidence of earlier life.

            a. Some fossils were puzzling; layers revealed increasing levels of complexity as you neared the surface.

            b. If all species were perfect, why do we observe these changes in similar organisms over time, and why are they now extinct?

16.3 A Flurry of New Theories

    A. Squeezing New Evidence into Old Beliefs

        1. Georges Cuvier was among a group of scientists trying to make sense of the growing evidence of evolution.

2. Cuvier further suggested that the abrupt changes in the fossil record in different rock strata reflected the concept of catastrophism.
    a. After each catastrophe, fewer species remained.
    b. The survivors were not new species; it was just that their ancestors' fossils had not been found.
3. Lamarck formulated a theory of inheritance of acquired characteristics—the idea that simple forms had changed into more complex ones by a built-in drive for perfection up the Chain of Being; for instance, a giraffe stretching its neck to reach higher branches would result in offspring with longer necks.

B. Darwin and the HMS *Beagle*
1. As a child (early 1800s), Charles Darwin was curious about nature, but in college, he first pursued medicine and finally received a degree in theology.
2. Botanist John Henslow arranged for Darwin (at age 22) to sail around the world as a ship's naturalist.
    a. Throughout the trip, Darwin studied and collected a variety of plants and animals, and a range of interesting fossils.
    b. He was also reading Lyell's *Principles of Geology*, which proposed a theory of uniformity—the notion of a gradual, lengthy molding of the Earth's geologic structure.
    c. Thus, the Earth was not thousands, but possibly millions of years old—enough time for evolution. This gradual change over time became known as the theory of uniformity.

16.4 Darwin, Wallace, and Natural Selection
A. Old Bones and Armadillos
1. Darwin returned after five years at sea with thousands of specimens and notes about his findings and travels. In time he was able to make enough connections to understand how species might evolve.
2. In Argentina, Darwin had observed extinct glyptodonts that bore suspicious resemblance to living armadillos; Darwin wondered if the present species had evolved from the extinct one.

B. A Key Insight—Variation in Traits
1. Thomas Malthus, a contemporary of Darwin, had suggested that as a population outgrows its resources, its members must compete for what is available; some will not make it.
2. Darwin deduced that any population has the capacity to produce more individuals than the environment can support.
3. Darwin had observed that artificial selection could alter an organisms traits.
4. In reflecting on his collection, it dawned on Darwin that variations in traits can influence an individual's ability to secure limited resources and thus survive.
    a. On the Galapagos Islands, the dozen or so species of finches all varied from one another to some extent but resembled the mainland finches to some degree also; perhaps they had descended from common ancestors.
    b. Darwin reasoned that conditions in the prevailing environment "select" those individuals that are best suited to that environment.
5. Darwin viewed this as nature's version of artificial selection, thus it was termed natural selection.

C. Great Minds Think Alike
   1. Ten years after developing (but not publishing) his idea, Darwin received a paper expounding the same idea from Alfred Wallace.
      a. Darwin and Wallace were jointly credited, though his publication of On the Origin of Species made Darwin the figurehead.
   1. The suggestion that natural selection was the force behind evolution was vigorously debated.

16.5   Fossils: Evidence of Ancient Life
   A. Fossils are Traces of Past Life
      1. The fossilization process is a slow one that starts when an organism dies and becomes covered by sediment or ash.
         a. Water infiltrates the remains and metal ions or other inorganic molecules replace the organic ones in bones or other hard tissues.
         b. The pressure increases from additional sediment deposited on top. This, in combination with the mineralization process, transforms the remains into stony fossils.
      2. Fossilization is favored when remains are buried quickly and remain undisturbed.
         a. Since these conditions are rare, fossils are rare.
         b. Other factors such as anaerobic conditions influence the fossilization process.
   B. The Fossil Record
      1. There are more than 250,000 species of fossils, yet the fossil record will never be complete.
         a. Odds are against finding one of every species due to the specific requirements of the fossilization process.
         b. Many ancient species had no hard parts to fossilize.
         c. The rare or dispersed nature of many species further compounds the likelihood of finding fossils of them.
         d. Lineages of organisms that were remote or lived for brief periods of geologic time are less likely to be represented in the fossil record.
   C. Radiometric Dating
      1. Fossil dating became more accurate with the discovery of radioisotope decay.
         a. Radioisotopes are a form of element with an unstable nucleus that decay and become other elements.
         b. The decay rate is not influenced by temperature, pressure, chemical bonding, or moisture.
         c. It represents a perfect clock since the decay rates are predictable and constant.
      2. The radiometric dating process is used to date rocks and fossils.
      3. More recent fossils may be dated using their ratio of carbon isotopes (carbon dating).

16.6   Putting Time in Perspective
   A. Placing Fossils in Geologic Time
      1. Early geologists counted backward through layers of sedimentary rock to observe transitions in the fossil sequence around the world.
         a. Similar transitions were observed in different locations around the world.
         b. These transitions became the basis for divisions in the geologic time scale.
         c. Macroevolution (major patterns, trends, and rates of change among lineages) can be correlated with the major divisions in the geologic time scale.

16.7 Drifting Continents, Changing Seas
  A. An Outrageous Hypothesis
    1. Major geologic patterns can be observed in looking at the jigsaw-like fit between the Atlantic Ocean coastlines of South America and Africa.
      a. One model suggests that all continents were once part of a large supercontinent called Pangea that eventually split and drifted apart.
      b. This model helped explain why the same fossils appear in sedimentary rocks on both sides of the ocean.
    2. The theory, called plate tectonics, was supported by similar evidence that kept turning up.
      a. Evidence includes the similar magnetic properties of solidified molten rock found in different places around the world.
      b. Also, the deep sea discovery of fissures where continents are pushing together or pulling apart.
      c. The plate tectonics theory holds that the thin outer surface of the earth is separated into immense plates that raft over the surface of the earth.
    3. Researchers applied this theory to help explain the distribution of fossils.
  B. A Big Connection
    1. We now know that continents collide, split, and move vast distances over the surface of the earth.
    2. Continental drift (plate tectonics) influences life and evolutionary forces on land and in the oceans.

16.8 Similarities in Body Form and Function
  A. Physical Similarities Suggest Common Ancestry
    1. Homologous structure is a term used to describe similar body parts shared among related organisms. The structures may be used differently, but the same genes direct their development.
  B. Morphological Divergence
    1. In time isolated populations begin diverging genetically.
      a. Over time differences appear in body form.
      b. This is a macroevolutionary process termed morphological divergence.
    2. In spite of changes in form a careful look reveals common heritage.
      a. An example is the four-legged ancestry of land vertebrates.
      b. Divergences led to the major vertebrate groups.
      c. The divergence seen in the five-toed limb provides an excellent example of this process. The same five-toed limb has been modified into a human arm, elephant foot, or bird wing.
      d. Although they differ in use, size, and shape they retain the same structure and positioning of bony elements.
  C. Morphological Convergence
    1. Similar body parts are not always homologous and do not always share a common lineage.
    2. They may have evolved independently in separate lineages.
      a. Analogous structures look alike in different lineages but did not evolve in a shared ancestor.
      b. Evolution of similar body parts in different lineages is known as morphological convergence.

      c.   An example are the wings of birds, bats, and insects. All act in flight but an examination of their structure reveals they are not homologous.

      d.   The unique adaptations for flight are evidence that wing surfaces in bats, birds, and insects are analogous.

16.9   Similarities in Patterns of Development

    A. Genes Guide Embryonic Development

      1. Mutations in one developmental gene can disrupt the form.

    B. Genes and Variation in Plants

      1. Homeotic genes guide the formation of flowers. In the laboratory, exceptionally fertile flowers can be developed by altering a single gene.

    C. Developmental Comparisons in Animals

      1. The embryonic development of many vertebrates is strikingly similar.

         a.   Their tissues form in the same way.

         b.   Differences in the adult forms result from heritable changes in the onset, rate, or completion of crucial steps in the developmental process.

         c.   Body parts as diverse as fish fins and mouse feet start out as clusters of cells that bud from the surface of the embryo.

         d.   An example gene is the Hox gene that controls the development of appendages.

    D. Forever Young

      1. In some animals, juvenile features persist into adulthood.

         a.   Compared to chimps, humans retain more juvenile features in adult skulls.

         b.   Some salamanders that do not leave the water retain external gills as adults.

Suggestions for Presenting the Material

   ♦ This chapter opens with a wonderful discussion on the huge amount of time included when we discuss evolution and geologic time scales. Take the time to show the video to help put this critical aspect in context for students. Refer students to the video as a refresher when studying for exams.

   ♦ Evolution can be a sensitive subject for many students; make it clear that in science classes we discuss evidence that supports lines of thought.

   ♦ Take the time to show the animated figures, such as 16.10, which lays-out the radiometric dating process so critical to validating the fossil record. Figure 16.12 helps students understand the process of plate tectonics, which is highly abstract to most.

   ♦ The authors discuss three areas (biogeography, comparative anatomy, and fossils) that were puzzling to early scientists. Your lectures could take the same approach as you introduce the material by asking for student response to those same questions.

   ♦ Before proceeding to the men who proposed a changing biological world, point out that the prevailing thought 200 years ago was "fixity of species." Because of the belief that species did not change, it was incumbent on humans to classify all living things. Although Linnaeus believed in this "fixity," his system is nevertheless still very valid and useful.

   ♦ One way to present the historical development of evolutionary thought is to chronicle the contributions of persons such as de Lamarck, Lyell, Malthus, Wallace, and of course, Darwin. Layout the timeline and discuss the major works of science that contributed to the acceptance of evolution theory.

- Students rarely hear about Darwin's life other than his famous journey. Present his biography *before* his theory to spark interest. Perhaps the videotape listed in the Enrichment section could be used. You can then proceed to *natural selection* by first recalling *artificial selection* (maybe using dogs rather than pigeons, as Darwin did in his book).

- Take the time to define and explain the process of natural selection and the Principles of Natural Selection of Table 16.1.

- Stress the ever-increasingly important role of molecular evidence in establishing evolutionary relationships among species. Discuss the significance of mutation rates and the conservation of important genetic information in this process.

- Take the time to explain cladistics to students. Have them consider the process in terms of their own family tree to provide context for this discussion.

- **Common Student Misconceptions:**
   - Students confuse the terms convergence and divergence. Take the time to go slowly through these very different processes presented in Section 16.8.
   - Reinforce the role of evidence in testing theories; students may still lack confidence in evolution because of the term *theory* used to define it.

Classroom and Laboratory Enrichment

- Show a video describing Charles Darwin's voyage on the HMS *Beagle* and his thoughts as he traveled.

- Present fossil evidence (actual samples from a teaching collection is best) that shows how a group of related organisms or a single genus (for example, *Equus*) has evolved and changed through time.

- Whales, like snakes, have pelvic girdles. Show a diagram of this portion of the whale skeleton. Ask students to consider the conservation of these features over such a long period of time.

- Have students pair up and develop a list of body parts that illustrate convergence or divergence. Have them discuss the evolution of these features and try to place them on the geologic time scale.

- In small groups, have students discuss what features are important in dividing up the six kingdoms of life into the three domains of life.

- Generate interest in Darwin's theory by bringing a copy of *On the Origin of Species* to class. Read selected chapter titles and portions of the text. Point out the lack of illustrations in the original edition.

Reflections of a Distant Past (revisited)

- Start the discussion by showing Figure 16.1.

- Have students reflect on the influence of large asteroid impacts on the evolutionary process. Have them create a list of extinct species and speculate about the forces needed to remove them from the record of life.

- Besides asteroid impacts, discuss what other factors, such as global climate change, may influence evolution and the fossil record.

Additional Ideas for Classroom Discussion

- Discuss the development of cultural ideas that relate to the fossil record.

- How did the widespread discoveries of fossils in the nineteenth century help to support Darwin's views on evolution?

- If you feel adventurous, discuss the idea that accepting the principle of evolution excludes belief in religion for some groups. Why or why not?

- Why was extensive travel a key ingredient in the development of Darwin's evolutionary thought?

- Can you think of any ideas commonly expressed today that are similar to Lamarck's understanding of evolution?

- How did the work of geologists such as Charles Lyell and others who were Darwin's contemporaries help Darwin to create his principle of evolution?

- Those who wish to berate certain scientific principles sometimes say, "It's only a theory." This statement is used by some when referring to evolution. Does the use of "theory" in biology mean the concept is in doubt? Explain the requirement for evidence and testing in the development of theories, using examples.

- Compare and contrast the principles of "uniformitarianism" and "catastrophism." Evaluate the physical evidence for each.

- How did Darwin's observation of variation among species help him to develop his principle of evolution?

- What did Darwin's study of the different finch species among the Galápagos Islands tell him about speciation? What conclusions can you make about the evolutionary histories of the different species of Galápagos finches, given what you now know about the process of speciation?

- Using a global map, find examples of current volcanic events, and have students relate the locations to tectonic plates.

- Reflect on earlier chapters and the significance of genetics in our discussion on evolution.

- Discuss the commonality between humans and chimps. Research the commonality with other primates and discuss the similarities. Based on this information have students help you construct a simple cladogram on the board.

How Would You Vote? Classroom Discussion Ideas

- Have students complete the online class polling. Discuss use of indirect evidence to evaluate a theory.

- Can a theory ever be proven? Ask students to discuss this commonly misunderstood aspect of theories.

- Evolution is a complicated theory as it depends on a large number of variables. Does the theory of evolution have strong predictive ability for specific cases?

Term Paper Topics, Library Activities, and Special Projects

♦ Describe how a trip through the Grand Canyon with a paleontologist would reinforce our modern understanding of evolution.

♦ To bring to life the ongoing developments in evolutionary science, have students use the internet to find articles related to current findings in this field. Have them develop a one-page paper that summarizes the information in one or more of the articles.

♦ How do today's biologists reconcile their personal faith in an organized religion with their belief in evolution? Research the viewpoints of some famous scientists on this issue.

♦ Can we see evolution actually happening? Find examples of natural occurrences in the wild or experimental situations in the laboratory in which we can observe evolution occurring.

♦ Learn more about the discovery of dinosaur fossils and the reactions of the scientific community to them and how that has changed over the last 160 years.

♦ Describe how Darwin's development of his principle of evolution was an example of the scientific method in action.

♦ The great "catastrophe" that dominated Cuvier's thinking was the flood of Noah as recorded in the Book of Genesis. This is still the cornerstone of creationist thinking. Investigate creationist writings to see how this event is critical to their theories.

♦ Darwin's emerging ideas on natural selection were not welcomed by the *Beagle* captain. Investigate how this challenge to his views strengthened Darwin's hypotheses.

♦ It is ironic that Darwin and Wallace would arrive independently at so important a concept as natural selection. Investigate the path each took.

Responses to *Data Analysis Activities*

1. The iridium content of the K-T boundary layer was 41.6 ppb.

2. The iridium content of the K-T boundary layer was 116 times higher in comparison to the sample taken 0.7 m above the K-T boundary layer.

Possible Responses to *Critical Thinking* Questions

1. If a rock is dated using radiometric dating ten times, and nine of the ten measures are in agreement, the tenth measure would be viewed as anomalous. The remaining nine measures are not invalidated. However, given the tremendous difference between the nine similar measures and the tenth, the researchers would likely want to return to their sample rock in an attempt to explain the odd outcome.

2. On this clock, the first humans appear at 11:59:59. This means that all humans, including myself, would appear within the most recent 1/1000 of a second. The human duration in comparison to the history of the planet is but a blink.

17

PROCESSES OF EVOLUTION

Chapter Outline

Objectives

1. Understand the role changing allelic frequency in microevolution.
2. Recognize the forces that drive and resist microevolution.
3. Understand what macroevolution is and the role it plays in species development.
4. Understand that macroevolution can cause the gain and loss of species.
5. Understand the use of cladistics in interpreting evolutionary relationships between groups.

Key Terms

population	balanced	sympatric	character
lethal mutation	polymorphism	speciation	cladogram
neutral mutation	genetic drift	parapatric	clade
gene pool	fixed	speciation	monophyletic
allele frequency	bottleneck	exaptation	group
microevolution	founder effect	stasis	evolutionary trees
genetic equilibrium	inbreeding	extinct	sister groups
natural selection	gene flow	adaptive radiation	
directional selection	speciation	key innovation	
stabilizing selection	reproductive	coevolution	
disruptive selection	isolation	phylogeny	
sexual selection	allopatric speciation	cladistics	

Lecture Outline

17.1 Rise of the Super Rats

  A. Rats are one of the most notorious pests of all time

    1. Most U.S. cities sustain rat populations of 1 for every 10 people. They cause many diseases, foul up to 30 percent of our food production, and cost us about $19 billion each year.

    2. The rodenticide warfarin was very effective when it was first introduced in the 1950s.

    3. Within a few years, rats developed resistance—the chemical would no longer kill.

  B. The resistant rats happened to inherit a gene that made the chemical ineffective

    1. The survivors passed on the gene to their offspring; soon resistant rats were the normal population.

    2. This is an example of evolutionary processes at work.

17.2 Individuals Don't Evolve, Populations Do

  A. Variations in Populations

    1. Populations refer to one group of individuals of the same species in a specified area.

      a. Species share morphological and physiological traits.

      b. They respond in the same way to stimuli.

    2. Populations show variation in shared traits.

      a. Examples of variations include coat color or amount of hair.

      b. Many traits show qualitative differences, having two or more different forms.

      c. In addition, many traits show qualitative differences, or range of incremental variations in a single trait.

    3. The genes of a population comprise the gene pool, a pool of genetic resources.

      a. Slightly different forms of the same gene are called alleles.

      b. An individual's collection of alleles is called its genotype.

      c. Alleles are the primary source of variation in appearance, called phenotype.

    4. Polymorphisms occur when genes have three or more alleles that persist in a population with a frequency of at least 1 percent.

      a. The ABO alleles for human blood type are an excellent example.

      b. Dimorphisms represent two distinct traits, like male-female sex.

      c. Mutations are the source of new alleles.

      d. Offspring inherit the genotype, not the phenotype.

  B. Mutation Revisited

    1. We can predict average mutation rates; remember the molecular clock concept presented in Chapter 16.

      a. The average mutation rate in humans is about 70 mutations per person per decade.

      b. Many mutations give rise to structural, functional, or behavioral alterations that reduce an individual's chances of surviving and reproducing.

    2. Mutations can be lethal, neutral, or beneficial.

      a. Lethal mutations usually arise from drastic changes in phenotype.

      b. Neutral mutations alter the base sequence of DNA but have no effect on survival or reproduction.

      c. Every so often a beneficial mutation occurs that enhances survival or reproduction. In these cases, natural selection will favor the transmission to the next generation.

  C. Allele Frequencies

    1. Researchers typically track allele frequencies in a population.

      a. The starting point is a reference point called genetic equilibrium, when a population is not evolving with respect to a gene.

      b. Genetic equilibrium can only occur when the following five conditions are met: mutations do not occur; the population is infinitely large; the population stays isolated from all others of the same species; mating is random; all members of the population survive and produce the same number of offspring.

      c. In nature all five conditions are never met; this results in small-scale changes in the population's allele frequency. This is called microevolution.

17.3 A Closer Look at Genetic Equilibrium

  A. The Hardy-Weinberg Formula can be used to track whether a population is in genetic equilibrium or not.

    1. The mathematical formula tracks allele frequency for a specific trait.

    2. Researchers can use the formula to estimate the frequency of carriers of alleles that cause genetic traits and disorders.

17.4 Natural Selection Revisited

  A. Remember that natural selection refers to differential survival and reproduction among individuals

    1. Some traits are more adaptive in prevailing environments.

    2. Natural selection influences all levels of biological organization.

  B. Selection can be directional, stabilizing, or disruptive. Each will be discussed starting in 17.5.

17.5   Directional Selection
  A. Directional selection occurs when allele frequencies shift in a consistent direction, and forms at one end of the range of phenotypic variations become more common than the intermediate forms
  B. The Peppered Moth
    1. The peppered moth is a classic illustration of the directional selection process.
        a. The moths feed at night and rest on tree trunks during the day.
        b. In preindustrial England, light colored moths were the most common.
        c. Due to the deposition of air pollution starting in the 1850s, the dominant allele shifted to dark colored moths.
        d. Since the advent of pollution controls in the 1950s, the allele frequency has begun to shift back to the light colored moths.
  C. Rock Pocket Mice
    1. Rock pocket mice emerge at night to forage for seeds.
    2. Those living on darker rocks have darker coats to hide from predators.
  D. Resistance to Antibiotics
    1. Human activities can influence directional selection, as with the super rats example.
        a. Antibiotics are toxins that kill bacteria by interfering in physiological processes.
        b. Since the 1940s antibiotics have been widely prescribed in the U.S.
        c. Overuse of antibiotics puts tremendous selection pressure on bacteria; over the course of a couple of weeks of antibiotic treatment, selective pressure can be put on thousands of generations of bacteria.
    2. Bacteria divide quickly and form huge populations.
        a. These large populations show great genetic variation.
        b. It is therefore likely some will survive antibiotic treatment.
        c. Resistant strains are becoming the norm rather than the exception.

17.6   Stabilizing and Disruptive Selection
  A. Stabilizing Selection
    1. With stabilizing selection, the intermediate forms of a trait in a population are favored.
        a. It does not result in evolutionary change.
        b. Body weight of sociable weavers are a good example of this concept, with mid-sized weavers selected for most often.
        c. Body mass represents a trade-off between risks of starvation and predation.
  B. Disruptive Selection
    1. In disruptive selection forms at both ends of a range of variation are favored. Intermediate forms are selected against.
        a. The selection for bill size in the black-bellied seedcracker finch in Africa provides an excellent example.
        b. Females and males have either large or small bills, no intermediate ones.
        c. Feeding performance maintains this dimorphism of beak size.

17.7   Fostering Diversity
  A. Nonrandom Mating
    1. Most species have distinctively male and female phenotypes—sexual dimorphism.
    2. Sexual selection is based on any trait that gives the individual a competitive edge in mating and producing offspring.
    3. Usually it is the females that are the agents of selection when they pick their mates.

B. Balanced Polymorphism
   1. With balanced polymorphism, two or more alleles of a gene persist at high frequencies in a population. Conditions favor heterozygotes.
   2. An example in humans is the heterozygous condition for the Hb^A/Hb^S.
      a. Hb genes code for hemoglobin; Hb^A is the normal condition and Hb^S is the mutated form, which causes sickle-cell anemia.
      b. Humans that are homozygous for sickle-cell anemia () develop the disease and die at an early age.
      c. However, individuals with alleles for both normal hemoglobin (Hb^A) and sickle-cell hemoglobin (Hb^S) have the greatest chances of surviving malaria.

17.8 Genetic Drift
   A. Genetic drift is the random fluctuation in allele frequencies over time, due to chance occurrences alone
      1. It is more significant in small populations; sampling error helps explain the difference.
      2. Genetic drift increases the chance of any given allele becoming more or less prevalent when the number of individuals in a population is small.
      3. Fixation means that one kind of allele remains at a specified locus in a population.
   B. Bottlenecks
      1. In bottlenecks, some stressful situation greatly reduces the size of a population, leaving a few (typical or atypical) individuals to reestablish the population.
      2. In the founder effect, a few individuals (carrying genes that may/may not be typical of the whole population) leave the original population to establish a new one.
   C. Inbred Populations
      1. Inbreeding refers to nonrandom mating among closely related individuals.
      2. It tends to increase the homozygous condition, thus leading to lower fitness and survival rates.
      3. Human populations that remain isolated and inbreed (such as the Old Order Amish in Lancaster County, PA) may concentrate disease, causing alleles.

17.9 Gene Flow
   A. Genes move with individuals when they move out of (emigration), or into (immigration), a population.
   B. The physical flow (and resultant shuffling) tends to minimize genetic variation between populations.

17.10 Reproductive Isolation
   A. Species and Speciation
      1. New species arise by the evolutionary process of speciation, which beings as gene flow ends between populations.
      2. Reproductive isolating mechanisms begin as two populations diverge from one another.
   B. Mechanisms of Reproductive Isolation
      1. Reproductive isolating mechanisms are any heritable features of body form, functioning, or behavior that prevent interbreeding between genetically divergent populations.
   C. Temporal Isolation
      1. Different groups may not be reproductively mature at the same season, month, or year (for example, periodical cicadas).

D. Mechanical Isolation
   1. Two populations are mechanically isolated when differences in reproductive organs prevent successful interbreeding (for example, floral arrangements in sage plants discriminate between different bee pollinators).
E. Ecological Isolation
   1. Potential mates may be in the same general area but not in the same habitat where they are likely to meet (for example, different species of manzanita shrubs live at different altitudes and habitats).
F. Behavioral Isolation
   1. Patterns of courtship may be altered to the extent that sexual union is not achieved.
G. Gamete Incompatibility
   1. Incompatibilities between egg and sperm prevent fertilization (for example, signals to pollen grains to begin growing toward the egg).
H. Hybrid Inviability
   1. Sometimes fertilization does occur between different species, but the hybrid embryo is weak and dies.
I. Hybrid Sterility
   1. In some instances, the hybrids are vigorous but sterile (for example, a mule produced by a male donkey and a female horse).

17.11 Allopatric Speciation

A. Physical Separation Encourages Speciation
   1. Allopatric refers to the "different lands" the two species occupy, and may be the most common way new species form.
      a. In this model, some physical barrier arises and prevents gene flow between populations.
      b. Reproductive isolating mechanisms evolve in the genetically diverging populations and will result in complete speciation when the two species can no longer interbreed.
   2. The pace of geographic isolation can vary depending upon the organism's means of travel.
      a. Isolation may be sudden as in an earthquake that results in separation of species.
      b. Studies of enzymes from fishes on the Atlantic and Pacific sides of the Isthmus of Panama reveal molecular differences that may have resulted from populations isolated as a function of plate tectonics.
B. Speciation in Archipelagos
   1. An archipelago is an island chain some distance away from a continent.
   2. The islands of Hawaii, which formed less than 1 million years ago, are an example.
      a. The islands' isolation is enough to favor divergence but not enough to stop the occasional colonizers.
      b. Thousands of species are unique to the Hawaiian archipelagos.

17.12 Sympatric and Parapatric Speciation

A. Sympatric Speciation
   1. In this model, species may form within the home range of an existing species, in the absence of a physical barrier.
   2. With polyploidy, speciation can occur in an instant with the change in chromosome number.
   3. Other mechanisms such as isolating environmental conditions can lead to divergence and the formation of new species.

B. Parapatric Speciation
1. Parapatric speciation may occur when one population extends across a broad region having diverse habitats. These different habitats exert selective pressures on these populations, which may result in divergence and new species.
2. Hybrids that form in a contact zone between habitats are less fit than individuals on either side.

17.13 Macroevolution
A. Patterns of Macroevolution
1. Macroevolution refers to large-scale patterns such as species giving rise to others.
2. Preadaptation or exaptation refers to a major evolutionary novelty that arises from some existing structure.
B. Stasis
1. Stasis refers to a long period with no evolutionary change.
C. Mass Extinctions
1. Extinction is the irrevocable loss of a species.
   a. Current estimates are that 99 percent of all species that have ever lived are extinct.
   b. Mass extinction events record the loss of many lineages of species.
D. Adaptive Radiation
1. We use the term coevolution where close ecological interactions among species cause them to evolve jointly.
   a. Each species adapts to changes in the other.
   b. Over time the two may become interdependent. Some may no longer be able to survive independently of the other.
E. Coevolution
1. Macroevolution refers to large-scale patterns such as species giving rise to others.
F. Evolutionary Theory
1. Evolutionary theorists do not doubt that macroevolution occurs; however, there are some disagreements about how it happens.

17.14 Phylogeny
A. Ranking Versus Grouping
1. A phylogeny is an evolutionary history of a species.
   a. Cladistics organize species based on shared characters.
   b. Cladograms organize species into clades, each with a common set of characters.
   c. A well-organized clade will represent accurate monophyletic groups – an ancestor and its decendents.
B. How We Use Evolutionary Biology
1. Our knowledge of evolutionary biology allows us to avoid scenarios that lead to extinction and the subsequent loss of diversity.
   a. History has shown we are slow to employ this knowledge.

Suggestions for Presenting the Material

◆ Stress the significance of the role of populations in the evolutionary process. How variations in a population are captured and passed along is a very significant concept.

- Several videos are available through the multimedia package that illustrates the major concepts in both microevolution and macroevolution. Students can use these videos to help place the material in context and as study tools for exams.

- Defining a species in terms of ability to interbreed may not seem as obvious to students as just saying two organisms "look alike." Perhaps the existence of various dog breeds is a good example of how very different individuals can look alike yet all be *Canis familiaris*.

- It helps to reinforce the role of natural selection as you move through the materials.

- The Hardy-Weinberg equation provides the baseline for calculating gene frequencies under unrealistic conditions. Non majors will find the mathematics intimidating.

  Several factors yield change in the real world:

  - mutation
  - genetic drift (founder, bottleneck)
  - gene flow
  - natural selection (stabilizing, directional, disruptive)

- Work a Hardy-Weinberg problem in the manner suggested in the Enrichment section below.

- Pesticide resistance in insects is perhaps the best and most recent example of natural selection. It should be presented clearly!

- Many students have the tendency to conclude that a population adapts to its environment because it "needs" to. They see adaptations more as Lamarck saw them instead of how Darwin saw them. This is a good place to give students practice in correcting their mistaken conclusions about natural selection. An example: Lamarck—Giraffes developed long necks by continually reaching for food that was higher in trees; Darwin—Giraffes born with longer necks were more effective in winning male-male fights for mates and thus, more reproductively successful in passing on those genes.

- Natural selection is, in many scientists' view, the most important concept for biology students to understand. Therefore, it is vital that you clear up any student misconceptions by providing many clear examples of microevolutionary processes.

- Emphasize to students that evolution occurs in populations, not individuals, even if they can see the changes in an individual's phenotype. Stress that selection pressures result in the survival of some individuals in the population over others.

- **Common Student Misconceptions**

  - Students often confuse microevolutionary processes with macroevolution. Find ways to reinforce the differences using multiple examples.

  - Students lose sight of the importance of selective pressures (stabilizing, disruptive, or directional), thinking they are all very similar.

Classroom and Laboratory Enrichment

- Choose an easy-to-see trait governed by one gene with two alleles such as tongue-rolling (the ability to roll one's tongue into a U-shape) or free earlobes (earlobes whose bases are not attached to the jawline), and ask students to determine their own phenotype. Determine the number of homozygous recessive individuals in the class (those who are non-tongue-rollers or have attached earlobes). Use the Hardy-Weinberg principle to calculate the frequencies of the dominant allele and the recessive allele.

- Demonstrate genetic drift by tracing changes in allele frequency throughout time. In small hypothetical populations, select a trait governed by two alleles and calculate the frequency of each allele. Different groups of students could be assigned populations of different sizes. Follow each population throughout several generations, as some of its members (selected by coin tosses) succumb to disease, predation, and other random causes of early death. How does population size affect genetic variation over time?

♦ Show slides or videos about endangered species that are threatened by sharp reductions in population size and subsequent loss of genetic variability. Highlight the directional selection forces that may act upon small populations that end up being geographically isolated.

♦ What happens to the genetic variability of small, isolated populations of laboratory organisms after many generations without the introduction of new organisms? Design and implement an experiment using any organism with a short generation time and several easy-to-see traits that can be followed from one generation to the next.

♦ How does artificial selection by humans affect gene frequencies of domestic plants and animals? Pursue this question with experiments or demonstrations.

♦ Present the results of a study where gene frequencies were determined by analyzing the proteins of an organism by gel electrophoresis.

♦ Explain why the analysis of proteins can be an indicator of gene variability.

♦ Consider the possibility that the Isthmus of Panama never existed. What kinds of organisms might, and might not, have been affected by this?

♦ Using the animated Figure 17.14, construct a small-group exercise to track rates of change for the flour beetle populations. Ask students to compare rates of change with the example for humans.

♦ Consider playing a DVD that highlights the concepts of evolutionary changes and the active science of evolution that investigates evidence for these processes.

Rise of the Super Rats (revisited)

♦ Would sporadic usage of warfarin improve its overall effectiveness?

♦ In the instance of resistance to warfarin, it was pointed out that the resistant strains gradually replaced the susceptible ones. Are these two strains different species? How could you prove/disprove your answer?

♦ If warfarin resistance could be bred out of the population by using biotechnology, should we pursue this?

Additional Ideas for Classroom Discussion

♦ How does phenotypic variation arise? Ask students to list as many sources of phenotypic variation as they can. They should be able to remember how genetic variation comes about from their earlier study of genetics.

♦ How are new alleles created? Is the creation of new alleles an important source of genetic change? Why or why not?

♦ What are some phenotypic variations that might have assisted the success of *Homo sapiens*? Ask your students to think of some imaginative examples of variations that might be useful in the future evolution of our species.

- How representative of the human population is your class? Discuss the importance of sample size with reference to determining allele frequencies. Ask your students to think about gene pool size and the founder effect if they were stranded forever on an uninhabited island. Would certain alleles be over- or under-represented? What would happen to allele frequencies after many generations?

- Think of examples of human alleles whose frequencies vary from one region to the next.

- Ask students to list the difference between natural selection and artificial selection?

- Is it legitimate to use the concept of *species* when naming bacteria? Why or why not?

- There are examples of animals with distinct species names, such as for the donkey and horse or the buffalo and Angus steer, but these animals can interbreed and produce living offspring. Are there other criteria that some authorities include in the definition of species to take care of these "exceptions"?

- What isolating mechanism(s) separate humans from other primates?

- What did Darwin's study of the different finch species among the Galápagos Islands tell him about speciation? What conclusions can you make about the evolutionary histories of the different species of Galápagos finches, given what you now know about the process of speciation?

- Why are conservationists concerned when the genetic variation within a population of rare or endangered organisms begins to decrease?

- How does sexual selection benefit a species? Would the introduction of alleles from a similar but different species introduce variety and thus help the species? Why or why not?

- How do reproductive isolating mechanisms help create new species?

- What type of isolation makes allopatry "thought [of as] the main speciation route," according to your text?

- Why is polyploidy referred to in the text as creating instantaneous species?

- Which of the models of speciation (gradual or punctuation) would be more likely to incorporate the necessity for "missing links"?

- Why do many evolutionary biologists believe that the punctuation model of evolution may explain the progression of different organisms better than the gradual model?

- Which evolutionary model is supported more fully by the fossil evidence—gradualism or punctuation?

- What was the impetus for Linnaeus to devise only two names for each organism rather than the taxonomy schemes in place during his day?

How Would You Vote? Classroom Discussion Ideas

- Have students complete class polling and monitor the online question. The banning of antibiotics in animal feed has been discussed for many years. Perhaps the first effort should be a voluntary move to limit the antibiotics that are of value to humans from those animals most likely to pass it on to humans. This has occurred in the new federal definitions and labeling of organic foods. Voluntary limits could be monitored to see it is making a difference in the quantities transferred. If not, then an outright ban may be necessary.

Term Paper Topics, Library Activities, and Special Projects

♦ Using the Internet, have students read about research of the founder effect in human populations isolated by geography or custom.

♦ What is the frequency of the allele for Tay-Sachs disease among Ashkenazic Jews? How do scientists explain the high frequency of this allele in this segment of the population?

♦ Have students investigate and report on other geographically or socially isolation human populations. What rare genetic conditions are more often expressed in those populations?

♦ How has the loss of genetic diversity (possibly resulting from a population bottleneck at some time in the past) affected cheetahs? Report on recent research efforts in this area.

♦ Describe how artificial selection in the genus *Brassica* has resulted in several very different vegetable varieties.

♦ What is the frequency of the allele for cystic fibrosis in the United States? Does the frequency of this allele differ among different segments of the population? Is the allele frequency changing over time?

♦ How do commercial plant breeders and agricultural biologists maintain genetic variability among the plants they raise?

♦ Why is inbreeding harmful to a species? Select a species or a group of organisms (a dog breed, for example), and discuss the results of inbreeding.

♦ Prepare brief biographies of G. H. Hardy and W. Weinberg. How is it that they discovered their principle "independently"? Did they ever collaborate?

♦ Consult a microbiology textbook to learn how bacteria are named and classified.

♦ What are the first recorded crossings of a donkey with a horse?

♦ What cellular mechanisms prevent mules from reproducing?

♦ There have been conflicting reports as to whether the squirrels on the North and South rims of the Grand Canyon are the same, or different, species because of geographical isolation. Research and analyze these claims.

♦ Have students investigate the commercial benefits of polyploidy in plants.

♦ Examine the role of geographic barriers (such as high elevations, mountaintops, isolated stream drainages, and islands) in the development of a group of closely related regional species or genera.

♦ Among invertebrates, there are several hermaphroditic (both sexes in the same animal) species, such as the common earthworm. How is self-fertilization avoided when these animals reproduce? (Answer: anatomical features and differential timing of gamete maturation)

♦ What is thought to be the current rate of species extinction today? Is the rate of extinction today higher than can be accounted for by background extinction? What areas of the Earth are experiencing the highest rates of species extinction?

♦ When reconstructing the past evolutionary history of the Earth and its living forms, vast periods of time are necessary to account for the amount of change. How do strict creationists view the geologic time scale?

♦ Have students report on current theories for the great mass extinctions of the past. Which is(are) the most plausible?

Responses to *Data Analysis Activities*

1.   Rats were most susceptible to warfarin in Ludwigshafen.
2.   Stadtlohn had the percentage of resistant rats.
3.   In Olfen, 79% of the rats were resistant to warfarin.
4.   Most likely, bromodiolone application was most intensive in Stadtlohn, leading to very high levels of resistant rats.

Possible Responses to *Critical Thinking* Questions

1.   Rama the cama is an animal that is not supposed to be. Camels and llamas are designated as two different species because they do not interbreed. But, alas, it appears as though Rama has nullified the definition. However, a more strict reading of the definition of a species may clarify things. Usually the words "naturally interbreeding" are included in the definition. Rama was the result of artificial insemination. Also, in order to be members of the same species, the offspring of a pairing must be living (truly Rama is) AND fertile (Rama has yet to demonstrate his procreative ability). So, just as in the case of horse + donkey = mule, the species are separate—albeit very close.

2.   What is needed here in the proposed experiment is to give the female human a choice— charming, witty man versus less flamboyant and dull man. Ideally, both types would be available and would differ *only* in similar phenotypic types. The female could be given a choice between flamboyant and dull men, in a range of social interaction situations. Observers would then record how many approaches and "interests" the female showed with each type of male suitor. If she chooses the flamboyant, witty man over the dull, dimwitted one, then sexual selection would be acting in favor of more flamboyant male. A similar experiment would need to be designed in which males are given the choice of females of more or less juvenile features. The problem with either experiment is that they impose the expectation that the selection pattern of modern males and females matches that of our ancestors.

18

LIFE'S ORIGIN AND EARLY EVOLUTION

Chapter Outline

Objectives

1. Describe the conditions on Earth approximately 3.8 billion years ago.
2. Describe the formation of organic subunits on the early Earth.
3. Describe the origins of cells.
4. Describe the early divergence and evolution of cells.
5. Discuss the origin of membrane-bound organelles and provide evidence supporting it.

Key Terms

astrobiology	protocells	stromatolites
big bang theory	RNA world	biomarker
hydrothermal vent	ribozymes	endosymbiosis

Lecture Outline

18.1 Looking for Life

  A. Astrobiology studies life's origins and distribution in the universe

  B. Life in extreme environments provides evidence that life can take hold almost anywhere

    1. Bacteria can tolerate extreme conditions.

    2. Scientists believe that anywhere there is liquid water to sustain chemical reactions life is possible.

18.2 Earth's Origin and Early Conditions

  A. From the Big Bang to the Early Earth

    1. The universe continues to expand and galaxies are still moving away from one another.

    2. The big bang describes the instantaneous distribution of all matter and energy throughout the universe that occurred 12-15 billion years ago.

    3. Dying stars left behind clouds of dust and gas, which began to cool and form our solar system some 5 billion years ago.

  B. Conditions on Early Earth

    1. About 4.6 billion years ago, one of the clouds formed by exploding stars began to condense into planets around our sun. One clump became our Earth.

      a. Earth was initially very hot, but cooled to form an outer mantle and partially-molten core.

      b. The first atmosphere probably consisted of gaseous hydrogen, nitrogen, carbon monoxide, and carbon dioxide.

      c. If free oxygen levels had been abundant, then the organic compounds necessary for life could not have formed.

      d. When the Earth's crust cooled rocks formed and rains began, forming the seas.

18.3 The Source of Life's Building Blocks

  A. Lightening-Fueled Atmospheric Reactions

    1. Miller and Urey proposed that the early Earth atmosphere would have produced organic compounds spontaneously.

      a. Miller's success in creating these amino acids and other small organic compounds caused scientists to revise their ideas about the first atmosphere's composition.

  B. Reactions at Hydrothermal Vents

    1. Hydrothermal vents spew hot, mineral-rich water.

    2. Wächtershäuser and Huber found hydrothermal vents produced amino acids rapidly.

  C. Delivery From Space

    1. Amino acids, sugars, and nucleotide bases are found in meteorites.

    2. Meteorites fell much more frequently in the past.

18.4 From Polymers to Cells

  A. Steps on the Road to Life

    1. All cells have a lipid bilayer plasma membrane, and DNA which is both hereditary and converted to RNA to make proteins.

    2. Chemistry can predict how these may have arisen.

  B. Origin of Metabolism

    1. Modern cells use proteins, which are polymers themselves, to assemble other polymers.

2. Proteins may have first evolved in polar clay-rich tidal flats. The negative charge of the clay would have attracted positively-charged amino acids, especially in the presence of sunlight. Research supports this hypothesis.
3. Other hypotheses suggest the development of simple metabolic pathways at thermal vents.

C. Origin of the Cell Membranes
1. The metabolism inside living cells cannot occur without a barrier of lipid membranes to protect against the chemical actions on the outside.
2. Protocells are simple membrane-bound sacs that capture energy, concentrate materials, engage in metabolism, and self replicate.
3. Experiments show that membrane-bound sacs can form spontaneously, incorporating proteins and fatty acids.

D. Origin of the Genome
1. From accumulated organic compounds emerged replicating systems consisting of DNA, RNA, and proteins.
2. An early RNA world may have preceded DNA's dominance as the main informational molecule. Ribosomes are evidence of early RNA molecules that have not changed much over time.
3. The discovery of ribozymes, a type of catalytic RNA, and subsequent research support the RNA world hypothesis.
4. How DNA entered the picture is not yet clear. DNA is a larger, more stable molecule that may have provided protection against early RNA viruses.

18.5 Life's Early Evolution
A. Origin of Bacteria and Archaea
1. Life on Earth is estimated to have began 4.3 billion years ago.
2. Australian rocks that date to 3.5 billion years ago contain microscopic filaments that some link to early cells. Other Australian rocks indicate early evidence of bacteria near deep sea thermal vents.
3. Over 3 billion years ago, the prokaryotic line split into bacteria and archaea
4. Evolution of the cyclic pathway of photosynthesis in bacteria tapped a renewable source of energy—sunlight; large accumulations of these cells are seen today as fossils known as stromatolites.
5. By the dawn of the Proterozoic eon (2.7 billion years ago), the noncyclic pathway had evolved among cyanobacteria that were producing oxygen.

B. Effects of Increasing Oxygen
1. By 2.4 billion years ago, increasing oxygen levels were impacting life.
    a. An oxygen-rich atmosphere stopped the further chemical origin of living cells.
    b. Free oxygen permitted aerobic respiration, which now became the dominant energy-releasing pathway .
    c. Oxygen formed ozone, which limited the penetration of UV radiation, allow life to move on to land.

C. The Rise of Eukaryotes
1. The oldest complete eukaryotic fossils are about 2.7 billion years old as indicated by the lipid biomarker they left behind.
2. The earliest known organism is filamentous red algae, about 1.2 billion years old.
3. Complex animals appear in the fossil record from about 570 million years ago.
4. By the dawn of the Cambrian, 543 million years ago, a large adaptive radiation of animals was taking place, leading to all major animal lineages.

18.6   Evolution of Organelles
    A. Origin of the Nucleus
        1. It is possible that the infoldings of the plasma membrane seen in prokaryotic cells could have led to the formation of narrow channels that permit the separation of tasks and materials seen in the ER of eukaryotic cells.
        2. Similarly, infoldings could have surrounded the DNA to become the nuclear envelope that serves to protect the cell from invasions of foreign DNA and shield the DNA from radiaton.
    B. The Role of Endosymbiosis
        1. Mitochondria are similar in size and structure to bacteria.
            a. Like bacterial chromosomes, mitochondrial DNA is a circle with few noncoding regions between genes and few or no introns.
            b. A mitochondrion does not replicate its DNA or divide at the same time as the cell.
        2. According to the theory of endosymbiosis, one species becomes a resident inside another cell to the benefit of both.
        3. Aerobic bacteria could have become the mitochondria; cyanobacteria could have become chloroplasts.
        4. The host would have begun to rely on ATP produced by the aerobic symbiont, and the symbiont would have relied on the host for raw materials.
    C. Evidence of Endosymbiosis
        1. A laboratory culture of *Amoeba* became infected with a bacterium; in the following five years some cells died but others thrived and became dependent on the invaders.
        2. However early symbiotic relationships arose, evidence indicates that early eukaryotes had a nucleus, endomembrane system, mitochondria, and in certain lineages, chloroplasts.

18.7   Time Line for Life's Origin and Evolution

Suggestions for Presenting the Material

♦   This chapter continues the theme of evolution but "steps back" in time to look at the origin and early evolution of life in preparation for the survey of life forms.

♦   Stress the conclusions that are in constant review as scientists attempt to reconstruct the past. Just as a good medical diagnosis is not based on one examination or one lab test, a good analysis of past evolutionary history is not based on any one line of evidence, but rather several lines of corroborating evidence.

♦   You may want to begin the topic of the origin of life by surveying the class for the explanations most frequently given to account for the origin of life on planet Earth. (Common responses include: (1) special creation, (2) arrival from distant planets, and (3) "just happened.")

♦   Based on the above survey, you may find that your students know the *least* about *spontaneous generation* and are indeed skeptical that "life could come from nonliving matter." Be sure you include some mention of the difference in possibilities of spontaneous generation in the *past* and *today*.

♦   Take time to stress the significant evolutionary advances seen in the development of photosynthetic pathways, aerobic respiration, and increases in complexity.

♦   Because of the rather theoretical and speculative nature of the "origin of life" section, students' minds often wander because they don't have any concrete terms to write down. Use of visual material of any kind will help to retain focus.

- Take the time to use the animated Figure 18.14 to pull students in and provide them context for the vast amount of times involved.
- Common Student Misconceptions
  - Students have difficulty imagining the huge amounts of time involved in the early evolution of life, the transition to eukaryotes and the first fossil evidence of complex life. Create a 12-hour clock example to illustrate the vast amounts of time involved (many examples are available in texts).

Classroom and Laboratory Enrichment

- Prepare an overhead or slide summarizing the work of Redi, Spallanzani, and Pasteur in disproving spontaneous generation under "recent" conditions on Earth.
- Assemble a replica (sans ingredients) of the apparatus Stanley Miller used in his famous experiment. Point out how elegant and simple his experiment was.
- Using modeling clay, make "templates" such as might have been available for molecules in the primordial earth as described in the chapter.
- To stimulate interest in "protocells," blow soap bubbles using the materials available in any store's toy section.
- Show actual fossils or photographs of fossils representing some of the life forms prevalent during the Paleozoic, Mesozoic, and Cenozoic eras.
- Have students create their own timeline or clock example that illustrates the major evolutionary trends.

Looking for Life (revisited)

- Describe the metabolic pathways used by the first living cells to obtain energy.
- What objections could you raise to the possibility of life arriving here millions of years ago from distant planets? Is there evidence to support this theory?
- Evolutionary biologists believe that life on Earth first evolved in the absence of oxygen. Where did the oxygen in our atmosphere come from?
- The lack of atmosphere on smaller planets suggest that only anaerobic life could evolve. What impact would this have on the complexity of life that could evolve?

Additional Ideas for Classroom Discussion

- Diagram the apparatus used by Stanley Miller to study the synthesis of organic compounds in an atmosphere like that of early Earth. Ask students how they summarize Miller's findings in light of the evolution of organic molecules.
- On what evidence do scientists reconstruct a primordial Earth depicted in Figure 18.3?
- Why was no free oxygen (O_2) included in Miller's experiment? What did the electrical spark simulate?
- What distinguishes a nonliving lipid-bound sphere containing nucleic acids and amino acids from a living cell?
- Name some organisms living today that are virtually unchanged from their earliest appearances in the fossil record millions of years ago. Why do some organisms fail to change significantly throughout geologic time?

- Why was aerobic respiration necessary for the evolution of eukaryotes?
- Describe the metabolic pathways used by the first living cells to obtain energy.
- Why do you think people believed as recently as 100 years ago that spontaneous generation still occurs on Earth?
- The branching of prokaryotes during the Archaean into archaebacteria, eubacteria, and eukaryotes (see Figure 18.14) is the basis for a new three-domain scheme of classification. Evaluate the merits of this scheme versus the more traditional five- (or six-) kingdom scheme.
- Do you think it is possible for scientists studying the evolution of life to also believe that God played a role in the creation of life? Why or why not?
- What triggered the rapid adaptive radiation of mammals beginning at the start of the Cenozoic era?
- Why is that body of thought known as "scientific creationism" not a science? List the types of evidence supporting the principle of evolution.
- How have extinctions facilitated the development of new species?

How Would You Vote? Classroom Discussion Ideas

- Have students complete class via the online question. On the one hand, the discovery of microbes in the Martian soil would be an absolutely momentous discovery in that it would confirm life outside the Earth. It is possible it may also reveal a shared common origin.
- The opposing view would involve pointing out the very high cost of such an undertaking that would most likely reveal information valuable only in an academic sense. There is also the potential danger of bringing a microbe from another planet to Earth as we would not be able to predict how it would interact with Earth life.

Term Paper Topics, Library Activities, and Special Projects

- Discuss the history of the experiments by Stanley Miller.
- See if you can locate the original article by Miller and Urey in which they reported their famous experiment. Read it carefully to see what speculative application they made for their experiment.
- Using the Internet, have students complete a search and report on current articles that discuss early evolution. Have them complete a one-page paper that summarizes one article focusing on the science presented.
- Although the idea of life originating on Earth from forms traveling from distant planets is highly imaginative, serious proposals have been advanced. Locate some of these and evaluate their merit.
- Discover what fossil evidence has revealed about the past history of your region of the planet. Present fossils in class and have students speculate about where on Figure 18.14 it would belong.
- When reconstructing the past evolutionary history of the Earth and its living forms, vast periods of time are necessary to account for the amount of change. How do strict creationists view the geologic time scale?
- What are the most plausible theories for the great mass extinctions of the past?
- Research the causes of extinction *today*. Are all, or most, of the causes the result of human intervention?
- Trace the evolutionary history of one group of plants or animals throughout geologic time.
- Prepare a time line tracing the geologic and biologic history of your section of the world.

Responses to *Data Analysis Activities*

1. Asteroid impacts declined long before oxygen levels began to rise.
2. Compared to conditions when cells first arose, O_2 levels are much higher while CO_2 levels are much lower.
3. At present, O_2 is far more abundant in the atmosphere than CO_2.

Possible Responses to *Critical Thinking* Questions

1. Plate tectonics involves the constant movement of geologic plates on the surface of the Earth. These plates collide, and rise over or move under adjoining plates. Where plates are separating, molten material from the core of the Earth makes its way to the surface. Over such long geologic time (many billions of years), the plates have moved dramatically, eliminating the earliest sedimentary rocks from the surface of the Earth.

2. These cells would have to contain genetic information to code for proteins, be able to obtain and process inputs for energy, engage in metabolic reactions, eliminate wastes, communicate and interact with its environment, and reproduce.

19

VIRUSES, BACTERIA, AND ARCHAEANS

Chapter Outline

Objectives

1. List the general characteristics of viruses and viroids, and describe their impact on living cells.
2. Describe the common features of bacteria.
3. Describe bacterial replication and their mechanism of gene exchange.
4. Recognize the diversity of bacteria, including their ability to cause disease.
5. Describe the diversity of the newly recognized archaeans.

Key Terms

bacteriophages	emerging disease	pandemic	pili
lytic pathway	vector	viroid	binary fission
lysogenic pathway	endemic disease	bacterial chromosome	horizontal gene transfer
pathogens	epidemic	nucleoid	conjugation

plasmid	proteobacteria	endospore	methanogens
cyanobacteria	normal flora	Spriochetes	extreme halophiles
nitrogen fixation	Gram staining	Chlamydias	extreme thermophiles

Lecture Outline

19.1 Evolution of a Disease

    A. HIV is the virus that causes AIDS in humans

        1. There are two subtypes HIV-1 and HIV-2.

        2. Genetic sequencing revealed that HIV strongly resembles SIV, a disease of chimpanzees.

    B. HIV may have evolved by ape-to-human transfer of HIV.

        1. Analysis of populations living near chimpanzees has revealed this is possible.

        2. HIV has been infecting humans since at least the 1950s, starting in Africa and slowly spreading.

        3. Today, 20 million people have died from AIDS, and 30 million are infected with HIV.

19.2 Viral Structure and Function

    A. Viral Traits and Diversity

        1. A virus consists of a nucleic acid core surrounded by a protein coat.

            a. The genetic material may be either DNA or RNA.

            b. The coat, or capsid, is a protein.

        2. Animal viruses infect human cells.

            a. They may have a coat or be naked.

            b. They may have RNA or DNA genetic material.

    B. Viral Replication

        1. A virus can replicate only after its nucleic acid has entered and subverted the host cell's biosynthetic apparatus to produce new viral particles.

    C. Bacteriophage Replication

        1. In the lytic pathway, the virus enters the host cell and replicates immediately, and then ruptures the cell by exiting.

        2. In the lysogenic pathway, the virus integrates in the host chromosome and then goes latent.

            a. During this time, it is copied during host replication, ending up in all subsequent cells.

            b. In the future, the virus can replicate and exit the cell.

    D. HIV Replication

        1. HIV replication follows these steps.

            a. The virus fuses to the host cell membrane, allowing its RNA to enter the host cell.

            b. Viral reverse transcriptase converts the viral RNA to DNA.

            c. New created viral DNA integrates in a host chromosome.

            d. Viral DNA is transcribed with host genes.

            e. Sme viral RNA is transcribed to form viral proteins.

            f. Other viral RNA becomes the genetic material of HIV viruses.

            g. Viral particles self-assemble at the plasma membrane.

            h. The virus buds, using the host plasma membrane as its envelope.

            i. The viral particle can now infect other host white blood cells.

19.3   Viral Effects on Human Health

A. Common Viral Diseases

1. Nonenveloped viruses can cause colds and warts.

2. Herpesvirus (responsible for genital herpes) is an example of an enveloped, lysogenic virus.

B. Emerging Viral Diseases

1. These viruses either rapidly expand their range or are newly detected in humans.

2. These are more apt to be RNA viruses due to their higher rate of mutation.

C. West Nile Fever

1. Mosquitoes serve as the vector for this virus, transferring it from birds to humans.

2. Most infected people are not sickened, but 1% may suffer fever and possibly die.

3. The disease entered the Western Hemisphere in 1999.

4. West Nile Fever is an endemic disease in the U.S. - present but at low levels.

D. SARS

1. SARS appeared in China in 2002.

a. SARS was first epidemic – widespread in one region.

b. It quickly became pandemic – threatening human health in many regions.

2. The coronavirus responsible for the disease it thought to have been native to rats, and then entered humans via other animal intermediaries.

E. Influenza H1N5 and H1N1

1. Influenza virus is responsible for causing the flu.

a. Mutations cause the virus to change slightly from year to year.

2. H1N5 was highly fatal, but transferred only from birds to humans.

3. H1N1 proved to be easily transmitted, but less lethal than first feared.

4. It is necessary to influenza viruses to be prepared should a highly transmissible and fatal virus develop.

19.4   Viroids: Tiny Plant Pathogens

A. Viroids are simpler than viruses, with a small circle of RNA that does not contain a protein coat. Viroids mainly cause plant diseases.

1. Viroid RNA does not encode proteins, the RNA itself has enzymatic activity.

19.5   Bacterial Structure and Function

A. Cell Size, Structure, and Motility

1. Bacteria are very small, and are described by their shape when viewed microscopically.

2. The most common prokaryotic cell shapes are a sphere (cocci), rod (bacilli), or a spiral (spirilla).

3. Nearly all bacteria have a cell wall, usually containing a tough mesh of peptides cross-linked with polysaccharides, overlaid with a slime layer.

4. Prokaryotes have no nucleus or other membrane-bound organelles.

a. Metabolic reactions take place in the cytoplasm or at the plasma membrane.

b. Proteins are assembled on floating ribosomes.

5. Two kinds of filamentous structures may be attached to the cell wall.

a. The *bacterial flagellum* rotates like a propeller to pull the cell along.

b. *Pili* help bacteria attach to one another in conjugation, during which plasmids may be transferred, or help them attach to surfaces.

B. Abundance and Metabolic Diversity

1. There are estimated to be 5 million trillion trillion bacterial cells on Earth.

2. Bacteria have four modes of nutrition; some are autotrophs (self-feeders) and some are heterotrophs (not self feeders).
   a. Photoautotrophs synthesize their own organic compounds, using sunlight as the energy source and carbon dioxide as the carbon source.
   b. Chemoautotrophs utilize carbon dioxide and produce organic compounds, using the energy in simple inorganic substances.
   c. Photoheterotrophs use sunlight as an energy source but their carbon must come from organic compounds—not CO_2.
   d. Chemoheterotrophs include parasitic types that draw nutrition from living hosts and saprobic types that are decomposers and obtain nutrition from products, wastes, or remains of other organisms.

19.6   Bacterial Reproduction and Gene Exchange
   A. Reproduction
      1. Bacteria reproduce by binary fission.
         a. The single, circular chromosome attaches to the plasma membrane.
         b. The chromosome duplicates, with the copy chromosome attaching adjacent to the original. New plasma membrane inserted between the two chromosomes.
         c. The membrane and wall invaginate between the two chromosomes.
         d. Two genetically identical cells result.
   B. Horizontal Gene Transfers
      1. Bacteria are capable of exchanging genetic material between individual cells.
         a. One cell extends a sex pilus to a second cell.
         b. The cell that made the sex pilus sends a copy of a plasmid – an extrachromosomal circular DNA – to the second cell.
      2. Bacteria can also take up DNA from the environment, and may receive DNA from viruses.
      3. This process accelerates that rate with which a valuable gene (e.g. resistance to antibacterial agents) can spread.

19.7   Bacterial Diversity
   A. Heat-Loving Bacteria
      1. If life evolved near hydrothermal vents, these may resemble the earliest cells.
      2. Enzymes from *Thermus aquaticus* are used in PCR.
   B. Oxygen-Producing Cyanobacteria
      1. Cyanobacteria both perform photosynthesis and release oxygen.
         a. Chloroplasts may have evolved from cyanobacteria.
      2. Some cyanobacteria can perform nitrogen fixation.
   C. Highly Diverse Proteobacteria
      1. Proteobacteria make up the largest, most diverse bacterial group.
         a. *Rhizobium* fixes nitrogen on the roots of legumes. *E. coli* makes vitamin K in the human gut.
         b. *Helicobacter pylori* cause stomach ulcers.
         c. *E. coli* makes vitamin K in the human gut.
   D. The Thick-Walled Gram Positives
      1. Gram staining can distinguish two major bacterial groups.
         a. Thick-walled gram positives stain purple.
         b. Thin-walled gram negatives stain pink.
      2. Most Gram positives are chemoheterotrophs.

3. Some Gram positives can form endospores
    a. Endospores can tolerate extremely harsh conditions.
    b. The endospore can germinate when conditions become favorable. Anthrax and *Clostridium* infections utilize this mechanism.
4. Disease causing Gram positives are becoming resistant to antibacterial drugs.
    a. Tuberculosis, flesh-eating bacteria, and staph infections are all diseases caused by Gram positive bacteria.
    b. Their resistance to antibiotics is rendering them increasingly problematic to treat.

E. Spring-Shaped Spirochetes
  1. This group includes both endosymbionts and disease-causing groups.

F. Parasitic Chlamydias
  1. Chlamydias can replicate only in eukaryotic host cells.
  2. They form the most common sexually transmitted bacterial disease in the U.S.

19.8 The Archaeans

A. Discovering the Third Domain
  1. Archaea are prokaryotes that differ from other bacteria in their ribosomal RNA.
  2. Some archaea may resemble the first cells on Earth.
  3. In many ways, archaea are more similar to eukaryotes than to prokaryotes. A third classification domain was established as a result.

B. Archaean Diversity
  1. Methanogens are "methane-makers."
    a. They inhabit swamps, mud, sewage, and animal guts.
    b. They make ATP anaerobically by converting carbon dioxide and hydrogen to methane.
  2. Extreme halophiles are "salt-lovers."
    a. These species can tolerate high salt environments such as brackish ponds, salt lakes, volcanic vents on the seafloor, and the like.
    b. Most are heterotrophic aerobes, but some can switch to a special photosynthesis, using bacteriorhodopsin, to produce ATP.
  3. Extreme thermophiles are "heat-lovers."
    a. These bacteria live in hot springs and other very hot places, such as the thermal vents of the sea floor where temperatures exceed 230°C.
    b. They use sulfur as a source of electrons for ATP formation.

Suggestions for Presenting the Material

♦ This chapter includes two quite diverse groups: one that is living (prokaryotes) and one that is not (viruses). Emphasize the fact that these groups are together not because of any taxonomic relatedness but because they traditionally lie at the beginning of discussions of living things.

♦ Students should be very interested in the viruses and bacteria covered in this chapter, especially those that are capable of causing well-known diseases.

♦ Most students are unfamiliar with the structure and function of the viruses and bacteria. Emphasize the nonliving nature of the viruses, a point that students often have trouble grasping.

♦ You may want to briefly review how taxonomists went from two kingdoms, to five kingdoms, to three domains.

- This chapter offers an excellent opportunity to discuss epidemiology and to show how scientists use the scientific method when attempting to find the causative agent of a disease. The recent widespread public awareness of AIDS also opens an avenue for discussion of the accuracy with which scientific stories are covered by the media.

- **Common Student Misconceptions:**
  - Many students may not be aware of that most bacteria are beneficial. Be sure to emphasize that not all bacteria are pathogens. Remind students of the beneficial aspects of bacteria, including their usefulness in producing products through genetic engineering, their role in decomposition/bioremediation, and their role in the human body.

Classroom and Laboratory Enrichment

- Videos are available through the PowerLecture that show the impact of bacteria and viruses in our students' lives. Introduce the chapter with one of these videos to put the topic in perspective.

- Use the tip of a toothpick to collect bacteria from sources such as plaque from the surface of a tooth or yogurt with live cultures. Prepare a simple bacterial smear, stain with crystal violet, and observe at 1000x.

- Prepare Gram stains of bacterial species of varying morphology and from cultures obtained from biological supply houses.

- Collect and examine cyanobacteria from stagnant ponds, tree trunks, and greenhouse flowerpots.

- Survey your environment for the presence of bacteria. This can be done with help from a microbiologist who can prepare media and plates. Then you and your students can: (a) take swabs of various surfaces, (b) allow dust to settle on a plate, (c) allow insects to land, (d) apply samples of food, (e) press a leaf onto a plate, and so on.

- Invite a health care worker to tell of experiences and precautions in the hospital or clinic setting.

- Visit an electron microscope in a research laboratory where research on viruses is being done. Ask the technician to discuss preparation techniques for viral specimens and to demonstrate the operation of the microscope. If possible, allow students to prepare their own viral suspensions of a plant virus (such as tobacco mosaic virus) in the laboratory for subsequent examination under the electron microscope.

- Prepare an exhibit of living organisms or portions of organisms, such as leaves, affected by viruses.

- Gather information from local health authorities about any of the diseases caused by bacteria and viruses that are found in your area. Sexually transmitted diseases such as gonorrhea, syphilis, and AIDS would be good examples. What is the number of cases per month within your city or state? Is the number of new cases rising or falling?

- Seek class members or faculty colleagues who may have traveled to a tropical area where diseases unknown in the United States are present. Ask them to report on any precautions taken before, during, and after their trip.

Evolution of a Disease (Revisited)

♦ HIV, like many disease-causing agents, has shown a powerful ability to evolve both to resist treatments designed to destroy them and to better match their host. Simultaneously, hosts evolve to combat the pathogens. What does this reveal about evolution ever reaching an end? Will we likely ever reach a point where pathogens are all eliminated or completely controlled?

♦ Given that HIV is a relatively recent disease-causing agent, why would some populations show greater resistance to HIV infection? (Hint: Look up the history of cowpox and small pox!)

♦ Recall that populations evolve, not individuals. What is the fate of infected individuals as a population is evolving to become increasingly resistant to a fatal disease?

Additional Ideas for Classroom Discussion

♦ In older classification schemes, bacteria were included with the plants. For what reason was this a rather poor "match"?

♦ Why is the "Gram" of Gram stain written with a capital letter?

♦ Why are bacteria said to be "the most metabolically diverse" of all living groups? Why are organisms of such varied metabolisms all placed in the same group?

♦ Why are the methanogens, halophiles, and extreme thermophiles grouped as archaeans?

♦ What are viroids? How are they similar to/different from viruses?

♦ What is the role of disease in limiting the growth of human and animal populations? (Remember Malthus!)

♦ What is epidemiology? Discuss the roles played by the World Health Organization and the Centers for Disease Control and Prevention in the study and treatment of outbreaks of disease.

♦ Discuss the possibility that the "age of antibiotics" may be drawing to a close.

♦ Are viruses alive? Use the characteristics of life to discuss whether or not viruses are alive.

How Would You Vote? Classroom Discussion Ideas

♦ Monitor the voting for the online question. Discuss the benefits of a voluntary testing program (greater awareness of infection and less spread) versus the cost (the majority of the people will test negative, and their tests will take money from treatment progams). Does the benefit of making people aware they have the disease override the funds for helping those who are infected manage the disease?

Term Paper Topics, Library Activities, and Special Projects

♦ Are public swimming areas (pools, lakes, spring-fed ponds, and rivers) in your area required to routinely check for evidence of pollution from sewage effluent? Discover the maximum *E. coli* count allowed by law before the facility must be closed to public swimming. How is this figure determined? What does it mean? Why is it unsafe to swim in waters that have a relatively large number of *E. coli* bacteria?

♦ How do antibiotics such as penicillin and tetracycline kill bacteria? Discuss the modes of action of several commonly used antibiotics.

♦ Describe the role of certain species of bacteria in producing food products such as buttermilk, sour cream, yogurt, and sauerkraut.

♦ Describe the morphology and physiology of any one of the pathogenic genera of bacteria. Discuss the diseases caused by the members of the genus and their treatments.

♦ Where did viruses come from? Discover what scientists know about the evolutionary origin of the virus.

♦ How are viruses destroyed? What kinds of chemicals and filters are used in the laboratory to ensure that an experimental liquid is virus-free?

♦ Research the history, mode of action, and treatment of several economically important viral diseases of crops.

♦ Discuss the role of the immune system in fighting viral outbreaks or bacterial infections. How does the immune system "recognize" viral strains or bacterial species that have caused disease within the individual on previous occasions?

♦ Discuss the worldwide Spanish flu epidemic of 1918–1920.

♦ Collect stories about AIDS from magazines and newspapers. Analyze the stories for scientific accuracy and completeness. In what areas do such stories effectively cover AIDS? In what ways do they mislead or fail to inform the reader?

♦ Report on the latest scientific research in the treatment of any one of the diseases caused by viruses discussed in your text.

♦ It is known that flu epidemics (and pandemics) tend to occur in 10- to 40-year cycles. Check an epidemiology or medical textbook to locate possible explanations for this periodicity.

♦ How does a retrovirus differ from other viruses in its operation?

♦ The following are diseases caused by spirochetes and transmitted in different ways: Lyme disease by ticks, relapsing fever by lice, and syphilis by human sexual contact.

  o Are the different spirochete species that cause these diseases able to interchange vectors? Explain why.

♦ Discuss the impact that bacteria have on food safety. What are the concerns and how can we handle food safely to prevent infection? Does proper food handling protect from prions?

Responses to Data Analysis Activities

1. Yes, during the late 1980s the number of children diagnosed with AIDS steadily increased.
2. The number of new AIDS diagnoses in children peaked in 1992.
3. In 1993, the use of antiretrovirals for HIV-positive women was introduced, and the number of AIDS diagnoses among children began to fall immediately.

Possible Responses to *Critical Thinking* Questions

1. Why viruses without a lipid envelope remain infective outside the body is curious. However, their ability to tolerate exposure to soap is likely due to the lack of a lipid for the aphphipathic soap molecules to act on.

2. Methanogens would only be found in low oxygen areas. Thus, the human mouth and surface waters would not be good locations for them to grow.

3. The harmless bacteria became dangerous by absorbing the DNA from the ruptured cells that provided them with the smooth coat to become pathogenic.

4. Cells treated with penicillin are unable to synthesize new cell wall material. As a result, the bacteria are unable to complete binary fission. By comparison, taxols interference with spindle formation would not impact bacteria as bacteria do not rely on a mitotic spindle to separate their chromosomes – bacteria rely on attachment to the plasma membrane.

5. I would expect more individuals to be heterozygous for this allele. The 1% that are homozygous represent the small fraction of the population that received two copies of a rare allele. It would be much more common to receive a single copy of a rare allele.

20

THE PROTISTS

Chapter Outline

Objectives

1. Describe the major categories of protistans.
2. Describe how protistans differ from bacteria, viruses, and multicellular eukaryotes.
3. Compare green algae to plants. Understand similarities and differences between these two groups of organisms.
4. Understand how amoeboid species compare to fungi and animals.
5. Gain an appreciation of the diversity of life on earth.

Key Terms

protist	foraminiferans	diatoms	amoebozoans
algal bloom	plankton	brown algae	amoebas
toxin	radiolarians	red algae	plasmodial slime molds
flagellated protozoans	alveolates	alternation of	cellular slime molds
pellicle	dinoflagellate	generations	
trypanosomes	ciliates	gametophyte	
euglenoids	apicomplexans	sporophyte	
contractile vacuoles	water molds	green algae	

Lecture Outline

20.1   Harmful Algal Blooms

   A.   Protistans are structurally the simplest eukaryotic cells.

   B.   Some protists cause disease or damage, but others are beneficial to nature.

   C.   An algal bloom, commonly known as a "red tide," is a population explosion of tiny aquatic producers.

   D.   The protist *Karenia brevis* makes brevetoxin, a substance which interferes with animal nerve cells.
   1.   Brevetoxin sickens and may even kill marine invertebrates, fish, sea turtles, sea birds, dolphins, and manatees.
   2.   Humans may be exposed to brevetoxin by eating shellfish or inhaled from onshore winds, causing the following symptoms: headache, vertigo, loss of coordination, temporary paralysis, irritation of the nasal membranes, constriction of the airways, and DNA damage

   E.   Although protists affect humans, the lineages and traits of protists had their origins long before humans evolved.

20.2   A Collection of Lineages

   A.   The classification of protists is a work in progress due to the incredible diversity within the group. Some lineages are more closely related to plants, fungi, or animals than to other protists.

   B.   Most protists are unicellular species that live independently or in colonies.

   C.   They have life cycles that include haploid and diploid stages.

   D.   Some lineages are heterotrophic, while others are autotrophic. Some even switch between these two modes.

20.3   Flagellated Protozoans

   A.   Flagellated protozoans are single-celled heterotrophic cells with one or more flagella.

   B.   A pellicle made of proteins helps these cells maintain their shape.

   C.   Haploid cells dominate the life cycle of these groups.

   D.   Diplomonads and parabasalids have multiple flagella and are among the few protists that can live in anaerobic habitats. These are heterotrophs that lack mitochondria and are types of human pathogens.
   1.   *Giardia lamblia* is a diplomonad that attacks humans, cattle, and some other mammals. It enters the body in cyst form from drinking feces-contaminated water, resulting in severe diarrhea.
   2.   *Trichomonas vaginalis* is a parabasalid that causes trichomoniasis and can be transmitted during sexual intercourse and lead to damage of the urinary and reproductive tracts.

   E.   Trypanosomes are typical parasitic representatives that are carried by biting insects or other vectors. For example, tsetse fly carries the trypanosome that causes African sleeping sickness And Chagas disease is caused by a trypanosome carried by blood-sucking bugs.

   F.   Euglenoids are free-living, flagellated cells. Most are asexual, colorless, and heterotrophic. About one-third of them have the same chlorophyll as green algae and plants. An eyespot detects the sunlight necessary for photosynthetic activities. A contractile vacuole helps to maintain water balance.

20.4   Mineral-Shelled Protozoans

A. Foraminiferans and radiolarians aretwo related lineages of heterotrophic marine cells with porous secreted shells.   They feed by capturing food with microtubule reinforced cytoplasmic extensions that protrude through the shell's many openings.

B. Foraminiferans have a shell of calcium carbonate.
   1. They live in sediments or drift as part of the plankton.
   2. They often live symbiotically with smaller photosynthetic protists.
   3. Foraminiferan shells have been accumulating on the sea floor over billions of years.

C. Radiolarians have delicate, glasslike shells of silica.
   1. Most are marine plankton drifting in seawater.
   2. Some have photosynthetic protists living inside them.

20.5   The Alveolates

A. Dinoflagellates, ciliates, and apicomplexans belong to this lineage. Alveolus means sac, the characteristic trait of alveolates is a layer of sacs beneath the plasma membrane acting to help stabilize the cell surface.

B. Dinoflagellates
   1. Single-celled, aquatic protist with cellulose plates and two flagella; may be heterotrophic or photosynthetic.
   2. Photosynthetic dinoflagellates, like *Karenia brevis*, sometimes undergo algal blooms.
   3. Bioluminescent dinoflagellates in the ocean can make the ocean waves shimmer at night by converting ATP energy into light.

C. Ciliates
   1. Ciliated protozoans are single-celled, heterotrophs with many cilia used for locomotion and feeding. Most are aquatic predators.
   2. *Paramecium,* a free-living ciliate, have many cilia that beat in synchrony on the cell surface. The cilia help them to acquire food. Other features include enzyme-filled vesicles for digesting food and contractile vacuoles to get rid of excess water.
   3. Ciliates contain two types of nuclei: a small micronucleus, which undergoes meiosis and serves in sexual reproduction, and a larger macronucleus that governs daily function.
   4. Ciliates reproduce asexually by binary fission and may demonstrate a primitive form of sexual reproduction in which partners swap micronuclei.

D. Apicomplexans
   1. Apicomplexans are single-celled protists that live as a parasite inside animal cells, and are sometimes called sporozoans.
   2. This type of alveolate possess a unique structure of microtubules that can attach to and penetrate the cells of host species.

20.6   Malaria and the Night—Feeding Mosquitoes

A. Malaria, caused by *Plasmodium*, a single-celled apicomplexan, and transmitted by mosquitoes, is a serious worldwide disease.

B. The female s mosquito transmits a motile infective stage (sporozoite) of *Plasmodium* to a human host during feeding.

C. After multiplying first in the liver and then in the red blood cells, the merozoite stage breaks out into the bloodstream, causing terrific bouts of chills and fever.

D. Malaria can be treated with drugs; however, many *Plasmodium* strains are now resistant to older drugs.

20.7 Stramenopiles
   A. This group of protists includes diverse lineages that are united on the basis of their genetic similarity rather than any visible traits. Water molds, diatoms, and brown algae belong to this group.
   B. Water Molds
      1. Water molds are filamentous heterotrophs that act as decomposers. Some are plant or animal parasites.
      2. Water molds have no chlorophyll and resemble fungi in their absorption of nutrients through filaments.
   C. Photosynthetic Stramenopiles: Diatoms and Brown Algae
      1. Photosynthetic stramenopiles possess a pigment in their chlorophyll (fucoxanthin) that masks the chlorophyll colors, giving shades of yellow color to the algae. This pigment is also in red algae suggesting the stramenopile chloroplasts evolved by secondary endosymbiosis from red alga.
      2. Diatoms are single-celled protists living in a two-part silica shell, which is commercially valuable as abrasives and filtering materials.
      3. Brown algae are multicelled marine protists ranging in size from microscopic filaments to giant kelps. The commercial use of brown algae includes thickeners, emulsifiers, and suspension agents derived from the alginic acid from their cell walls.

20.8 Red Algae and Green Algae
   A. Red and green algae are photosynthetic protists that deposit cellulose in their cell walls, store sugars as starch, and have chloroplasts containing chlorophyll a. The chloroplasts evolved from a cyanobacterial ancestor by primary endosymbiosis.
   B. Red Algae
      1. Red algae are typically multicellular and live in warm marine currents at great depths.
      2. In addition to containing chlorophyll a, red algae has phycobilin pigments which traps sunlight in deep marine waters.
      3. Red Algae have commercial uses.
         a. Some yield agar, a polysaccharide used in baked goods, cosmetics, jellies, and medicines.
         b. Carrageenan is used as a stabilizer in ice cream, soy milk, and other dairy foods. It is also used on airplanes to prevent ice formation.
         c. *Porphyra*, dry sheets of red alga, is cultivated as a food.
      4. The modes of reproduction are diverse, with complex asexual and sexual phases, but the multicelled stages do not have tissues or organs. This alternating between haploid and diploid state is known as an alteration of generations.
   C. Green Algae
      1. Green algae include single-celled, colonial, and multicelled species. They range in size from microscopic cells to multicelled filamentous species that are several meters long.
      2. In addition to containing chlorophyll a, green algae has chlorophyll b as well.
      3. *Chlamydomonas* are a flagellated single-celled green alga that lives in standing fresh water. *Chlamydomonas* can reproduce asexually or sexually.
         a. When nutrients and light are plentiful, spores reproduce asexually.
         b. When conditions are suboptimal, gametes develop and fuse to form a diploid zygote with a tough outer wall.
         c. When conditions are favorable, meiosis occurs to produce the next generation of haploid, flagellated spores.

4. The spherical *Volvox* is colonial and lives in freshwater ponds. Daughter cells form inside the parental sphere and rupture to form new colonies.
5. Sheets of the multicelled species Ulva cling to rocks along marine coasts and commonly known as sea lettuce. It has an alterantion of generations with large, sheetlike bodies in both the haploid and diploid generations.
6. Charophyte algae are a subgroup of fresh water green algae which are the closest living relatives of land plants.

20.9   Amoebozoans

A. Amoebozans are shape-shifting heterotrophic protists with no pellicle or cell wall, including solitary amoebas and slime molds.
B. Solitary amoebas are single-celled protists that extend a pseudopod to move and to capture prey.
C. Slime molds are social amoebas, including plasmodial slime molds and cellular slime molds
    1. Plasmodial slime molds appear as a large multinucleate mass, creeping along the ground engulfing food particles; at times it will produce spore-bearing fruiting bodies.
    2. Cellular slime molds spend most of their lives as a slug-like mass, feeding and reproducing asexually; at times a stalk will arise from the mass to release spores.
D. *Dictyostelium* and other amoebozoans provide clues on how cell signaling pathways evolved.
E. Molecular comparisons suggest that animals and fungi descended from an ancient amoebozoan ancestor.

Suggestions for Presenting the Material

♦   Because the protistans are sometimes "...viewed as the rag-bag of classification schemes..." it is important to assure the students that water molds do in fact resemble fungi, and brown algae do have plant-like parts. Rather than dwelling on the imprecision of this situation, use it to emphasize the continuum of evolution.

♦   It is very difficult for students to get a sense of the relative size and shape of protists unless the instructor makes liberal use of photos, especially ones that give some comparison to objects of known size.

♦   To make the names of these protistans more real, seek practical uses and applications for as many as you can. For example, foraminiferans seem to be just lying at the bottom of the ocean, but to a geologist exploring for oil reserves, they tell a valuable story.

♦   **Common Student Misconceptions:**
    o   Students may not think of protists as multicellular. Be sure to point out the colonial lifestyle of many and the large multicellular algae that make up the kelp beds.

Classroom and Laboratory Enrichment

♦   Obtain samples of water from decorative fountains, flower pots, and small ponds to examine them for protistans.
♦   Kits for growing slime molds are available from biological supply houses.
♦   Show videos of living protists.
♦   View protozoa in a hay infusion.
♦   Look for slime molds on moist logs and fallen trees in damp forest areas.

- Collect diatoms from the edges of quiet ponds and slow-moving streams.

- Gather information from local health authorities about any of the diseases caused by protists that are found in your area.

- Many protists are highly mobile creatures and fun to watch. If you have a small class, secure some cultures and allow students to make their own preparations for microscopic observation. If your class is large, use a videotape (several biological supply houses offer these).

- Search the web for protest images and movies. Several are available that will give an appreciation of the diversity this group displays.

Harmful Algal Blooms (revisited)

- What coastlines are affected by algal blooms?
- What are the consequences on humans of the algal blooms?
- What causes algal blooms?

Additional Ideas for Classroom Discussion

- What makes the water in a decorative fountain turn green?
- Algae occur in tremendous quantities in nature. To what extent have they been used for human or animal food? Are there any "algae farms"?
- Of what ecological value are the water molds and slime molds?
- What are some steps that tropical countries can take to reduce the rate of malaria?
- Why did the effort to eradicate malaria fail? Which of Darwin's ideas was ignored in the eradication proposal?
- How is amoebic dysentery transmitted to humans?
- Why are the red, brown, and green algae more properly considered protists than plants?

How Would You Vote? Classroom Discussion Ideas

- Monitor the voting for the online question. It only seems reasonable that states should enact regulations to protect the interests of its citizens and their environment. Do you think it is fair to farmers, developers, industries, and water treatment plants to bear the cost of tighter regulations on governing nutrient discharge into coastal waters?Have students complete classroom polling using the JoinIn clickers.

Term Paper Topics, Library Activities, and Special Projects

- Investigate the nutritional value of kelp.
- Prepare a report on the Irish potato famine.
- Chronicle the rise and fall of the campaign to eradicate malaria.
- Compare the extent and severity of problems caused by viruses, bacteria, and protists.

- Discuss the geographic distribution and economic impact of "red tides" in the United States.

- Write a report on any one of the diseases caused by protozoans. Discuss the historical roles played by these diseases in situations such as the colonization of new lands, wars, and the building of the Panama Canal.

- Prepare an analysis of why water molds are more properly considered protists than fungi.

- Historically, the multicelled algae (red, brown, and green) were considered plants. Enumerate the reasons why they are more properly considered protistans.

- Prepare a report on the impact that protistans have on humans in terms of medical and commercial terms.

Responses to *Data Analysis Activities*

1. The average concentration of *K. brevis* increased from approximately 30,000 cells per liter to 750,000 cells per liter, in areas less than 5 kilometers from shore.

2. The average concentration of *K. brevis* increased from zero cells per liter to approximately 120,000 cells per liter, in areas more than 25 kilometers from shore.

3. These data support the hypothesis that human activity increased the abundance of *K. brevis* by adding nutrients to coastal waters.

4. If the two graph lines became farther apart as distance from the shore increased, then that would suggest the nutrient source was not coming from the coastal cities.

Possible Responses to *Critical Thinking* Questions

1. Typically when you travel to places with poor sanitation, you do not want to drink the water or eat raw vegetables. Since parasitic flagellates live in water and soil they could easily be consumed. Boiling water for five minutes will kill off any unwanted bugs. In terms of the vegetables, if they are not boiled, I would avoid them.

2. Since this group lives in freshwater, does not have chloroplasts, and has cilia, it probably belongs to the alveolates and more specifically the ciliates. The information provided also tells us to look for a heterotroph that is a predator.

3. The carotenoids could be protecting the cells from the intense rays of the sun.

21

PLANT EVOLUTION

Chapter Outline

Objectives

1. Outline the evolutionary advances that converted marine algal ancestors into plants that could live on land.
2. State the advances of the bryophytes that converted primitive marsh plants into dry-land plants.
3. Understand the life cycle of the seedless vascular plants.
4. Characterize the seedless vascular plants (gymnosperms), and their success in dry climates.
5. Discuss why the angiosperms are the most successful of all plants presently found with regard to dispersion and diversity.

Key Terms

embyrophytes	mosses	megaspores	stamens
cuticle	rhizoids	ovule	carpel
stomata	peat	pollination	ovary
vascular tissue	seedless vascular	gymnosperms	pollinators
xylem	plants	conifers	fruit
phloem	rhizome	cycads	eudicots
lignin	epiphytes	ginkgo	endosperm
pollen grain	coal	gnetophytes	secondary
seed	pollen sacs	angiosperms	metabolite
bryophyte	microspores	flower	

Lecture Outline

21.1   Speaking for the Trees

   A.   Forests take up CO_2 and release O_2

      1.   Life all over the planet relies on this.

   B.   Economies of many countries rely on cutting down forests for fuel and lumbar

      1.   Deforestation rapidly reduces species diversity.

      2.   Deforestation affects evaporation rates, runoff, and regional rainfall patterns.

   C.   Our management of forests will impact the future of all life on Earth.

21.2   Adaptive Trends among Plants

   A.   Structural Adaptations to Life on Land

      1.   Charophyte, a simple branching plant, were evolving at the water's edge by 430 million years ago and gave rise to plants.

      2.   Land plants developed a cuticle to retain water and stomata to facilitate CO_2 uptake with a minimum of water loss.

      3.   Vascular tissue – xylem and phloem – was developed to facilitate the movement of fluids within the plant.

      4.   Lignin stiffened cells, allowing the plant to resist gravity.

   B.   The Plant Life Cycle

      1.   All plants show an alteration of haploid and diploid multicelled stages.

         a.   The haploid body, called the gametophyte, produces gametes by mitosis.

         b.   Fusion of gametes produces a diploid sporophyte that produces spores by meiosis.

         c.   A spore is a haploid cell that may germinate, divide by mitosis, and produce a new gametophyte plant body.

      2.   The history of plants shows a shift from gametophyte dominance of the life cycle to one of sporophyte dominance.

   C.   Pollen and Seeds

      1.   Reproductive traits among some vascular plants convey an advantage.

         a.   All nonvascular plants and some vascular (example ferns) release spores.

         b.   Seed-bearing vascular plants hold spores; one type gives rise to an egg-producing female gametophyte and the other develops into a male pollen grain.

      2.   Production of pollen puts seed plants at an advantage in dry environments.

         a.   The male gametophytes—pollen grains—are released from the parent plant to be carried by whatever means to the female gametophyte.

         b.   Plants that do not produce pollen require water to allow sperm to swim to eggs.

3. Seeds help plants survive in dry time.
    a. The seed contains an embryo sporophyte and some nutrient tissues.
    b. One seed-bearing lineage gave rise to gymnosperms, and another gave rise to angiosperms—the most widely distributed and diverse plant group.

21.3 The Bryophytes
  A. Bryophyte Characteristics.
    1. Although they resemble more complex land plants, they do not contain xylem or phloem.
    2. The largest and longest lived phase of the bryophyte is the gametophyte.
    3. After fertilization, the zygote remains attached to the gametophyte.
        a. Most species do have *rhizoids*, rootlike parts that attach the gametophytes to the soil and absorb water and minerals.
        b. Most live in moist places; others can tolerate periodic drought.
        c. Drought tolerance and wind-dispersed spores make bryophytes important pioneer plant species in many habitats.
  B. Mosses
    1. Mosses form rhizoids, which anchor like roots but do not absorb nutrients or water.
    2. Peat bogs are used for commercially grown crops due to the unique pH.
  C. Liverworts and Hornworts
    1. Liverworts and hornworts grow in moist climates like mosses.
    2. Liverwort sporophytes rely on the gametophyte, hornwort sporophytes do not.

21.4 Seedless Vascular Plants
  A. Seedless vascular plants require water for sexual reproduction like bryophytes.
    1. They release spores directly into the environment.
    2. They have true vascular tissues.
  B. Club Mosses
    1. Despite their name, these plants are true vascular plants.
    2. They have a rhizome – a horizontal stem that runs along the ground.
    3. Club mosses are used for a variety of economic purposes.
  C. Horsetails and Rushes
    1. Horsetails, *Equisetum*, are familiar plants that grow in wet or moist places.
        a. Most horsetail rhizomes spread through the soil.
        b. They have hollow stems, often with leaflike branches.
        c. Strobili, the site of spore production, form at the tips of stems.
        d. Silica deposits inside the stems provide support.
  D. Ferns—The Most Diverse Seedless Plants
    1. With about 12,000 species, ferns are the most diverse group of seedless vascular plants.
        a. Most fern sporophytes have leaves and roots that grow from rhizomes.
        b. Fern leaves are often called fronds; they start out in a tight coil called a fiddlehead.
    2. Sori (singular, sorus) are clusters of spore-forming chambers that form on the lower surface of fern fronds.
        a. They open and distribute haploid spores.
        b. Following germination, the spore develops into a small, heart-shaped gametophyte.
    3. Many tropical ferns are epiphytes, which attach and grow on another plant.

21.5 History of Vascular Plants
  A. From Tiny Branches to Coal Forests
    1. Vascular plants began forming forests roughly 400 million years ago.

2. The rise and fall of the seas compressed the undecayed remains of these ancient forests into coal.

3. It has taken a remarkably short time for human technology to extract coal, one of the non-renewable fossil fuels, from the ground.

B. Rise of Seed Plants

1. Flowering plants arose by about 120 million years ago.

2. Successful adaptations included structural modifications like a cuticle and the two kinds of spores formed by meiosis.

    a. Microspores become pollen grains, which contain the male gamete.

    b. Air currents or animals disperse pollen.

    c. Pollination refers to the arrival of pollen grains to the female reproductive parts of a plant.

    d. The development of pollen removed the reliance on water for this process.

3. Megaspores form inside ovules and stay attached to the parent plant.

    a. The ovule starts as a small mass of sporophyte tissue.

    b. A megaspore inside the mass gives rise to a female gametophyte that contains an egg cell.

    c. When fertilization occurs, an embryo forms inside the ovules. A seed is a mature ovule.

21.6 Gymnosperms—Plants with Naked Seeds

A. Gymnosperms are vascular seed plants that have no ovaries like flowering plants.

B. Conifers

1. Conifers (cone-bearers) are woody trees with needlelike or scalelike leaves.

    a. Most are evergreens; some are deciduous.

    b. Examples of conifers: pines, redwoods, firs, and spruces.

C. Lesser Known Gymnosperms

1. Cycads are palmlike trees that flourished during the Mesozoic era.

    a. Only about 130 species still exist—confined to the tropics and subtropics.

    b. They bear massive cone-shaped strobili that produce either pollen (transferred by air currents or insects) or ovules.

2. Ginkgos have been reduced in diversity from the Mesozoic to only one surviving species today, *Ginkgo biloba*.

    a. They are unusual, having fan-shaped leaves and in being deciduous.

    b. They are remarkably hardy, showing resistance to insects, disease, and air pollutants.

3. Gnetophytes are the most unusual gymnosperms; they live in tropical and desert areas.

D. A Representative Life Cycle

1. The life cycle of the pine is typical of gymnosperms.

2. The pine tree (sporophyte) produces two kinds of cones.

    a. Male cones produce sporangia, which yield microspores that develop into pollen grains (male gametophyte).

    b. Female cones produce ovules that yield megaspores (female gametophyte).

3. Pollination is the arrival of a pollen grain on the female reproductive parts, after which a pollen tube grows toward the egg.

4. Fertilization, which is delayed for up to a year, results in a zygote that develops into an embryo within the conifer seed.

21.7 Angiosperms—The Flowering Plants

A. Angiosperms Traits and Diversity
  1. They are the only plants that make flowers.
    a. 90% of modern plants are angiosperms
  2. A flower is a specialized reproductive shoot.
    a. Stamens hold the pollen.
    b. The ovary is found at the base of the carpel.

B. Coevolution with Pollinators
  1. Coevolution refers to two or more species jointly evolving because of their close ecological interactions.
    a. Changes in one exert adaptive pressure on the other.
    b. Plants developed fragrance and nectar.
    c. Successful recruitment of pollinators help plants reproduce sexually.
    d. Ultimately, fruits were developed to disperse seeds.

C. Major Lineages
  1. Most flowering plants arose belong to one of two lineage.
    a. Eudicots (170 000 species) include familiar shrubs, trees (except conifers), and herbaceous plants.
    b. Monocots (80 000 species) include grasses, lilies, and the major food-crop grains.

D. A Representative Life Cycle
  1. Pollen (microspores) forms in the stamen.
  2. Megaspores form in the ovaries.
  3. The pollen grain delivers two sperm to the ovary
    a. One fertilizes the egg.
    b. The second fertilizes a diploid cell to form the triploid endosperm – food for the developing embryo.

21.8 Ecological and Economic Importance of Angiosperms

A. Of the approximately 150 plant species that are grown as crops for food, 12 represent the main food source for humans

B. C3 plants are grown in cool conditions, while C4 plants are grown in hot environments
  a. Rice, wheat and oats are C3 plants.
  b. Corn and sorghum are C4 plants.

C. Legumes are eudicots that provide proteins and fats
  a. These include soybeans, lentils, and peas.

D. Other plant parts compliment the human diet
  a. Root crops provide starches.
  b. Fruits and leaves provide carbohydrates and vitamins.
  c. Fibers, oils, and secondary metabolites are also products of flowering plants.

Suggestions for Presenting the Material

♦ Make time to show the opening image (Figure 21.4) that shows plants through time. This will help diminish student misconceptions about plants and reinforce the immense amounts of time involved in the evolution of plants.

♦ When students think of plants, almost all of the examples that come to mind will be angiosperms. Counter this tendency by asking for examples of plants that do NOT have flowers.

- ◆ Bring several non-flowering plant examples to lab or class. Illustrate the differences that separate these plant groups from one another.

- ◆ Review the evolutionary trend from gametophyte dominance to sporophyte dominance (Figure 21.4). If students still find this confusing, they will have trouble comparing one plant life cycle to another. Highlight evolutionary hallmarks (summarized in Figure 21.4) such as development of vascular tissue, dominant sporophyte, heterospory, nonmotile gametes, and seeds that distinguish simple plants from those that are more complex.

- ◆ Make use of Figure 21.3 to frame the difficult concept of the alternating haploid, diploid life cycles seen in plants.

- ◆ Be sure to show each of the animated figures: Figures 21.5 on the life cycle in moss, and 21.19 on the life cycle of conifers. They will help students visually place the material in context.

- ◆ Because of the numerous classification categories included within this chapter, it is easy to get lost. To alleviate this difficulty, you may wish to make a transparency of Figure 21.4 and have it in view as you proceed through the different groups of plants.

- ◆ Because of their natural geographic locations, many of the plants mentioned in the earlier sections of this chapter are not familiar to students. Transparencies of representative species, even made from photos in the book, will help to remove the abstract quality of a ginkgo or cycad.

- • **Common Student Misconceptions**

  - o Students have a great deal of difficulty relating to the alternating haploid, diploid life cycles in plants. Try to frame the discussion around the reproductive focus of this process.

  - o Students often fail to grasp the significant evolutionary diversity in the plant kingdom because they are surrounded by flowering plants.

  - o You will need to stress the important transitions in plant evolution and the contribution these adaptive changes provide in plant radiation.

Classroom and Laboratory Enrichment

- ◆ Look at fossils of ancient lycophytes, horsetails, ferns, and gymnosperms. Discuss how changing climates influenced the geographic distributions and the sizes of these plants.

- ◆ Prepare a small display of portions of bryophytes, lycophytes, horsetails, ferns, and gymnosperms from local areas where plant collection is allowed. Prepared slides and live materials ordered from biological supply houses can supplement your collection.

- ◆ Collect reproductive structures of gymnosperms (use photos, drawings, or models to represent those taxonomic divisions for which structures are unavailable). Compare them to the reproductive structures of angiosperms (students can dissect flowers).

- ◆ Use models, photos, drawings, or overhead transparencies to discuss the life cycle of pine (a good representative gymnosperm because it is familiar to students). Compare it to the life cycle of a typical angiosperm.

- ◆ Bring in a piece of coal and describe the long-term processes involved in its production, where we find it, and its economic significance in energy production.

- ◆ Obtain a set of pictures that will provide a survey of the plant world, including algae.

- ◆ Redraw several of the life cycle figures in this chapter, but omit several key labels. Photocopy these and distribute as a labeling exercise.

Speaking for the Trees (revisited)

- Plants can store an enormous amount of carbon. If plants are burned or otherwise destroyed, where does this carbon ultimately end up?
- On which products of photosynthesis do animals rely?
- What are the local and global effects of deforestation?
- Can the timber industry and good ecological conservation practices abide together?

Additional Ideas for Classroom Discussion

- What are the only land plants with a dominant, independent gametophyte and a dependent sporophyte?
- What major structural difference separates the bryophytes from the ferns?
- What are some differences and similarities between a pine cone and a fruit?
- Which type of pollination is more efficient—wind pollination, as seen among conifers, or insect pollination, as seen among some of the angiosperms?
- Describe the similarities and differences between fungal spores and spores found among members of the plant kingdom.

How Would You Vote? Classroom Discussion Ideas

- Have students complete class and monitor the voting results online. Balancing carbon productions and absorptions between countries is admirable in that it considers the global consequences of our actions. However, does this program keep less developed countries permanently in that state? Similarly, does it truly make CO_2 emitting countries responsible for their actions (considering the variable value of currencies between countries)?
- Consider your own personal carbon offsets. On which side do you contribute?

Term Paper Topics, Library Activities, and Special Projects

- Prepare a list of the vascular plant flora on your campus or some other local area.
- Find vegetation maps showing the worldwide distributions of major vegetation associations of gymnosperms and angiosperms (for example, grasslands, temperate forests, coniferous forests, and so on).
- Investigate the extent of removal of trees and small plants in your vicinity that has occurred in the past few years in preparation for commercial property development.
- Assess the balance between producing healthy, oxygen-yielding lawn plants and the fertilizers and pesticides used to keep them that way.
- Read about the "balanced terrarium" concept. Set up one and attempt to prove if the theory is workable.
- Evaluate the effects of possible global warming on the world's grain-producing regions. Will all areas be affected negatively? Some positively?

- Estimate the number of acres of land that is not available for food production because it is part of the right-of-way of the USA interstate highway system.

- Have the students use the Internet to research current articles on plant evolution. Have them create a short report on their findings.

- Have students visit a local arboretum or greenhouse facility and compile a digital picture collection of plants that fit in each of the major plant groups.

Responses to *Data Analysis Activities*

1. In 2005, there were 677 hectares of forested land in North America.
2. Between 1990 and 2005, the area of forested land increased most dramatically in Europe, though the change was not particularly dramatic.
3. The world lost 125 hectares of forested land between 1990 and 2005.
4. No, while China did slightly increase their area of forested land between 2000 and 2005 (by 5 hectares across all of Asia), this is far short of the 2002 goal of a 76 million hectare increase.

Possible Responses to *Critical Thinking* Questions

1. My dear fellow plant enthusiasts: Your interest in fern reproduction and discovery of "dustlike" seeds confuses many. Having just completed studying the evolution of plants, I can help you understand what it is you are seeing. Ferns create reproductive structures called spores; these are the "dustlike" seeds you are seeing. These spores, however, do not represent the sexual reproductive phase for this plant. Instead, this asexual reproduction occurs via meiotic cell division inside the sori, located on the underside of the leaves. These spores do germinate under favorable conditions, but instead of creating a recognizable fern, they produce a haploid phase of the plant's life cycle, called a gametophyte.

2. The mildly disadvantageous mutation would be more likely to survive in a fern as compared to a moss as the fern spends a greater fraction of its life cycle in the diploid stage where the mutation could be 'hidden' at present.

3. The red-stained structure is the secondary wall of the xylem. This structure would be present in corn plants, but not in moss which lack a true xylem.

22

FUNGI

Chapter Outline

Objectives

1. Recognize the unifying features of all fungi, and the characteristics on which the group is subdivided.
2. Describe the characteristics and physiology of the groups of fungi which lack cell walls.
3. Describe the characteristics and physiology of the diverse sac fungi.
4. Describe the characteristics and physiology of the club fungi.
5. Describe mutualistic and parasitic relationships between fungi and other organisms.

Key Terms

fungi	dikaryotic	sac fungi	mycorrhiza
saprobe	chytrids	club fungus	
mycelium	zygote fungi	lichen	
hypha	glomeromycetes	mutualism	

Lecture Outline

22.1   High-Flying Fungi

    A. Fungal spores can travel amazing distances

        1. The spread of fungal spores on the wind can cross oceans.

        2. Lichens feed animals; other fungi feed other animals.

    B. This mobility makes the spread of pathogens difficult to contain

        1. In 1999, a new and highly virulent strain of wheat rust was discovered in Uganda.

        2. By 2009 it had spread to the Asia.

        3. Continued spread could threaten the global food supply.

22.2   Fungal Traits and Diversity

    A. Structure and Function

        1. Fungi are heterotrophs that utilize organic matter.

           a. Most are saprobes; they feed on and decompose organic wastes.

           b. Most fungi are made of a network of hypha, collectively forming a mycelium.

           c. Materials are able to flow from cell to cell in a fungus.

        2. Chytrids are one of the more ancient lineages of fungi. Some are saprobes and some are parasites. Parasitic chytrids endanger amphibians. Some also live in the stomachs of sheep and cattle, helping them to digest cellulose.

        3. The majority of fungi fall into three groups: zygote fungi, sac fungi, and club fungi. These are detailed below.

    B. Life Cycles

        1. Haploid or dikaryotic (possessing two identical nuclei) stages dominate the fungal life cycle.

        2. Most fungi disperse by producing spores – a thick-walled cell or cluster of cells.

           a. Asexual spores form by mitosis.

           b. Sexual spores form by meiosis.

           c. One way each group is classified is by its structure that produces spores.

    C. Fungal Diversity

        1. Chytrids are one of the more ancient lineages of fungi. Some are saprobes and some are parasites. Parasitic chytrids endanger amphibians. Some also live in the stomachs of sheep and cattle, helping them to digest cellulose.

        2. The majority of fungi are either club fungi or sac fungi, both of which have fungi with cross-walls.

22.3   Chytrids, Zygote Fungi, and Relatives

    A. Chytrids

        1. Chytrids are an ancient fungal lineage that makes flagellated spores.

        2. Most are aquatic decomposers.

        3. Some are mutualists or pathogens.

           a. Global decline in frog populations is suspected to be due to a chytrid parasite.

    B. Zygote Fungi

        1. The majority of zygote fungi are saprobes, some are parasites.

        2. Their life cycle is as follows:

           a. Haploid mycelia produce asexual spores.

           b. Sexual reproduction begins if hyphae of compatible mating strains meet.

           c. Those hyphae fuse to form an immature, dikaryotic zygospore.

       d. Following meiosis, the zygospore liberates haploid spores.

       e. Those spores germinate to form a haploid mycelia.

  C. Glomeromycetes

    1. Glomeromycetes form a mutualistic association with plant roots.

       a. The plant provides sugars for the fungus, the fungus provides mineral nutrients from the soil.

22.4 Sac Fungi

  A. Life Cycle

    1. Sac fungi are the most diverse fungi, with over 32,000 species.

    2. Sac fungi and club fungi have hyphae divided by cross walls, allowing them to form large spore-producing body called an ascus.

    3. In sexual reproduction, the dikaryotic cell that results from hyphal fusion undergoes mitosis to form the ascocarp.

    4. In asexual reproduction, haploid mycelia can produce spores.

  B. A Sampling of Diversity

    1. Morels and truffles are sac fungi with edible ascocarps.

    2. Other sac fungi have important uses.

       a. *Penicillium* is used to flavor some cheeses.

       b. Other members of this genus produce the antibiotic drug penicillin.

    3. Some yeasts are sac fungi. *Candida* causes yeast infections and *S. cerevisiae* is used as baking yeast and for alcohol fermentation.

    4. *Arthrobotrys,* a predator that traps roundworms, may be helpful in controlling crop damage from roundworms.

22.5 Club Fungi

  A. Life Cycle

    1. While the fruiting body (basidiocarp) is the conspicuous component, the complete life cycle is as follows:

       a. Hyphae of compatible mating strains fuse to form a dikaryotic cell.

       b. The dikaryotic cell undergoes mitosis to form the basidiocarp (commonly a mushroom).

       c. Club-shaped spore-making cells form on the gills of the basidiocarp.

       d. In these specialized cells, the nuclei fuse to form diploid cells.

       e. The diploid cells undergo meiosis to form sexual, haploid spores.

       f. These spores are released and germinate to form a mycelium.

  B. Diversity

    1. Many club fungi are saprobes.

       a. One exceptional example has a mycelium that spans 2000 acres and may be over 2000 years old.

    2. While many club fungi are edible, many produce dangerous toxins that may be fatal or mind-altering.

22.6 Fungi as Partners

  A. Symbiosis refers to species living together in close association throughout their life cycle

  B. Lichens

    1. Lichens are mutualistic associations between fungi (usually a sac fungi) and cyanobacteria, green algae, or both.

       a. The fungus parasitizes the photosynthetic alga upon which it depends entirely for its food.

       b. The algae derive very little benefit other than a protected place to survive.

Fungi   **171**

2. Lichens disperse by fragmentation – releasing small packages of both partners.
   a. Lichen can also make fungal spores for which survival depends on germinating near a suitable partner.
3. Lichens live in inhospitable places such as bare rock and tree trunks.
   a. By their metabolic activities, lichens can change the composition of their substrate.

C. Mycorrhizae: Fungus + Roots
   1. A mycorrhiza is a symbiotic relationship in which fungi hyphae surround roots of shrubs and trees.
      a. The plant provides carbohydrates to the fungus.
      b. Because of its extensive surface area, the fungus can absorb mineral ions and facilitate their entry into the plant.
      c. Over 80% of plants form mycorrhiza, and many plants grow poorly in its absence.

22.7   Fungi as Pathogens
A. Plant Pathogens
   1. Molds grow on live plants and harvested fruits and vegetables.
      a. Wheat stem rusts and powdery mildews dramatically impact crops.
      b. Chestnut blight virtually eliminated the American chestnut.
   2. *Claviceps purpurea* parasitizes rye, producing a toxic alkaloid.
      a. Peter the Great's soldiers and their horses became so ill that it thwarted the effort of conquering ports along the Black Sea.

B. Human Pathogens
   1. Fungal infections typically involve the skin.
      a. Athlete's foot and ringworm feeds on the dead outermost skin layers.
      b. Fungal vaginitis is caused by the growth of yeast in the vagina.
   2. Inhaled spores can cause a respiratory disease such as histoplasmosis.

Suggestions for Presenting the Material

♦ Be sure to spend ample time discussing the parasitic and saprobic lifestyles found among the fungi; students will be much more familiar with the autotrophic mode of nutrition among photosynthetic green plants.

♦ Ask students to name examples of fungi, and use these examples when discussing fungal diversity. Students will be surprised at the variety of organisms found in this kingdom.

♦ Students commonly struggle to understand the alternation of generations in the fungal life cycle due to the many specialized terms. Try to emphasize the familiar terms haploid, diploid, sexual reproduction, and asexual reproduction to reduce difficulties.

Classroom and Laboratory Enrichment

♦ Gather information from about human illnesses caused by fungi.

♦ Invite an agricultural extension officer to the class to report on fungi that cause problems in the local area to crops.

♦ Demonstrate variety within the Kingdom Fungi by growing cultures of representative fungal species or ordering them from a biological supply house. Use color pictures to survey the fungi. Use prepared microscope slides to look at vegetative hyphae and reproductive structures of representative fungi.

- Collect samples of plant tissues exhibiting signs of pathogenic fungi. Examples may include leaves infected with powdery mildew, rusts, or black spot; young seedlings killed by *Pythium* causing "damping off"; and citrus fruits covered with blue-green *Penicillium*.

- Ask the produce manager of a local supermarket to save rotting or damaged fruit for one or two days. Place the fruits on display in lab, and allow students to look at fungi with a dissecting scope or to make wet mounts and view them under the compound scope.

- Start a culture of bread mold *(Rhizopus)* by wiping a small piece of preservative-free bread across a dusty floor or cabinet top, misting with water, and placing in a covered Petri dish for several days.

- Grow *Pilobolus* on extremely fresh horse manure that has been placed on filter paper in a culture dish covered with an upside-down beaker. Soon after *Pilobolus* has started to appear, sporangia ejected by *Pilobolus* stalks will appear on the inside of the beaker.

- Collect fungi from forests and fields after cool, damp weather conditions. Lichens can be collected from a wide variety of locations regardless of weather conditions.

- Prepare a yeast culture in lab by dissolving an envelope of baker's yeast and a small amount of sugar in a beaker of warm water. Keep the beaker warm. Make a wet mount, and observe budding yeast cells under the microscope.

- Demonstrate the ability of yeast to perform fermentation by making beer or wine in the laboratory.

- Use various mushrooms from the grocery store as classroom props. Pass them around the classroom or lab, and ask students to observe the stalk, cap, and gills. Have students investigate each type—where they grow, whether they are decomposers, what organisms they feed off of, etc.

High-Flying Fungi (revisited)

- Fungal spores are capable to tremendous dispersion. Is there any practical means to limit the spread of fungi?

- How did spores survive in contact lens solution?

- *Fusarium* is not strictly a pathogen of humans. Investigate the literature to discover its impacts in agriculture and pig farming?

Additional Ideas for Classroom Discussion

- Describe the similarities and differences between fungal spores and spores found among members of the plant kingdom.

- What feature is the basis for classification of the fungi?

- What do we mean when we say a fungus is "imperfect"?

- Wildlife biologists have occasionally observed wild bears that appear to stagger and walk unsteadily after consuming large quantities of fallen fruit in late summer and early autumn. What has happened to them?

- The relationship between the algae and fungi that compose lichens is mutualism. What is the symbiotic relationship of the entire *lichen* to the *tree* to which it is attached?

◆ Is it true that lichens grow only on the north side of trees? What is the basis of this? Is this also true of lichens in the Southern Hemisphere?

How Would You Vote? Classroom Discussion Ideas

◆ Monitor the voting for the online question. At first blush, the prospect of reducing the production of opium and heroin in Afghanistan is highly favorable. However, introducing a plant pathogen would be environmentally irresponsible. In addition, our history at using biological pathogens in such broad circumstances has not been good – e.g. the use of myxomatosis on Australian rabbits.

Term Paper Topics, Library Activities, and Special Projects

◆ Discuss the economic importance of fungi, both as agents of decay and disease and as organisms important in research and industry.

◆ Discuss the diagnosis and treatment of fungi that grow on the human skin and mucous membranes.

◆ Describe the role of yeasts in the making of beer and wine.

◆ Compile a list of wild mushrooms found in your area.

◆ Consult a textbook on insect control methods to investigate the use of fungi as biocontrol agents for insects.

◆ Obtain a listing of the active ingredients in an antifungal medication for athlete's foot. Consult the Merck Index to learn how these chemicals inhibit fungal growth.

◆ Obtain a field guide to the edible mushroom. What easily-seen features warn us of poisonous varieties?

◆ Write a report about the use of lichen species as indicators of pollution.

Responses to *Data Analysis Activities*

1. In the control forest, larch had the highest percent cumulative mortality while birch had the lowest percent cumulative mortality.
2. In the control forest, *A. ostoyae* was responsible for approximately 27% of the larch deaths, while it was responsible for only 3% of the deaths in the experimental forest.
3. Yes, removing the stumps dramatically reduced tree mortality by *A. ostoyae* in all species examined.

Possible Responses to *Critical Thinking* Questions

1. Bacteria are prokaryotes, and fungi and humans are eukaryotes. When drugs are made from bacteria they can target prokaryotic mechanisms and not harm the human. When drugs are made from fungi they are more likely to act upon healthy human cells as well.

2. The mushroom protects itself from predators by emitting a strong odor. A foul odor is unattractive and can deter predators. If the smell is not foul but is just strong, the predator can associate the strong smell with the sick feeling it gets when it consumes the fungi.

23

ANIMALS I: MAJOR INVERTEBRATE GROUPS

Chapter Outline

Objectives

1. Define what an animal is and how it differs from other forms of life.
2. Describe the basic body plans of animals.
3. Describe the major advances in body structure and function that made invertebrates and vertebrates increasingly large and complex.
4. Discuss the relationship between segmentation and the development of paired organs and paired appendages.
5. List the functions of a coelom, and describe the role coelomic development played in animal evolution.
6. For each major phylum, list the name, distinguishing characteristics, and common examples.

Key Terms

vertebrates	coelom	planarians	exoskeleton
invertebrates	segmentation	annelids	antennae
animal	choanoflagellates	closed circulatory	metamorphosis
ectoderm	placozoans	systsm	chelicerates
endoderm	sponges	mollusks	arachnids
mesoderm	hermaphrodite	gastropods	crustaceans
radial symmetry	larva	open circulatory system	insects
bilateral symmetry	cnidarians	bivalves	echinoderms
cephalization	nematocysts	cephalopods	water-vascular system
protostomes	nerve net	roundworms	
deuterostomes	hydrostatic skeleton	molting	
pseudocoelom	flatowrms	arthropods	

Lecture Outline

23.1 Old Genes, New Drugs
   A. Animals with backbones are vertebrates; those without a backbone are invertebrates.

   B. Cone snails are a group of invertebrates with considerable value.
      1. These snails are valued form their beautiful shells.
      2. These are predators and many produce venom that helps to subdue their prey.
      3. Synthetic versions of the venom are now a source of new drugs targeting pain relief and control of seizures.
      4. A gene that codes for an enzyme in the venom production pathway has been conserved through evolutionary time, showing up today not only in the snail, but in humans and fruit flies. This point reinforces that all organisms interconnect.

23.2 Animal Traits and Trends
   A. What Is an Animal?
      1. Animals are multicellular (diploid) with tissues arranged into organs and organ systems.
      2. Animals are aerobic and heterotrophic.
      3. Animals reproduce sexually, and in some cases, asexually or both; their embryos develop through a series of stages.
      4. Most animals are motile during at least part of their life cycle.

B. Evolution of Animal Body Plans

1. Most animals have tissues, specific cell types arranged to carry out a specific task. Tissues develop from embryonic germ layers: ectoderm (outer layer), mesoderm (middle layer), and endoderm (inner layer).

2. Body Symmetry

   a. Animals show either radial (round) or bilateral (right and left sides) symmetry; bilateral animals also show anterior (head end), posterior (tail end), dorsal (back), and ventral (belly) orientations.

   b. Cephalization means having a definite head end, usually with feeding and sensory features.

3. Type of Gut

   a. The place where food is digested is the gut; some are saclike with one opening—a mouth—where food enters and waste exits.

   b. Incomplete digestive tracts only have one opening. Complete digestive tracts have two openings (mouth and anus) for continuous food processing, often through specialized regions.

4. Body Cavities

   a. Two lineages of bilateral animals developed based on the differences on digestive system.

      i. In protostomes, during development the first opening develops into the mouth

      ii. In deuterostomes (echinoderms and chordates), the first opening develops into the anus.

   b. Most bilateral animals have a coelom, a space between the gut and body wall that allows internal organs to expand and operate freely.

   c. Others, such as roundworms, have a "false" coelom, known as a pseudocoelom.

   d. Some animals (flatworms) do not have a coelom but instead are packed solidly with tissue between the gut and body wall.

5. Segmentation

   a. A segmented animal is composed of repeating body units (for example, the earthworm). This repetition allowed specialization.

   b. The segments may be grouped and modified for specialized tasks, as for example in insects.

23.3 Animal Origins and Early Radiations

A. Colonial Origins

   1. One hypothesis is that they evolved from colonies of flagellated cells.

   2. DNA evidence points to choanoflagellates as the group involved in early stages of animal evolution.

B. Perhaps the earliest animals resembled the present-day placozoan, *Trichoplax adhaerens*.

   1. Two layers of cells make up its flattened body, which displays no symmetry, no tissues, and no mouth. It has four cell types.

   2. Genetic studies of *T. adhaerens* revealed the genetic foundations for traits that evolved in more recent animal lineages.

C. Fossil Evidence

   1. Six-hundred million years ago, tiny animals known as Ediacarans were living in seafloor sediments.

   2. By the end of the Cambrian, all the major groups of animals had originated in the seas.

   3. Drifting continents, shifting sea levels, and changing climates perhaps triggered this explosion of adaptive radiation.

23.4   Sponges

A. General Characteristics
   1. Sponges (phylum Porifera) are aquatic animals that have an asymmetric body with no true tissues, no organs.
   2. Between two layers of body cells there is a jellylike matrix with fibrous proteins oar glassy silica spikes for support.
   3. Flagellated collar cells line the interior chambers.
       a. By means of their beating flagella, these cells move large volumes of water in through body pores and out through the large opening at the top of the body.
       b. They also trap suspended food particles in their collars and transfer the food to amoeba-like cells in the matrix.
       c. All digestion is intracellular.
   4. The skeletal spikes s also provide a defense mechanism, used to deter predators.

B. Sponge Reproduction
   1. Sexual Reproduction—Sperm are released into the surrounding water to be picked up by a nearby sponge and directed to the egg within the matrix; the zygote develops into a free-swimming larva.
   2. Asexual Reproduction—Sponges can produce buds or fragments that break away and grow into new sponges. Some freshwater species produce gemmules, which later grow into a new sponge when the conditions are favorable.

23.5   Cnidarians

A. Cnidarians are tentacled, radial animals including corals, sea anemones, and jellyfish
   1. Cnidarians have simple body plans.
       a. The medusa resembles an umbrella and floats like a tentacle-fringed bell in the water; oral arms surround the central mouth.
       b. The polyp is tubelike and is usually attached to some substrate; it may be solitary or part of a colony.
       c. The digestive cavity is saclike (only a mouth) and can accommodate prey larger than the cnidarian itself.
       d. An outer epidermis covers the body, and an inner gastrodermis lines the digestive cavity.
           i.   A nerve net running through both layers coordinates the animal's response to stimuli.
           ii. Some also have a nerve net and contractile cells.
   2. A jellylike mesoglea lies between the outer and inner body layers.
       a. Medusae have abundant mesoglea, helpful in providing buoyancy and in swimming.
       b. The water in their cavities serves as a hydrostatic skeleton.

B. Unique Cnidarian Weapons
   1. Most cnidarians are predators.
   2. The phylum name comes from their ability to sting by discharging nematocysts. Nematocysts allow cnidarians to capture prey and defend themselves.

C. Life Cycles and Diversity
   1. The life cycle of a cnidarian may have a polyp and medusa stage, or it may have just the polyp or the medusa.
       a. The medusa is usually the sexual form with gonads.
       b. Most zygotes develop into a bilateral ciliated swimming larva.
   2. Many cnidarians, such as the Portuguese man-of-war and coral reefs, grow as colonies often harboring photoautotrophic protist guests.

23.6 Flatworms
A. Organs and organ systems are present in flatworms.
   1. Flatworms (phylum Platyhelminthes) are the simplest bilateral, cephalized animal. They have no segments and no coelom.
   2. Turbellarians, flukes, and tapeworms are the main groups. All flukes and tapeworms are parasites of animals.
B. Structure of a Free-Living Flatworm
   1. Planarians are turbellarians that are free-living and aquatic, found in ponds and streams.
   2. The gut is saclike with a single (mouth) opening through which a pharynx extends for food gathering. The pharynx also expels waste. They have an incomplete digestive system.
   3. A pair of nerve cords runs the length of the body sending signals to the ganglia, which serves as a simple brain.
   4. Planarians are hermaphrodites with female and male sex organs. Some can reproduce asexually.
C. Flukes and Tapeworms—The Parasites
   1. Flukes and tapeworms are internal parasites that require a primary host (such as a human) for sexual reproduction and an intermediate host (such as a snail) for development.
   2. They absorb predigested nutrients from the host because they have no digestive tract.
   3. The tapeworm body consists of an anterior scolex, solely for attachment to the host's gut, and a string of proglottids, each of which possesses both male and female organs.

23.7 Annelids
A. Simple to Highly Modified Segments
   1. Annelids are bilateral worms with a coelom and a highly segmented body.
   2. The majority of species are marine worms called polychaetes. This group also includes the oligochaetes (earthworms and leeches).
   3. The repeating segments invited modification, and many annelids have a variety of appendages for handling food and locomotion.
B. Marine Polychaetes
   1. The sand worm uses its many appendages to burrow into sediment on marine mudflats. It is an active predator with its hard jaws.
   2. The feather duster worm secretes and lives inside a hard tube. Feathery extensions on the head capture food from the water, and cilia help move captured food to the mouth.
C. Leeches
   1. Commonly live in freshwater and most are scavengers and predators of small invertebrates
   2. The *Hirudo medicinalis* leech attaches to a vertebrate, pierces the skin, and suck the blood from its prey. The saliva of these leeches contains a protein that prevents blood from clotting during feeding, and this attribute has lead to the use of these animals in medicine.
D. Earthworms
   1. Include marine and freshwater species, although the land-dwelling earthworms are most familiar.
   2. The outer body surface is covered with a cuticle; internal partitions define individual coelomic chambers filled with fluid to provide a hydrostatic skeleton against which the muscles act during movement.

3. The digestive system is complete and the circulation closed (blood confined to hearts and vessels). Gas exchange occurs across the cuticle.

4. Nerve cords extend from the brain through the length of the body with a ganglion in each segment.

5. Earthworms are hermaphrodites, but cannot fertilize themselves. During mating, a secretory organ, the clitellum, produces mucus that glues two worms together while they swap sperm.

23.8   Mollusks

A. Mollusks (phylum Mollusca) have a fleshy, soft bilateral body with a small coelom.
   1. Some have a head with eyes and tentacles; some have a shell.
   2. All have a mantle, a skirtlike tissue covering the body.
   3. Some have a food scraping tongue-like organ called the radula.
   4. This group consists of more than 100,000 named species.

B. Gastropods
   1. Gastropods have a muscular foot for locomotion and burrowing. Most have a head with eyes and sensory tentacles.
   2. They have an open circulatory system and cells exchange substances with the blood while it is outside of vessels.
   3. This subtype of mollusk includes the only terrestrial mollusks, land-dwelling snails and slugs.

C. Bivalves
   1. This subtype includes scallops, oysters, mussels and have a hinged, two-part shell. This shell is lowered by muscle contractions when the animal has been disturbed.
   2. Bivalves have no obvious head and many have simple eyes arranged around the edge of the mantle.
   3. Water and suspended food are drawn in, and waste voided, through openings called siphons by the action of the cilia on the gills.

D. Cephalopods
   1. This subtype includes squids, nautiluses, octopuses, and cuttlefish.
   2. All are predators and most have beaklike, biting mouthparts in addition to a radula.
   3. They move by a type of jet propulsion caused by mantle contractions.
   4. Cephalopods include the fastest (squids), biggest (giant squid), and smartest (octopus) invertebrates.

23.9   Roundworms

A. Roundworms (phylum Nematoda) are also known as nematodes.
   1. They are bilateral and possess a slender tapered body.
      a. The digestive tract is complete—mouth and anus for continuous food processing.
      b. A collagen-rich cuticle covers and protects the body. The cuticle is repeatedly molted between growth spurts.
   2. *Caenorhabditis elegans* is a rather famous nematode because its simplicity of body plan and small genome make it an excellent organism for research studies.

B. Most roundworms are small and free-living, but some are parasitic on plants and animals.
   1. In trichinosis, undercooked pork is the source of a roundworm that moves from the digestive tract of the host to the muscles.
   2. Elephantiasis is a severe swelling of the legs due to blockage of lymph flow by small roundworms deposited by a mosquito during feeding.
   3. Hookworms, pinworms, and ascaris are other examples of parasitic roundworms that can infect humans.

23.10 Keys to Arthropod Diversity

A. Arthropods (phylum Arthropoda) are bilateral animals with a hardened, jointed external skeleton, a complete gut, and a reduced coelom. The major lineages are trilobites (now extinct), chelicerates (spiders and relatives), crustaceans (crabs, shrimp, and relatives) and uniramians (insects).

B. Key Arthropod Adaptations
1. A hardened exoskeleton:
    a. It is a combination of protein and chitin (plus calcium in some) that is flexible, lightweight, yet protective.
    b. It is a barrier to water loss and can support a body deprived of water's buoyancy.
    c. Exoskeletons restrict growth and so must be shed periodically (molting process).
2. Jointed appendages:
    a. Arthropod appendages are jointed at membranous areas where body parts abut.
    b. Appendages became specialized for feeding, sensing, locomotion, sperm transfer, and spinning silk.
    c. Arthropod means jointed leg.
3. Highly modified segments:
    a. Body segments became more specialized, reduced in number, and grouped together.
    b. In some lineages, this has resulted in head, thorax, and abdomen regions. Wings, the appendages for flight, are also a result of these modified segments.
4. Respiratory structures:
    a. Aquatic arthropods have a type of gill for gas exchange.
    b. Land dwellers have special tubes which supply oxygen directly to body tissues.
5. Specialized sensory structures:
    a. Most arthropods have one or more pairs of eyes. The compound eye provides a wide angle of vision.
    b. Most have paired antennae that detect touch and odors.
6. Specialized developmental stages:
    a. Metamorphosis transforms insects from immature larval stages through a pupal stage to adult.
    b. Larval stages concentrate on feeding and growth, whereas the adults specialize in dispersal and reproduction.
    c. Differences among stages of development are adaptations to the environment (food, water, shelter).

23.11 Spiders and Their Relatives

A. Chelicerates include some marine species such as horseshoe crabs and the more familiar arachnids.

B. Paired feeding appendages, called chelicerae, near the mouth give the group its name.

C. Horseshoe crabs are an ancient chelicerate lineageand the only one that is marine.
1. They have a horseshoe-shaped shield covering over their cephalothorax.
2. The last body segment, the telson, has evolved into a long spine that acts as a rudder during swimming.

D. Arachnids include spiders, scorpions, ticks, and mites.
1. Spiders are keen predators that trap insects in their webs, produced as silk strands from the abdomen; some are poisonous such as the brown recluse and black widow.
2. Ticks and mites are the smallest, most diverse, and most widespread. Some mites are free-living, others are serious pests of plants and animals; ticks are notorious blood-suckers and disease-carriers (Lyme disease).

23.12 Crustaceans

    A. Crustaceans include krill, copepods, shrimps, lobsters, crayfishes, crabs, and barnacles.

        1. The name is derived from the crusty exoskeleton.

        2. Most are important components of food webs, and several serve as human food also.

        3. Unusual crustaceans include the tiny copepods that are integral to marine food webs and the shell-encased barnacles that cause problems when they attach to wharf pilings.

    B. The crustacean body is divided into many segments.

        1. Like other arthropods, they repeatedly molt and shed the exoskeleton.

        2. Appendages on the body include two pairs of antennae, a pair each of mandibles and maxillae, and five pairs of legs.

23.13 Insect Traits and Diversity

    A. Insects have several unique features.

        1. The body is divided into three regions: head (sensory and feeding), thorax (locomotion by six legs, usually two pairs of wings), and abdomen (digestive and reproductive organs).

        2. Some spend time in the water, but the group is overwhelmingly terrestrial.3. A respiratory system consisting of tracheal tubes carries air from openings at the body surface to tissues deep inside the body.

    B. Insects are enormously successful.

        1. With more than a million species, insects are the most diverse arthropod group.

        2. Their great success is due to their ability to exploit nature's resources during different stages of metamorphosis, such as larvae, nymphs, and pupae.

            a. Incomplete metamorphosis means that the alterations in body form take place a bit at a time.

            b. Complete metamorphosis includes a larval and pupal stage prior to complete tissue remodeling in the formation of the adult.

        3. The most successful insects have wings. Flight allows the use of widely ranging food sources.

23.14 The Importance of Insects

    A. Ecological Services

        1. Flowering plants coevolved with insect pollinators. The close interactions between pollinator lineages and flowering plants contributed to an increased rate of speciation in both.

        2. Insects serve as food for a variety of wildlife (e.g., songbirds, fish, amphibians, reptiles, and humans).

        3. Insects dispose of waste and remains, helping to distribute nutrients through the ecosystem.

    B. Competitors for Crops: Insects are our main competitors for food and other plant products. They devour about 25% of all crops grown in the United States.

    C. Vector for Disease: Some insects spread human pathogens (e.g., mosquitoes transmit malaria).

23.15 Echinoderms

    A. The name of this phylum, Echinodermata, refers to the "spiny skin" made of calcium carbonate.

        1. Members include sea stars, sea urchins, brittle stars, and sea cucumbers.

        2. Most adults are radially symmetrical, while the larvae are bilateral.

B. Internally, echinoderms have a simple design.
1. The nervous system is decentralized; there is no brain.
2. The unique water-vascular system operates the tube feet, which have suction disks that can be used in locomotion and prey capture.
3. Sea stars are active predators and can push their stomachs out of their mouth and around prey.
4. Sea urchin roe are used in sushi. Overharvesting threatens some species.

Suggestions for Presenting the Material

♦ This diverse chapter begins with definitions of some basic terms used in describing animals. Then the "march through the phyla" begins. This can be a tedious and overwhelming experience unless you exercise special care to add those little extras that will hold student interest.

♦ In a survey that reduces volumes of information to about 20 pages, there must be brevity that will certainly shortchange someone's favorite animal group. However, the authors have been fair in presenting the chief characteristics for which each phylum is noted. Even so, the few features may be too many, and further reduction may need to be made by the individual instructor.

♦ If the instructor has a good grasp of animal diversity, especially invertebrates, the chapter may seem oversimplified, but to a botanist it may be quite the opposite. No matter where you find yourself in this spectrum, remember the naive student, and have compassion.

♦ One way to enliven your presentation is to relate the members of each phylum to the students' daily lives. This may be more difficult for sponges than arthropods, but with a little forethought, it can be done. See samples in the Enrichment section.

♦ **Common Student Misconceptions:**
   o When students think of animals they automatically think of vertebrates. Remind them that invertebrates make up the majority of the animal species.
   o Students also think of invertebrates as small organisms, yet there are many large invertebrate species to discuss.

Classroom and Laboratory Enrichment

♦ There is no scarcity of visual material depicting the diversity of animal life. It ranges from professionally made transparencies, to single-phylum videos, to full-length video surveys of the animal kingdom such as David Attenborough's *Life on Earth* (available at retail outlets).

♦ If you are fortunate to live in or near a large city with a zoo, arrange a field trip, but this time with a difference. Prepare the students for note-taking on various topics such as classification, body symmetry and cavities, body system development, ecological niche, and so on. Comment on the lack of animal representatives from the invertebrate phyla (at least ones that are plainly visible).

♦ Most, or perhaps all, of your students should have an accompanying laboratory experience where they can see, touch, and dissect representatives of the various phyla. If not, it will be even more crucial that you present adequate visual material.

- Have students list the "famous firsts" for each evolutionary advancement. For instance, which group was famous for first having a complete digestive system? This will help students learn the important adaptations that lead to evolutionary advancements.

- As mentioned in the Presentation section, relating animals to daily life will enhance your lectures. Below is a sampling that you can build upon.

  PORIFERA: Natural *sponges* (expensive) are still the best for cleaning purposes.

  CNIDARIA: We wouldn't want to tangle with a *jellyfish*, but a valuable piece of *coral* on your ring finger is OK.

  PLATYHELMINTHES: The *tapeworms* and *flukes* have disgusting parasitic habits but are all a part of nature's balance.

  NEMATODA: Everyone is familiar with *roundworms* as parasites of pets, but do you know that humans can get them too?

  ANNELIDA: The familiar *earthworm* is a very beneficial tiller of the soil, but is its relative the *leech* so well respected?

  ARTHROPODA: The largest phylum contains pesky *insects* as well as tasty *lobsters*.

  MOLLUSCA: *Snails* and *clams* are quite familiar—we even eat them! But what about the *squid* and *octopus?*

  ECHINODERMATA: *Sea stars* seem exotic because they and their relatives are found only in the sea.

  CHORDATA: Finally, "familiar" animals, but they constitute less than 5 percent of all the animals on the earth.

Old Genes, New Drugs (revisited)

- How would complete destruction of marine invertebrates impact humans?

- How can a toxin like conotoxin, which kills, be the potential source of new drugs?

- What measures can be taken to explore the marine biodiversity, yet protect the habitats of these animals and prevent overharvesting?

Additional Ideas for Classroom Discussion

- Why are protozoans no longer included in the Kingdom Animalia?

- Even if you cannot remember all the details concerning the members of each phylum, can you tell the major niches that each phylum seems to fill?

- When a pet owner says, "My animal has worms," what worm is most likely present? How could you distinguish between a flatworm and a roundworm, other than by shape?

- Some people don't consider an organism as a true animal unless it bleeds red when injured. Which animals presented in this chapter would fit this "definition"?

- Arthropods as a group have more unique features than perhaps any other group. Name as many of these features as you can.

- Why do persons you know refuse to eat insects when close relatives such as crayfish and lobsters, and near relatives such as snails and oysters, are gourmet items?

- Have students design, name, and present a science fiction super-insect with adaptations for survival.

How Would You Vote? Classroom Discussion Ideas

- Monitor the voting for the online question. It only seems reasonable that bottom trawling ought to be banned, since this form of fishing can destroy invertebrate habitats. What are the costs associated with a ban on this fishing method? Who should pay for these costs?
- Have students complete classroom polling using the JoinIn clickers.

Term Paper Topics, Library Activities, and Special Projects

- In the early days of biological investigation, sponges and even some cnidarians were classified as plants. Search some older textbooks to see why scientists changed their minds.
- Prepare a report on the extent of flatworm parasitic infestations in humans. List the condition, number of cases, and economic loss to society.
- The phylum Echinodermata is unique in not possessing any freshwater representatives. Find the reasons for this in an invertebrate biology textbook.
- Chordates dominate our thinking when the word *animal* is used. But they constitute about 5 percent of the total species. Relate this fact to the concept of pyramids (energy, biomass, numbers) as presented in Unit VII.
- Divide the invertebrates among your class and have students prepare a profile of an organism including its body plan, symmetry, habitat, diet, predators, etc.

Responses to *Data Analysis Activities*

1. Trial 5 had the most control crabs die. Trial 5 had the most bled crabs die.
2. Fifteen more crabs died if they were bled on the day of capture, as compared with crabs that were simply handled and not bled on the day of capture.
3. These data indicate that bleeding harms horseshoe crabs more than capture alone does.

Possible Responses to *Critical Thinking* Questions

1. Self-fertilization allows the animal to reproduce without the need of a partner and produce many offspring; however, this will limit the potential for genetic mutation leading to beneficial adaptations.

2. The eyes of birds and squids have a lens, and these structures are analogous. The lens serves the same function in each of these species but evolved independently rather than from the same embryological material or from the same structures in a common ancestor.

3. Most pesticide chemicals attack the nervous system of the pest. Even though insects and lobsters are very different in size and live in different habitats, their nervous systems work by the same mechanisms. Therefore, we would expect any nerve poison to work the same in both. If the levels of pesticide were high enough in the water it could be the culprit of killing the lobsters. Further toxicology and lab tests could confirm this speculation.

24

ANIMALS II: THE CHORDATES

Chapter Outline

Objectives

1. Describe the four characteristics that are distinctive of chordates.
2. Describe the characteristics of jawless and jawed fishes.
3. Describe the evolutionary adaptations that allowed the transition from life in water to life on land.
4. Recognize the characteristics of the amniotes that allowed them to expand to dry habitats.
5. Understand the general physical features and behavioral patterns attributed to early primates and their transition to early humans.

Key Terms

chordates	hagfishes	dinosaurs	hominids
notochord	lampreys	ectotherms	bipedalism
lancelets	cartilaginous fishes	endotherms	culture
tunicates	bony fishes	birds	australopiths
craniates	ray-finned fishes	mammals	humans
vertebrates	lobe-finned fishes	monotremes	multiregional model
endoskeleton	amphibians	marsupials	replacement model
tetrapods	amniote eggs	placental mammals	
amniotes	reptiles	primates	

Lecture Outline

24.1   Windows on the Past

    A. The absence of transitional forms was an early obstacle to Darwin's theory of evolution.

        1. The discovery of *Archaeopteryx* specimens, which display both reptilian and bird features, was significant.

        2. The transitions have been aided by the discovery of *Sinosauropteryx* and *Confuciusornis* fossils.

    B. Such fossils are witness to the history of life.

        1. They, along with structural, biochemical, and genetic evidence, contribute to the scientific theory of evolution

24.2   The Chordate Heritage

    A. Chordate Characteristics

        1. Chordates are bilateral animals.

        2. All chordates, at some time in their lives, have four distinctive features.

            a. A notochord is a long rod of stiffened tissue that supports the body; later it changes to bony units in vertebrates.

            b. A dorsal, tubular nerve cord lies above the notochord and gut.

            c. A muscular pharynx with gill slits is positioned at the entrance to the digestive tract.

            d. A tail, or rudiment thereof, exists near the anus.

        3. Most chordates are vertebrates.

    B. Invertebrate Chordates

        1. Lancelets are small fishlike animals with tapered bodies.

            a. They lie buried in the sand, filtering food from the stream of water passing through the pharynx.

            b. Lancelets display all four of the vertebrate characteristics throughout their lives.

            c. Lancelets may be the most ancient chordates.

        2. Tunicates, or sea squirts, are marine organisms covered with a gelatinous tunic.

            a. The larval stage swims around and has all the chordate traits.

            b. The adult is sessile, maintaining a constant flow of water entering through the gill slits bringing in food particles (filter feeding) and oxygen, and carrying away wastes.

            c. Metamorphosis to the adult results in a loss of the notochord and tail, a regression of the nerve cord, and an expansion of the pharynx for filter feeding.

C. Overview of Chordate Evolution
1. Craniates have a cranium that is a braincase protecting the brain. Fishes, amphibians, reptiles, birds, and mammals are all craniates.
    a. Hagfishes are a jawless fish that are unique because they have a cranium, but no backbone.
2. Vertebrates possess an endoskeleton.
3. The single, continuous notochord was replaced by a column of separate, hardened vertebrae, parts of which became modified near the head to form jaws.
    a. Jaws allowed new feeding possibilities, coupled with better eyes for detecting both prey and predators.
4. Gradually, there was less reliance on gills and more on lungs and the circulatory system (heart, blood vessels), which work in connection.
5. The fins of fishes select fishes developed bony supports within them.
6. Those organisms that developed walking limbs formed the tetrapods.
7. Amniotes developed a series of water-proof membranes to allow them to expand on land.

24.3 The Fishes
A. Jawless Fishes
1. These fishes have cylindrical bodies with no fins or scales.
2. Hagfishes have a cranium with no backbone.
    a. Hagfishes feed on soft invertebrates or dead/dying fish.
3. Lampreys have a cartilaginous backbone.
    a. Many lampreys are parasite like, extracting food from a living host.

B. Fishes With Jaws
1. Jaws are modified gill supports.
2. Most jawed fishes also have paired fins.

C. Cartilaginous Fishes
1. All possess a streamlined body with a cartilaginous endoskeleton, gill slits, and fins.
2. This group includes the sharks and rays.
    a. Scales do not grow; new ones emerge between existing scales and are made of dentin and enamel.

D. "Bony Fishes"
1. The bony fishes have jaws and a bony endoskeleton.
    a. They generally possess a bony covering over the gills have scales that grow.
    b. A swim bladder offsets the weight of the bone skeleton.
2. Bony fishes are the most numerous and diverse of the vertebrates.
    a. The ray-finned fishes are highly maneuverable thanks to their fins, which are supported by rays that originate from the dermis.
    b. The lobe-finned fishes bear fleshy extensions, with internal supporting bones, on the body.
    c. Lungfishes have gills and one or a pair of "lungs" that are modified gut wall outpouchings.

24.4 Amphibians—The First Tetrapods
A. The Move Onto Land
1. Amphibians are thin-skinned vertebrates that were the first to evolve from lobe-finned fishes.
2. Over time structural modifications allowed the early amphibians to spend more time out of water.

Animals II: The Chordates   **189**

3. Natural selection favored changes in sensory systems.
   a. A three-chambered heart improved circulation and reliance on the lungs.
   b. Vision sharpened and eyelids developed.
4. The move to land may have been to escape predators or to eat newly-evolved insects.

B. Modern Amphibians
   1. Salamanders have an elongated body with a tail that persists into adulthood.
      a. When they walk, the body bends from side to side, much like a fish moving through water.
      b. Adults may retain larval features including gills and a tail.
      c. Some salamanders retain juvenile traits as an adult. For instance, they have gills and they may breed before reaching a true adult stage.
   2. Frogs and toads are the best known and belong to the most diverse group of amphibians.
      a. These animals possess long hind limbs capable of responding to powerful muscles.
      b. Larval frogs and toads have gills and a tail but no limbs.

C. Declining Amphibian Diversity
   1. Amphibians are in trouble.
      a. Several frog, toad, and salamander species are currently listed as threatened or endangered.
      b. Many declines correlate with shrinking and deteriorating habitats.
   2. Newly introduced species, long-term changes in climate, increases in ultraviolet radiation, the spread of more diseases, and chemical pollution may be affecting amphibians sooner than other organisms.

24.5   Evolution of the Amniotes

A. Amniotes arose from some amphibians
   1. Three traits were critical to help amniotes adapt fully to land.
      a. They produce amniote eggs with covering membranes and a shell, which allow the eggs to be laid in dry habitats.
      b. Amniotes have a toughened, dry, or scaly skin that is resistant to drying.
      c. Their kidneys are good at conserving water.
   2. The amniote lineage branched quickly.
      a. One branch formed the mammals.
      b. The other includes the dinosaurs and birds, crocodilians, turtles, tuataras, snakes and lizards.

24.6   Nonbird Reptiles

A. General Characteristics
   1. Reptiles include turtles, lizards, tuataras, snakes, and crocodiles.
   2. Reptiles are cold-blooded.

B. Major Groups
   1. Lizards and Snakes.
      a. Most lizards are small-bodied insect eaters; their most usual habitats are deserts and tropical forests.
      b. The Komodo dragon is an ambush predator, attacking deer and wild pigs.
      c. Snakes are descended from short-legged, long-bodied lizards.
      e. All are carnivores, many with flexible jaws that permit swallowing quite large, whole prey.
      f. Most lizards and snakes lay eggs.
   2. Turtles
      a. Turtles possess a distinctive shell that offers protection while conserving water and body heat.

      b.   Instead of teeth, turtles have horny plates that are used to grip and chew food.

   3. Crocodilians.

      a.   They are thought to be relatives to birds.

      b.   Crocodilians are the only animal other than birds and mammals with a four-chambered heart.

      c.   They show complex behavior, such as guarding nests and assisting hatchlings.

      d.   They can be quite large, over 1000 kg.

24.7   Birds—Reptiles With Feathers

  A. Birds are evolved for flight

    1. Feathers covering the wings make a good flight surface and conserve metabolic heat in the body.

    2. Heat is generated and regulated from within the body.

    3. The heart is four-chambered, and the lungs are highly efficient because of their "flow-through" design.

    4. Bones in the bird body are lightweight because of air cavities within them.

    5. Powerful muscles are attached at strategic places on the bones for maximum leverage.

  B. Birds evolved from reptiles.

    1. The oldest known bird (*Archaeopteryx*) resembled reptiles in limb bones and other features.

    2. Birds still resemble reptiles: horny beaks, scaly legs, cloacas, and they lay eggs.

    3. Birds are incredibly diverse in color, courtship, song, and size, including the very large flightless ones such as the ostrich.

24.8   Mammals – The Milk Makers

  A. Mammalian Traits.

    1. Modern mammals are characterized by the following:

      a.   Hair covers at least part of the body (whales are an exception).

      b.   Milk-secreting glands nourish the young.

      c.   Dentition (incisors, canines, premolars, and molars) is extensive and specialized to meet dietary habits.

  B. Three Mammalian Lineages

    1. Monotremes (egg-laying mammals) are represented today only by the platypus and spiny anteater in Australia.

      a.   They are practically toothless.

      b.   They lay eggs but suckle their young.

    2. Marsupials (pouched mammals), such as the opossum of North America, give birth to tiny, blind, hairless young that find their way to the mother's pouch where they are suckled and finish their development.

    3. Placental mammals nourish their young within the mother's uterus by the placenta—a composite of maternal and fetal tissue.

      a.   The placenta is the organ of exchange of nutrients and wastes between the maternal blood and the fetal blood.

      b.   Placental nourishment is more efficient than nourishment of the pouched animals.

      c.   Representatives of this group are found in virtually every aquatic and terrestrial environment.

24.9 Primate Traits and Evolutionary Trends

  A. Primate Classification

    1. Prosimians (literally: before apes) are small tree dwellers (arboreal) that use their large eyes to advantage during night hunting.

2. Tarsiers (tarsioids) are small primates with features intermediate between prosimians and anthropoids.

3. Anthropoids include monkeys, apes, and humans.

    a. Hominoids include apes and humans.

    b. Hominid refers to human lineages only.

B. Key Trends in Primate Evolution

  1. Enhanced vision:

    a. Early primates had an eye on each side of the head.

    b. Later ones had forward-directed eyes, resulting in better depth perception and increased ability to discern shape, movement, color, and light intensity.

  2. Modified jaws and teeth:

    a. Monkeys have rectangular jaws and long canines.

    b. Humans have a bow-shaped jaw and smaller teeth, reflecting the changes in diet.

  3. Upright walking:

    a. Bipedalism is possible because of skeletal reorganization in primates ancestral to humans.

    b. A monkey skeleton is suitable for a life of climbing, leaping, and running along tree branches with palms down.

    c. An ape skeleton is suitable for climbing and using the arms for carrying some body weight; the shoulder blades allow the arms to swivel overhead.

    d. Humans have a shorter, S-shaped, and somewhat flexible backbone.

  4. Better grips:

    a. Prehensile movements allowed fingers to wrap around objects in a grasp.

    b. Opposable thumb and fingers allowed more refined use of the hand.

    c. The precision and power grip movements of the human hand allowed for toolmaking.

  5. Brain, behavior, and culture:

    a. Brain expansion and elaboration produced a brain of increased mass and complexity, especially for thought, language, and conscious movements.

    b. Human brain development led to patterns of human behavior known collectively as culture.

24.10 Emergence of Early Humans

A. Early Hominids

  1. Most of the earliest known hominids lived in Central Africa, beginning roughly 6 million years ago.

  2. The first known hominids are designated australopiths (southern apes).

    a. They had a large face but smaller braincases and protruding jaws.

    b. They possessed improved dentition for grinding harder foods, upright walking, bipedalism (leaving footprints), and increased manual dexterity.

  3. *Australopithecus afarensis* is one of the species that walked across the African plane some 3.9 million years ago.

B. Early Humans

  1. Differentiating the earliest humans is hard – perhaps duplication for specific brain protein genes was the key.

  2. The first toolmaker is referred to as "handy man" or *Homo habilis*.

    a. Early *H. habilis* had a smaller face, more generalized teeth, and larger brain.

  3. "Manufactured" tools have been found at Olduvai Gorge in Africa.

  4. *Homo erectus* was a very successful early human.

24.11 Emergence of Modern Humans

  A. Branchings of the Human Lineage

    1. *Homo erectus* ("upright man") is a species related to modern humans that migrated out of Africa into Europe and Asia.

    2. Selection pressures triggered adaptive radiations resulting in physical changes as well as cultural shifts.

      a. *Homo erectus* had a longer, chinless face, thick-walled skull, heavy brow ridge, but narrow hips and long legs.

      b. *Homo erectus* made advanced stone tools and used fire as they migrated out of Africa into Asia and Europe.

    3. By about 195,000 years ago, *Homo sapiens* had evolved from *Homo erectus*.

      a. Early *H. sapiens* had smaller teeth, a chin, thinner facial bones, larger brain, and rounder, higher skull.

      b. Neanderthals were similar to modern humans and lived 200,000 to 30,000 years ago.

  B. Where Did Modern Humans Originate?

    1. Fossil and genetic evidence points to the origin of humans in Africa.

    2. Two models are used to interpret the evidence.

      a. In the multiregional model, *Homo sapiens* evolved from *H. erectus* in Africa. Other regions evolved into *H. sapiens* populations gradually over more than a million years.

      b. In the more widely accepted replacement model, *H. sapiens* originated from a single *H. erectus* population in sub-Saharan Africa within the past 200,000 years. Bands of *H. sapiens* then migrated out to replace the *H. erectus* populations already there.

  C. Leaving Home

    1. Long-term shifts in climate drove human bands away from Africa.

    2. Cultural means were developed to survive the extraordinary hardships they faced.

    3. Cultural evolution is still ongoing.

Suggestions for Presenting the Material

♦ In contrast to the information given in the text on invertebrates, students should be more familiar with the vertebrates. In fact, they may be overly confident and not listen as attentively as they should.

♦ Interest can be sparked by use of slides and videos to show exotic animals in their natural habitats.

♦ Additional interest can be generated by allowing any students that have cared for, or studied, vertebrates to share their experiences.

♦ The authors have gone to special lengths to present the vertebrates based on their evolution. This should be emphasized in lecture.

♦ Depending on the region of the country and your particular institution, the discussion of human origins may, or may not, spark some controversy in your class. Whether we acknowledge it or not, this is an area where religious beliefs and scientific explanations can conflict. If confronted, don't get emotional, and stick to the scientific evidence that is available.

♦ Be sure to distinguish "hominoid" from "hominid."

♦ Because there are several genus and species names associated with primate evolution, each with distinguishing characteristics, perhaps you or the students could construct a table summarizing this data.

Classroom and Laboratory Enrichment

- If you are fortunate to live in or near a large city with a zoo, arrange a field trip, but this time with a difference. Prepare the students for note-taking on various topics such as classification, body symmetry and cavities, body system development, ecological niche, and so on.

- Nearly every campus has some kind of vertebrate collection. Bring some of the specimens to the classroom or arrange for a tour of the museum.

- There is no scarcity of visual material depicting the diversity of animal life. It ranges from professionally made 2 x 2 transparencies, to single-phylum films, to full-length video surveys of the animal kingdom such as David Attenborough's *Life on Earth*, or Animal Planet's *Planet Earth* (available at retail outlets).

- Because of the interest in human origins, numerous videotapes and slide sets are available (check supply catalogs in your A/V center). Some may be more technical; others may be for the general public.

- If you are fortunate to have an expert in human evolution available, by all means arrange for an illustrated lecture on this complex subject.

- View museum displays depicting early human evolution and life.

- Many lab manuals have activities for that trace fossil evidence and are helpful in tracing the evolutionary history of humans.

- In lab, review each of the phyla and classes of animals discussed in this chapter. To learn each of the major adaptations have students identify the "famous firsts." For instance: Which animal was the first to show internal fertilization? Which was the first to have metabolic processes to internally regulate body temperature?

Windows on the Past (revisited)

- Do you think the fossils of human ancestors create more controversy than non-human fossils? Explain.

- Based on what you know of fossils, why are they difficult to compare and categorize?

- Think of how you would interpret 'modern fossils'. Imagine you were an alien found the skeleton of a professional basketball player and a jockey. If those were your only samples, would you think they were the same species?

- Rarely are entire fossil skeletons found in one geographical site. Rather, a skeleton is a composite of many "finds." How do scientists know what bones to group together?

- Think back to our definition of a species. Do fossil finds make that definition useful in classifying them as the same or different species?

Additional Ideas for Classroom Discussion

- Organize a debate on the use of vertebrate animals as subjects of medical and scientific research. Are there alternatives to their use? Are these alternatives practical?

- Evaluate the extent to which humans should go in breeding unusual animals simply for "show." Are there any breeds that you know of that suffer anatomical or physiological anomalies just for the sake of a good show animal?

- What kinds of animals are the animal-rights movements concerned about? Which ones do they not see as worthy of their protests?

- What role do hunters and fishermen play in the ecological balance of nature? Is their contribution to game management significant?

- Why do you think it is that the unusual reptiles and mammals are found on islands and island continents?

- What characteristics define a "primate"? Why are chimpanzees and humans classified into different genera?

- What characteristics distinguish *Australopithecus* from *Homo?*

- Have students speculate on how we are evolving and what adaptations we may incorporate into our genome over the next many years.

How Would You Vote? Classroom Discussion Ideas

- Monitor the voting for the online question. In the United States, with its strong emphasis on individual land rights, it would be difficult to impose a sanction on landowners that would prohibit them from taking possession of the fossils found on their private property. Perhaps a compromise could be reached whereby the "owner" would share his finds with authorities but retain ownership. Certainly the advancement of science is aided by the finds of private collectors. It would be a shame to drive these persons "underground."

Term Paper Topics, Library Activities, and Special Projects

- Chordates dominate our thinking when the word *animal* is used. But they constitute about 3 percent of the total species. Relate this fact to the concept of pyramids (energy, biomass, numbers) as presented in Unit VII.

- What is the relative extent of extinction of vertebrates compared with that of invertebrates?

- Evaluate the literature of the animal rights movement. Is it scientifically sound? Does it place emotion above the public good?

- Research the ethical basis (if there is any) of how we should treat animals. If you come to any conclusions about treatment of vertebrates, can you formulate as strong an argument for invertebrates?

- Prepare an analysis of the contribution that hunters and fishermen make to the management of animals.

- Research the creationists' arguments against evolution of humans, and rebut each one using scientific evidence and arguments.

- Prepare a report on the methods illustrators use to reconstruct fossil humans. Assess the degree of freedom individual artists use in their work (check the "Readings" list at the end of this chapter).

- Investigate the controversy surrounding the skeleton called "Lucy."

- The Institute of Human Origins produced a downloadable documentary called "Becoming Human." Have you students work through this activity.

- Divide the vertebrates among your class and have students prepare a profile of an organism including its body plan, symmetry, habitat, diet, predators, etc.

Responses to *Data Analysis Activities*

1. The average life span of a lemur is 20 years, and for a gibbon it is 30 years.
2. Lemurs reach adulthood most quickly.
3. Humans have the longest expanse of reproductive years.
4. Only humans survive past their reproductive years.

Possible Responses to *Critical Thinking* Questions

1. Because placental mammals evolved after the breakup of Pangea, they were not able to access that land mass which had already been occupied by marsupials and monotremes. This was fortunate for the marsupials and monotremes of Australia, as their relatives were generally out-competed by placental mammals across the rest of the globe.

2. Alaska would have many more native birds than reptiles. Reptiles are ectotherms and would not thrive in Alaska's cold climate, while endothermic birds would be able to tolerate the low temperatures.

3. Assuming that modern humans and Neanderthals had intercourse, there are two mechanisms that could prevent hybrid births. One is gamete incompatibility, perhaps the sperm of the male involved would be either unable to handle the vaginal environment of the female, or was unable to fertilize the egg. A second possibility is hybrid inviability, which assumes the sperm did fertilize the egg, but that the developing embryo was the victim of too many genetic incompatibilities and died in the womb.

25

PLANT TISSUES

Chapter Outline

Objectives

1. Describe the generalized body plan of a flowering plant.
2. Define and distinguish among the various types of ground tissues, vascular tissues, and dermal tissues.
3. Explain how plant tissues develop from meristems.
4. Know the basic structure and functions of stems, leaves, and roots.
5. Explain what is meant by primary and secondary growth. Describe how secondary growth occurs in woody dicot roots and stems.

Key Terms

ground tissue system	cotyledons	sclerenchyma	phloem
vascular tissue system	meristems	epidermis	sieve tubes
dermal tissue system	primary growth	mesophyll	companion cells
	secondary growth	sylem	vascular bundles
	parenchyma	tracheids	veins
	collenchymas	vessel members	taproot system

fibrous root system	endodermis	wood	cork
root hairs	lateral meristems	cork cambium	heartwood
vascular cylinder	vascular cambium	bark	sapwood

Lecture Outline

25.1 Sequestering Carbon in Forests

   A. Carbon in the atmosphere occurs mainly as carbon dioxide gas (CO_2). The amount of CO_2 in the atmosphere is increasing exponentially due to the burning of fossil fuels and other plant-derived materials. This is producing unintended and potentially catastrophic effects on Earth's climate.

   B. Efforts are now under way to reduce the amount of CO_2 in the atmosphere, including carbon offsets.

      1. Companies and individuals buy carbon offsets to "offset" the activities that release greenhouse gases, like CO_2.

      2. Any process by which CO_2 is removed from the atmosphere is called carbon sequestration.

      3. Plants remove CO_2 already in the atmosphere, thus acting as natural carbon sequesters.

25.2 Organization of the Plant Body

   A. The Basic Body Plan

      1. The aboveground parts of plants—shoot—consist of stems, leaves, and flowers with internal pipelines for conduction.

         a. Stems are frameworks for upright growth and display of flowers.

         b. Photosynthetic cells in leaves are exposed to light.

         c. Flowers are displayed to pollinators.

      2. The plant's descending parts—roots—usually grow below ground.

         a. They absorb water and minerals from soil and conduct them upward.

         b. They store food; they also anchor and support the plant.

   B. Overview of the Plant Tissue Systems

      1. Plants consist of three basic tissue types.

         a. The ground tissue system makes up the bulk of the plant body.

         b. The vascular tissue system contains two kinds of conducting tissues that distribute water and solutes through the plant body.

         c. The dermal tissue system covers and protects the plant's surfaces.

      2. All three systems incorporate simple and complex tissues.

         a. Parenchyma, collenchyma, and sclerenchyma are simple tissues.

         b. Xylem, phloem, and epidermis are complex tissues, composed of two or more cell types.

   C. Eudicots and Monocots

      1. Eudicots include common trees and shrubs (other than conifers).

      2. Monocots include grasses, lilies, irises, and palms.

      3. Monocot seeds have one cotyledon ("seed leaf"), and eudicot seeds have two.

   D. Introducing Meristems

      1. Plant tissues originate from meristems—localized regions of undifferentiated, rapidly dividing cells.

         a. Primary growth is the seasonal lengthening of shoots and roots.

         c. Secondary growth is the increase in diameter of older roots and stems.

25.3   Components of Plant Tissues

A.   Cells of Simple Tissues

1.   Parenchyma makes up most of the soft, moist primary growth of plants.

a.   Its thin-walled, pliable cells.

b.   Various types participate in photosynthesis, storage, secretion, and other tasks.

c.   Its cells are alive at maturity, metabolically active and retain the capacity to divide (e.g., wound healing).

2.   Collenchyma cells are thickened and help strengthen the plant (for example, "strings" in celery).

a.   It is commonly arranged at strands or cylinders beneath the dermal tissue of stems and stalks.

b.   The primary cell walls of collenchyma become thickened with cellulose and pectin at maturity, often at their corners.

c.   These cells are alive at maturity.

3.   Sclerenchyma cells provide mechanical support and protection in mature plants.

a.   The secondary walls are thick and often impregnated with lignin, which strengthens and waterproofs cell walls.

b.   Sclerenchyma cells form *fibers* such as in hemp and flax; others called *sclereids* form strong coats around seeds, as in a peach pit.

c.   These cells are not alive at maturity.

B.   Complex Tissues

1.   A dermal tissue system called epidermis covers all primary plant parts. This is the first dermal tissue to form.

a.   A waxy cuticle covers the external surfaces of the plant to restrict water loss and resist microbial attack.

b.   Pairs of specialized epidermal cells form stomata, openings that permit water and gaseous exchange with the air.

2.   Ground tissue accounts for the bulk of a plant, and consists of everything other than dermal and vascular tissue. Mesophyll is the only photosynthetic ground tissue, consisting of chloroplast-containing parenchyma cells.

3.   Vascular tissues function in the distribution of substances throughout the plant.

a.   Xylem uses two kinds of cells (dead at maturity) to conduct water and minerals absorbed from the soil.

i.   Vessel members are shorter cells joined end to end to form a vessel with perforation plates at the ends of each member.

ii.   Tracheids are long cells with tapered, overlapping ends.

b.   Phloem transports sugars and other solutes throughout the plant body.

i.   Phloem contains living, conducting cells called sieve tube members that bear clusters of pores in the walls through which the cytoplasm of adjacent cells is connected.

ii.   These are joined end to end at sieve plates to form tubes.

iii.   Companion cells, adjacent to the sieve tube members, help to load sugars produced in leaves and unload them in storage and growth regions.

25.4   Primary Shoots

A.   Internal Structure of Stems

1.   A vascular bundle is a multistranded cord of primary xylem and phloem running lengthwise through the ground tissue of shoots.

2.   The arrangement of vascular bundles is genetically different in eudicots and monocots.

a.   The cortex is the parenchyma between the vascular bundles and the epidermis.

      b. Pith refers to the parenchyma inside the ring of vascular bundles.

      c. The stems of most dicots have vascular bundles arranged as a ring that divides the ground tissue into the outer cortex and inner pith.

      d. In most monocots, the vascular bundles are scattered throughout the ground tissue.

  B. Primary Growth of a Stem

    1. Terminal buds are a shoot's main zone of primary growth.

      a. Beneath a terminal bud's surface are cells that divide continually during a growing season.

      b. These cells divide and differentiate into specialized tissues.

    2. Below the terminal bud are small regions of tissue that bulge outward.

      a. Each bulge is the start of a new leaf.

      b. Each stem region where one or more leaves form is a node.

    3. Lateral, or axillary, buds are dormant shoots.

      a. Each forms in a leaf axil, the point at which the leaf is attached to the stem.

      b. The axillary buds may form branches, leaves, or flowers.

      c. Hormones secreted by the terminal bud keep lateral buds dormant.

25.5   A Closer Look at Leaves

  A. Similarities and Differences

    1. Leaves are shaped like cups, needles, blades, spikes, tubes, and feathers.

    2. Leaves are metabolic factories equipped with photosynthetic cells.

      a. Most have a thin, flat blade, which is attached to the stem by means of a stalk, or petiole.

      b. Leaves are adapted to local environmental conditions and can orient themselves for maximum exposure to the sun for photosynthesis.

      c. Leaves of most species offer a high surface-to-volume ratio.

  B. Fine Structure

    1. Epidermis covers all leaf surfaces that are exposed to the surroundings.

      a. Its surface may be smooth or covered with a variety of hairs and scales.

      b. The cuticle coats the epidermis and minimizes water loss.

      c. Stomata are located mostly on the lower epidermis, with guard cells on either side.

    2. Mesophyll is a photosynthetic ground tissue.

      a. Photosynthetic parenchyma cells (in the mesophyll layer) are located between the extensive surface areas of the upper and lower epidermis.

      b. Air spaces participate in gaseous exchange.

      c. Columnar parenchyma cells attached to the upper epidermis (palisade cells) have more chloroplasts than the spongy cells below.

    3. Veins are the leaf's vascular bundles.

      a. Veins form a network for water, solutes, and photosynthetic products.

      b. In eudicots, the veins repeatedly branch into smaller ones embedded in the mesophyll; in monocots, veins are quite similar in length and run parallel with the leaf's long axis.

25.6 Primary Roots

  A. Root primary growth results in one of two kinds of root systems, taproot and fibrous roots systems.

    1. Taproot systems of eudicots consist of a primary root and its lateral branchings. The taproot is characteristic of woody plants and typically is long lasting.

2. Monocots have primary roots that do not last as long; instead they develop a root system described as fibrous where the primary and lateral roots are similar in diameter and length.

B. Roots provide anchorage for the plant while absorbing water and minerals.
1. Typically, the roots do not penetrate more than five meters deep.
2. In an experiment with potted rye plants, after four months the surface area of the roots measured over 600 square meters.

C. Internal Structure of Roots
1. The root epidermis, with its extensions called root hairs, increase surface area and the absorptive interface with the soil.
2. Vascular tissues form a vascular cylinder arranged as a central column.
   a. The column is surrounded by root cortex (ground tissue), which has abundant air spaces within it.
   b. The endodermis—the innermost layer of the cortex—surrounds the vascular cylinder and helps control water movement into it.
   c. Just inside the endodermis is the pericycle, a layer of parenchyma cells one or more layers thick. This layer is meristematic and can give rise to lateral roots.

25.7 Secondary Growth

A. Woody plants such as dicots and gymnosperms show secondary growth by developing lateral meristems—vascular cambium and cork cambium.
1. Vascular cambium is a cylinderlike lateral meristem.
   a. It produces secondary xylem on its inner face and secondary phloem on its outer.
   b. The secondary growth displaces the cells of the vascular cambium toward the stem or root surface.
   c. A core of secondary xylem, or wood, contributes up to 90 percent of the weight of some plants.
2. Periderm, formed from cork cambium, plus secondary phloem make up the bark.
3. Cork cambium also produces cork. Cork contains suberin and protects, insulates, and waterproofs the stem or root surfaces.

B. Wood's appearance changes as the stem grows older.
1. Heartwood lies at the center of older stems and roots.
   a. It is a depository for resins, oils, gums, and tannins.
   b. It makes the tree strong and able to defy gravity.
2. Sapwood is secondary growth located between heartwood and the vascular cambium.
   a. It is wet, pale in color, and not as strong.
   b. It is rich in the sugar-rich fluid of the phloem (for example, maple trees).
3. In regions with cool winters or dry spells, the vascular cambium is inactive during part of the year.
   a. Early wood (start of growing season) contains xylem with large diameters and thin walls.
   b. Late wood contains xylem with small diameters and thick walls.
   c. Growth rings appear as alternating light bands of early wood and dark bands of late wood.
4. Hardwood (such as oak) has vessels, tracheids, and fibers in its xylem; softwood (such as conifers) has no vessels or fibers.
5. Softwoods (such as pine) have xylem with tracheids and parenchyma rays but no vessels or fibers. This makes their wood weaker.

25.8   Variations on a Stem

   A.   Stolons are stems that branch from the main stem of the plant and may look like roots. Example: strawberry plants (*Fragaria*).

   B.   Rhizomes are fleshy stems that typically grow under the soil and parallel to its surface. Example: turmeric plant (*Curcuma longa*).

   C.   Bulbs are short sections of an underground stem encased by overlapping layers of thickened, modified leaves (called scales). Example: onion plant (*Allium cepa*).

   D.   Corms are a thickened underground stem that stores nutrients and is a solid structure (lacking scales). Example: arrowroot plant (*Colocasia esculenta*).

   E.   Tubers are thickened portions of underground stolons and function as the primary storage tissue. Example: potato plant (*Solanum tuberosum*).

   F.   Cladodes are flattened, photosynthetic stems that store water. Example: prickly pear plant (*Opuntia*).

25.9   Tree Rings and Old Secrets

   A.   Tree rings can be used to estimate the age of a tree.

   B.   The relative thickness of a tree's rings hold clues to environmental conditions during its lifetime.

Suggestions for Presenting the Material

♦   The information in this chapter is very visual in nature, so use pictures, models, and diagrams whenever possible. Even if students are seeing many of these structures in lab while they are covering this chapter in lecture, they will gain much reinforcement by seeing diagrams and photos of plant cells, tissues, and systems.

♦   Bring a large potted plant to class and ask students to create a list of terms that describe plant components being studied in this chapter. Follow this up by showing the animated Figure 25.2 on the plant body plan.

♦   Emphasize the link between structure and function. Stress the differences between plants and animals, particularly in regard to growth. The concept of growth only at plant meristems, so different from the way in which animals grow, is initially puzzling to many students. Introduce useful and familiar plant examples as you go through this chapter. Students are aware of the importance of plants in our day-to-day existence, but many forget the role plants play in our lives. Use "grocery store" examples; students will be intrigued to hear more about the plants and plant parts that they have taken for granted. Bring in plants and fruits and vegetables whenever possible to demonstrate plant structures.

♦   Another area that is familiar to students, particularly those who have done woodworking, is wood. You can use many examples in this area to introduce points on plant structure and growth.

♦   **Common Student Misconceptions**

    o   This chapter presents a large number of new terms related to plant cells, tissues, and other structures that students are unfamiliar or uncomfortable with. Be sure to emphasize those you consider most important and reinforce with repeated use.

Classroom and Laboratory Enrichment

♦ Distribute different types of plant tissues around the lecture classroom or lab room. Some possible examples include a fresh celery stalk cut in two (notice strands of collenchyma running along the "ribs" of the stalk), hemp used in making rope (fibers), cotton bolls (fibers), and nutshells (sclereids).

♦ Obtain information about wood from lumber and paper companies. Several companies can supply posters and other materials about trees used for lumber and paper.

♦ Demonstrate dendrochronology. Using an overhead transparency (or in small groups of students, an actual portion of a tree cross-section), discuss how interpretation of growth rings can reveal drought; fire; loss of trees due to disease, windfall, or harvesting; and periods of normal growth. Show students a tree-boring device; let them interpret trunk samples obtained with it.

♦ Pass varied samples of leaves around the room. Ask students how leaf morphology varies between eudicots, monocots, and gymnosperms. Have student speculate about the differences in morphology as a function of climate.

♦ If the number of students in the class permits it and the physical environment is suitable, take a short walk to examine the plants and trees on your campus.

♦ Make ample use of plant structure models that will emphasize the 3-D quality lacking in flat photos. This is especially true of conducting tissue.

Sequestering Carbon in Forests (revisited)

♦ Discuss the classification of forests as a type of "carbon sink." Is this an effective analogy? What effect does burning wood have on the rate of tree decomposition and release of carbon?

♦ Discuss methods, other than forests, of carbon sequestration.

Additional Ideas for Classroom Discussion

♦ How did companion cells acquire their name?

♦ How does growth in plants differ from growth in animals? What would humans look like if they grew like plants?

♦ What is the difference between primary growth and secondary growth? What kind(s) of growth occur(s) in a maple tree? Where would you look in the maple tree to find primary growth? Secondary growth? What is the difference between an apical meristem and a lateral meristem?

♦ What causes "growth rings" in wood? Does one ring always represent one growing season? Does some wood lack growth rings? Why or why not?

♦ What is the purpose of the root cap? Is there such a thing as a "shoot cap"? Why or why not? Is there any structure on the shoot tip that is analogous to the root cap?

♦ What plants have root systems and shoot systems that can be used as food? Many of these plants have modified structures such as roots (for example, carrot), stems (for example, ginger), or leaves (for example, celery, an enlarged petiole) that are eaten.

- Present some familiar examples of common and/or economically important plants such as corn, tomatoes, lettuce, rice, and wheat, and ask students to classify them as monocots or eudicots.

- How useful are plant parts such as leaves, stems, and roots when one is attempting to identify a plant? Are such plant parts a reliable indicator of species?

- Ask your students if pines, firs, and spruces are monocots or eudicots. (The answer, of course, is that conifers are gymnosperms and hence are not classified as either monocots or eudicots.) The ensuing discussion will help students to learn the differences, not yet covered in the text, between gymnosperms and flowering plants.

- When you eat an apple, what ground tissue are you eating?

- What is the biggest monocot you can think of? (Some possible answers might be bamboo or palm.)

- What is cork? Where does the cork used in wine bottles come from?

- Why are plants "taken for granted" in our culture?

How Would You Vote? Classroom Discussion Ideas

- Have students complete class polling using the JoinIn clickers. Are carbon offsets a good idea, or do they just give companies and individuals an excuse to continue emitting greenhouse gases?

Term Paper Topics, Library Activities, and Special Projects

- Have students use Thomson's InfoTrac College Edition to find articles related to a range of plant topics such as drought impacts on food production or plant biotechnology. Have them write a short paper that summarizes their findings.

- Assign students the task of creating a position paper that requires them to take a stand on the How Would You Vote topic related to the use of carbon offsets.

- What are some of the woody plant species used for lumber? Find the names of as many as you can; you may be surprised at the number! Describe some of these species and discuss their uses.

- Many plant parts provide dyes that can be used to color fabrics. Prepare a demonstration or an exhibit of plant species used as sources for dyes.

- Learn more about the history of paper making, and discuss how modern papers are made.

- Describe some of the morphological adaptations found among plants of extreme climates (for example, tundra, deserts, and bogs).

- Describe some of the plant species whose leaves, stems, and/or roots can be used as sources for drugs. Just a few of the many examples to include in your research are coca plant, marijuana, *Ephedra*, foxglove, and opium poppy.

- Can plant parts such as leaves, roots, and stems be used to grow new plants? Discuss techniques of vegetative propagation; describe its role in commercial greenhouses and nurseries.

- Investigate the effects on plants that the gypsy moth has had in the northeastern United States.

- What factors make the vast majority of the United States suitable for intensive agriculture?

Responses to *Data Analysis Activities*

1. The tree ring data reflect a drought condition around 770 A.D., the time the Mayan civilization began to suffer a massive loss of population. This condition was more severe than the "dust bowl" drought.
2. The most severe drought occurred between 1550 and 1600 A.D.

Possible Responses to *Critical Thinking* Questions

1. The plant with the yellow flower is a eudicots (pattern of five) and the purple-flowered plant is a moncot (pattern of three).

2. The initials carved into the *tiny* tree at a particular height should be at about the same height 10 years later because the tree does not "stretch" or grow from the bottom, but rather adds height at the top. However, if the tree was very young and did not have much bark, it is possible that the initials are obscured by the addition of more bark. If he cuts down the tree, Oscar should be able to count the growth rings indicating the approximate 10 years that have elapsed.

3. The stems are bulbs.

26

PLANT NUTRITION AND TRANSPORT

Chapter Outline

Objectives

1. Know which elements are essential to plant health.
2. Explain how water and mineral ions are absorbed, transported, used, and lost by a plant.
3. Understand how plants balance water loss with the need for gas exchange.
4. Know how translocation of organic substances occurs, according to the pressure flow theory.

Key Terms

soil	leaching	root nodules	translocation
humus	soil erosion	cohesion-tension theory	pressure flow theory
loams	mycorrhiza	transpiration	
topsoil	nitrogen fixation	guard cells	

Lecture Outline

26.1 Mean Green Cleaning Machines

A. The United States Army inadvertently contaminated soil during weapons testing and disposal at a Maryland facility.
   1. In a process called phytoremediation, hybrid popular trees are taking up organic solvents and degrading them.
   2. Alternatively, certain contaminants can be absorbed and stored in plant tissues, which are then removed from the site and disposed.

B. Plants such as the alpine pennycress are being genetically engineered to remove heavy metals from soil; perhaps the gene can be transferred to other, faster growing species.

26.2 Plant Nutrients and Soil

A. Nutrients are elements essential for a given organism because they have roles in metabolism.
   1. Sixteen essential elements are needed for plant growth.
      a. Nine elements are called macronutrients (used in significant quantities): carbon(C), hydrogen (H), oxygen (O), nitrogen (N), potassium (K), calcium (Ca), magnesium (Mg), phosphorus (P), and sulfur (S).
      b. Seven are used only in trace quantities (micronutrients): chlorine (Cl), iron (Fe), boron (B), manganese (Mn), zinc (Z), copper (Cu), and molybdenum (Mb).
   2. Deficiencies in any nutrient can cause problems.

B. Properties of Soil
   1. Soil consists of particles of minerals mixed with humus (dead organisms and their litter).
      a. Soils differ in their proportions of mineral particles and how compacted they are.
      b. Particles come in three sizes: sand, silt, and clay.
      c. Clay, the smallest, carries a negative charge and holds onto nutrients as water percolates through the soil.
      d. Plants do best in loams, soils with nearly equal proportions of the three particle types. Loam soils have the best oxygen and water penetration.
      e. Humus, also negatively charged, absorbs water, releases nutrients, and helps aerate the soil.

C. How Soils Develop
   1. Soils develop over thousands of years.
   2. Layers of soil can be classified by profile properties; topsoil, the uppermost, is the most essential layer for plant growth as it contains the most nutrients.
   3. Leaching refers to the removal of some of the nutrients from soil as water percolates downward through it.
   4. Soil erosion is the movement or loss of land under the force of wind, running water, and ice.
   5. Nutrient losses from leaching and soil erosion affect plants and other organisms that rely on soils for survival.

26.3 How Do Roots Absorb Water and Minerals?

A. Root Specializations
   1. Root hairs are often produced by the billions, act as extensions of the root epidermal cells, and greatly increase the absorptive surface.
      a. Root hairs are fragile and do not become long-lasting roots.
      b. As the root lengthens, new root hairs develop behind the root tip.

2. Mycorrhizae (fungi growing around plant roots) aid in absorbing minerals that are supplied to the plant in exchange for sugars; this symbiotic relationship is beneficial to both.

3. Root nodules of legumes harbor bacteria that convert gaseous nitrogen to ammonia useful in the growth of the plants. This is a form of mutualism. The metabolic conversion of gaseous nitrogen to ammonia is called nitrogen fixation.

B. Control Over Uptake
   1. Water moves from the soil across the root epidermis to the vascular cylinder, a column of vascular tissue in the center of the root.
   2. A sheetlike layer of cells, the endodermis, surrounds the vascular cylinder separating it from the cortex.
   3. Endodermal cells deposit a waxy layer called the Casparian strip, which forces water to move through the cytoplasm of the cells of the endodermis.
   4. Membrane transport proteins help control the types of absorbed solutes that will become distributed throughout the plant.

26.4 Water Movement Inside Plants

A. Cohesion–ension Theory
   1. Water moves through pipelines called xylem, composed of cells (dead at maturity) called tracheids and vessel members.
   2. The cohesion–tension theory of water transport explains water movement in plants.
      a. The drying power of air causes transpiration (evaporation of water), which puts the water in the xylem in a state of tension leading from leaves to stems to roots.
      b. Unbroken, fluid columns of water show cohesion (aided by the hydrogen bonds); they resist rupturing as they are pulled upward under tension.
      c. As water molecules escape from the plant, molecules are pulled up to replace them.

B. Movement of water through vascular plants is driven mainly by transpiration, but evaporation is only one of many other processes in plants that involve the loss of water molecules. Metabolic activities that use water also contribute to the negative pressure that results in water movement.

26.5 Water-Conserving Adaptations of Stems and Leaves

A. Most (90 percent) of the water absorbed by a plant is evaporated out at the leaves. Only about 2 percent is used in photosynthesis, growth, membrane functions, and other events.

B. The Water-Conserving Cuticle
   1. The cuticle is a translucent, water-impermeable layer secreted from epidermal cells.
   2. It coats the outer walls, which are exposed to the environment.
      a. Waxes, pectin, and cellulose are embedded in a matrix of cutin, a lipid polymer.
      b. The cuticle does not bar the entry of light rays but does restrict water loss, the inward diffusion of CO_2, and the outward diffusion of oxygen.

C. Controlled Water Loss at Stomata
   1. Stomata regulate the passage of water, carbon dioxide, and oxygen.
   2. A pair of guard cells defines each opening.
      a. When guard cells swell with water, they bend slightly, forming the opening of the stoma.
      b. When the guard cells lose water they collapse against one another, closing the opening.
      c. Environmental cues such as water availability, CO_2 levels in the plant, and light influence the opening of the stomata. The stomata of most plants are closed at night.

3. In CAM plants (cacti, for example), the stomata open at night when cells of these plants fix carbon dioxide; the stomata close during the day to conserve water in the arid habitats where these plants live.

26.6 Movement of Organic Compound in Plants

A. Conducting Tubes in Phloem
 1. Phloem tissue consists of organized arrays of conducting tubes, fibers, and strands of parenchyma cells.
 2. Phloem has sieve tubes through which organic compounds flow.
    a. Sieve tube cells are alive at maturity and are interconnected from leaf to root.
    b. Companion cells press up against sieve tubes and help load them with organic compounds.
 3. Storage forms of organic molecules (for example, starch, fats, and proteins) are not easily transported throughout the plant body; therefore, they are converted to more soluble forms, such as sucrose. Sucrose is the main form of carbohydrate being transported in plants.

B. Translocation
 1. The term translocation is the name for the transport of sucrose and other compounds through phloem.
 2. Movement of molecules through phloem is from sources (mostly leaves) to sinks (flowers and fruits).
 3. According to the pressure flow theory, translocation depends on pressure gradients.
    a. Solutes are loaded by active transport into the phloem from a source; water follows.
    b. As pressure builds in the tubes it pushes the sucrose-laden fluid out of the leaf, into the stem, and on to the sink.

Suggestions for Presenting the Material

♦ Students should be able to make an easy transition to this material if the role of function in determining plant morphology was stressed in presenting the previous chapter. Emphasize that plants are supported by a "skeleton" formed by a continuous column of water inside sturdy xylem tubes. Review, if necessary, some of the terms learned earlier that relate to water movement, such as osmosis and turgor pressure.

♦ Stress the fact that plants have dietary requirements for inorganic compounds just like in the animal kingdom. Challenge students to consider why this is.

♦ Have students consider the physical properties of soils they are familiar with. What do the soils look like? Are they compacted or loose? Show them pictures of a road cut through a hill where the soil horizons are visible.

♦ Show the animated Figure 26.7 to provide visual context for how plants take up water from the soils where they grow.

♦ To help students understand the large surface area of a plant's root system, provide data on the surface areas of some typical plant root systems. Ask them to guess the ratio of shoot surface area to root surface area of a typical plant.

♦ This chapter provides many good opportunities to discuss the selective role of the environment in shaping such features as stomata and root systems, and the response of plants to their environment.

♦ **Common Student Misconceptions**

  o While students have likely heard of the cohesion tension theory of water movement, they do not understand the interaction between the anatomy of the plant, environmental conditions, and the basic chemical properties of water that contribute to the movement of water through plants.

Classroom and Laboratory Enrichment

♦ Demonstrate the abundance and fragile nature of root hairs. Germinate radish seedlings in a Petri dish lined with paper toweling. Pass the dish around the classroom, and allow each student to take a seedling and examine the root hairs. What happens to the root hairs minutes after the seedling is removed from the dish? Why?

♦ Demonstrate how species adapt to their surroundings by discussing the number, size, location, and distribution patterns of stomata in leaves of different species. Include some unusual examples, such as aquatic plants with stomata on upper leaf epidermis, conifers with sunken stomata, and plants with pubescent leaves.

♦ Examine tomato seedlings suffering from a deficiency of one of the macronutrients. This can be prepared as a lab experiment of several weeks duration, or a demonstration (slides) of the results can be shown instead.

♦ Use a simple soil-testing kit in lab to test samples of several different local soils. What are some steps that could be taken to improve each of the soils tested, if necessary?

♦ Set up demonstrations of root pressure or transpiration in lecture or lab.

♦ Show pictures of chloroplasts containing starch grains. Where did the starch come from? Would you be more likely to see such grains in the morning or in the afternoon? What will happen to the starch grains?

♦ In lab, provide prepared microscope slides of the undersides of plant species from different environments, and in lecture, pictures or diagrams of the lower leaf epidermis.

♦ Compare the rates of recovery after wilting among three tomato seedlings that have each been cut off at the base of the main stem, as described below, and then placed in a beaker of water:
(1) seedling is cut; (2) seedling is cut while plant is briefly submerged underwater; and (3) seedling is cut, then allowed to sit on desktop for 15 minutes before being placed in water. Which seedling exhibits the least amount of wilting at the end of the lab period? The most? Why?

♦ Test slices of various fruits and vegetables for starch content by applying an iodine solution (should turn blue-black).

♦ Obtain a chart showing color photos of the symptoms of mineral deficiencies as listed in Table 26.1. Perhaps a plant nursery or fertilizer supplier can help you. If you cannot obtain a copy of some chart you would like, ask permission to photograph it for a slide.

Mean Green Cleaning Machines, Revisited

- How could responsible government agencies allow such an ecological disaster as the Aberdeen Proving Grounds contamination to happen? Have students consider the changing cultural perceptions of waste disposal and pollution that culminated in the ecological awakening of the 1960s.

- Have students consider local industrial or governmental activities that may influence their environment.

- What is so bad about having lead, arsenic, mercury, and other metals in drinking water?

- Are consumers of individual well water necessarily at more risk than consumers of municipal supplies?

- Is it possible that the scenario described in "Mean Green Cleaning Machines" could result in exchanging contaminated water for contaminated plants?

Additional Ideas for Classroom Discussion

- How do the tracheids and vessel members found in xylem conduct water even though they are dead at maturity?

- Desert plants must balance the need for carbon dioxide against the threat of desiccation. What are some adaptations of desert plants that allow them to open their stomata often enough to get the carbon dioxide sufficient for photosynthesis? Discuss how alternative photosynthetic pathways such as C4 and CAM photosynthesis have evolved in response to environmental pressures.

- What happens to transpiration rates on hot days? Dry days? Humid days? Breezy days?

- Ask students who have raised tomatoes or other garden plants if they have ever observed "midday wilt," a phenomenon in which even well-watered plants temporarily wilt during the late afternoon. Ask them why this happens. (Midday wilt occurs when transpiration exceeds the rate of water uptake.)

- What are some crop plants that are particularly adept at storing sugars or starches?

- In what ways are animals dependent on plants for survival?

- Reports of topsoil erosion and mineral leaching are numerous. Are there finite amounts of soil and soil nutrients? Will we ever completely exhaust our sources of plant sustenance?

How Would You Vote? Classroom Discussion Ideas

- Have students complete class polling using the JoinIn clickers. Plants can be genetically engineered to take up toxins more effectively. Do you support the use of such plants to help clean up toxic waste sites? The general idea of genetic engineering is usually not as debatable as human uses of this technique. Have students compile a list of benefits and potential costs to bioengineering plants for phytoremediation.

Term Paper Topics, Library Activities, and Special Projects

♦ Discuss the role of each of the macronutrients in plant metabolism and growth.

♦ What role has the fibrous root system of grasses played in the establishment and maintenance of prairies in the United States? What happens to the species composition of prairies if such areas are interrupted by roads, farming, or railroads? Discuss the history of the American prairies.

♦ Using Thomson's InfoTrac College Edition, have students research phytoremediation activities in the news. Have them compile a list of articles and summarize in a short paper.

♦ Have students work in small groups to debate the use of bioengineering plants for human activities like crop production or phytoremediation.

♦ Learn more about soil testing. Describe how a typical soil-testing kit works.

♦ Visit a nursery or garden center where lawn and garden fertilizers are sold. List the N-P-K ratio for each of the different fertilizers. Explain differences among N-P-K ratios of fertilizers for lawns, vegetables, and flowers. Why do fertilizers for different purposes have such different N-P-K ratios? Summarize. the roles of nitrogen, phosphorus, and potassium in plant functioning and development.

♦ What are the effects of acid rain on plant functioning?

♦ Discuss the effects of extremely cold climates, such as Arctic tundra, on the ratio of shoot systems to root systems. Why is so much of the plant underground in such climates?

♦ Locate a report (USDA documents?) showing the decline in soil fertility in the United States in the past 100 years.

♦ Insects such as aphids can be controlled by insecticides introduced into the plant via uptake by the roots. They are called "systemic" insecticides. How do these chemicals accomplish their control? Give an example.

Responses to *Data Analysis Activities*

1. The researchers tested one type of transgenic plant.
2. The vector control group displayed the slowest rate of TCE uptake and the planted, transgenic group had the fasted rate of TCE uptake.
3. Approximately 10,000 $\mu g/m^3$.
4. These data demonstrate that the transgenic poplar plants are effective in removing TCE from the air; however, require planting in soil. A wild-type poplar could have served as another control in this experiment.

Possible Responses to *Critical Thinking* Questions

1. Insufficient nitrogen in a plant will have a negative impact on the synthesis of amino acids and the proteins from which they are assembled. This will in turn affect the structure of the plant, which is incorporating proteins, plus it will curtail the synthesis of enzymes needed for metabolic activities. Lack of nitrogen will also adversely affect the synthesis of nucleic acids needed for information storage (DNA) and decoding (RNA).

2. Wilted plants are always a disappointment. Fortunately, if the wilting has not been prolonged, a good drink of water and the plant perks right up. Of course, what has happened is this: While you were on vacation (nice hot summer days at the beach), the plants continued to transpire and lose water to the air. For the first day or so, the molecules of water continued to move up the xylem columns, showing off their cohesion and tension properties. Alas, on about day three, there was insufficient water entering the roots to replace the water being lost, and the column was broken, resulting in the wilting.

3. When moving a plant from one location to another, it is a good idea to take as much soil as practicable with the root mass. This will ensure that the mycorrhizae are substantially intact and can continue functioning in the new location and the fragile root hairs so essential for water/mineral absorption are not stripped off.

4. If stomata remained open all the time, excessive amounts of water might be lost especially on hot days in the sun. If they remained closed, no carbon dioxide would enter to keep the photosynthetic process going.

5. Transpiration is a process of evaporation of water from the leaves of plants. The rate would be affected by environmental factors, somewhat like sweating from human skin. If the surrounding air is dry, more moisture can leave the surface and be taken up by the air. Conversely, humid air already contains large amounts of moisture and cannot take on much more. Additionally, a breeze moving over the surface will take any moisture-laden air away and replace it with drier air, capable of absorbing moisture.

27

PLANT REPRODUCTION AND DEVELOPMENT

Chapter Outline

Objectives

1. Describe the typical patterns of life cycles in flowering plants.
2. Draw and label the parts of a perfect flower. Explain where gamete formation occurs in the male and female structures.
3. Define and distinguish between *pollination* and *fertilization*.
4. Trace embryonic development from zygote to seedling.
5. Describe the general pattern of plant growth, and list the factors that cause plants to germinate.
6. List the various chemical messengers that regulate growth and metabolism in plants. Explain how plants respond to changes in their environment.
7. Know the factors that cause a plant to flower, to age, and to enter dormancy. Describe each process.

Key Terms

pollinators	double fertilization	auxins	circadian rhythm
flowers	endosperm	abscisic acid (ABA)	phytochromes
stamens	seed	cytokinins	photoperiodism
carpels	fruit	ethylene	vernalization
ovary	vegetative reproduction	tropisms	systemic acquired
ovule	tissue culture	gravitropism	resistance
megaspores	propagation	phototropism	abscission
microspores	germination	solar tracking	senescence
dormancy	hormones	thigmotropism	
pollination	gibberellins	biological clock	

Lecture Outline

27.1 Plight of the Honeybee

    A. Recently, beekeepers have noticed a significant decline in the honeybee populations, and have termed this phenomenon as colony collapse disorder.

    B. Honeybees are pollinators, which mean they carry pollen from one plant to another, pollinating flowers as they do.

        1. Honeybees are very important pollinators of crops in the United States, pollinating most crops.

        2. Honeybees tolerate man-made hives that can be moved to crops requiring pollination.

    C. Hundreds of plant species are listed as endangered because of disturbances in relationships with coevolutionary pollinators.

        1. The exact causes of colony collapse disorder are still unknown.

        2. Evidence indicates that a variety of parasites and diseases that infect honeybees may be part of this problem.

        3. Also, pesticides that are very toxic to honeybees may contribute to the decline of the honeybee populations.

27.2 Reproductive Structures of Flowering Plants

    A. Life Cycle of a Flower

        1. Flowers are specialized reproductive shoots of the angiosperm sporophyte.

        2. Meiosis of cells within flowers produces the small haploid gametophytes, which in turn produce either sperm or eggs (gametes).

        3. Male and female gametes meet at fertilization, resulting in a diploid zygote that grows into a new sporophyte.

    B. Anatomy of a Flower

        1. Flowers result from lateral buds along the stem of a sporophyte as a modified branch called a receptacle.

        2. Flower parts are arranged in whorls, spirals or rings.

            a. Sepals are the outermost green, leaflike parts.

            b. Petals are the colored parts located between the reproductive structures and the sepals.

            c. Male parts consist of the stamens—a slender stalk (filament) capped with an anther, inside which pollen sacs enclose pollen grains.

      d.   The female parts are the carpels, vessel-shaped structures with an expanded lower ovary (with ovules), a slender column (style), and an upper surface (stigma) for pollen landing.

   C. Pollinators

     1.   Pollination is the act of delivering pollen grains to structures that house female gametophytes.

       a.   Wind is a common pollination method for grassland plants.

       b.   Many flowering plants are pollinated by specific insects which coevolved with the plant.

     2.   Bright colors (carotenoids and anthocyanins), fragrant oils, and sugar-rich nectar attract pollinators.

     3.   Nectar, a sucrose-rich secretion from the flower is a nutrient for many pollinators.

     4.   Pollen is rich in vitamins and mineral ions, and represents a desirable food source.

27.3   A New Generation Begins

   A. Microspore and Megaspore Formation

     1.   Female gametes are produced by this method:

       a.   In the ovary of a carpel, a mass of tissue forms ovules (potential seeds).

       b.   A diploid mother cell divides by meiosis to produce four haploid megaspores, one of which will eventually produce the egg, and others typically disintegrate.

       c.   The remaining megaspore undergoes three rounds of mitosis without cytoplasmic division, the outcome being a single cell with eight haploid nuclei.

       d.   The cytoplasm of this cell divides unevenly, forming a seven-celled embryo sac that constitutes the female gametophyte.

       e.   One of the cells in the gametophyte, the endosperm mother cell, has two nuclei and another cell is the egg.

     2.   Pollen, the male gametes, is produced by this method:

       a.   In anthers, each diploid "mother" cell divides by meiosis to form four haploid microspores.

       b.   Mitosis and differentiation of a microspore produces a pollen grain.

       c.   A pollen grain consists of two cells, one inside the cytoplasm of the other. After formation, pollen grains enter dormancy, a state of suspended metabolism.

   B. Pollination and Fertilization

     1.   Pollination refers to the arrival of a pollen grain on a receptive stigma.

     2.   After a pollen grain lands on a stigma, the pollen grain exits dormancy and a pollen tube forms, producing a path that the two sperm nuclei will follow to the ovule. A pollen tube together with its contents of male gametes constitutes the mature male gametophyte.

     3.   Guided by chemical cues, the pollen tube grows through the tissues of the carpel and ovary to an ovule.

     4.   When the pollen tube penetrates the embryo sac, the two sperm are released to accomplish double fertilization.

       a.   One sperm fuses with the egg nucleus to form a diploid zygote.

       b.   The other sperm nucleus fuses with the two endosperm nuclei to yield a triploid endosperm, which will nourish the young sporophyte seedling.

27.4   From Zygotes to Seeds in Fruits

   A. The Embryo Sporophyte Forms

     1.   The zygote undergoes repeated divisions to form an embryo sporophyte inside an ovule.

     2.   Cotyledons (seed leaves) develop for the purpose of utilizing the endosperm during germination. Dicots will have two and monocots will have one.

      a. From zygote to embryo, the plant supplies nutrition until the time when the connection between the ovule and ovary wall is broken.

      b. The mature ovule's integuments thicken into seed coats surrounding the seed (a mature ovule containing embryo and food reserves).

B. Fruits

    1. A fruit is a mature ovary with seeds (ovules) inside, often containing accessory tissue.

    2. Only flowering plants form seeds in ovaries, and only they make fruits.

    3. There is tremendous diversity in fruit structure.

      a. Botanists categorize fruits by how they originate, their tissues, and appearance.

         i. Simple fruits are derived from one ovary (e.g., pea pod).

        ii. Aggregate fruits form from the separate ovaries of a single flower and mature as a cluster of fruits (e.g., strawberry).

        iii. Multiple fruits form from fused ovaries of separate flowers (e.g., pineapple).

      b. True fruits consist of just the ovary wall and its contents (e.g., cherry).

      c. Accessory fruits contain additional floral parts (e.g., apple).

    4. Fruit classification based on appearance fall into two categories: dry or fleshy.

    5. The function of fruit is to protect and disperse seeds.

      a. Some fruits are dispersed by sticking on animal bodies or by passing through the digestive tract to be deposited in the feces.

      b. The wall of maple seeds extends out like wings to catch the wind and be transported far from the parent tree.

      c. Winds can transport fruits, as in the dandelion's pluming "parachute."

      d. Specialized fruits with waxy coating can disperse in water.

27.5 Asexual Reproduction of Flowering Plants

A. Asexual Reproduction in Nature

    1. Many plants can reproduce asexually by vegetative growth, where new roots and shoots grow from extensions or fragments of a parent plant. In this mode of reproduction, all of the plants produced from the parent material are clonal.

    2. Strawberry plants send out runners; stands of aspen are clonal forests. Most houseplants, woody ornamentals, and orchard trees are grown from cuttings or fragments of shoot systems.

B. Induced Propagation

    1. Tissue culture propagation can result in whole plants produced from a group of cells.

    2. This technique is used today to improve food crops that have desirable characteristics such as disease resistance.

27.6 Patterns of Development in Plants

A. Seed Germination

    1. Germination is the resumption of growth after a time of arrested embryonic development.

    2. Environmental factors influence germination.

      a. Rains provide the water amounts necessary to swell and rupture the seed coat.

      b. Oxygen diffuses in and allows the embryo to switch to aerobic metabolism.

      c. Increased temperatures and number of daylight hours are also influential.

    3. Germination ends when a primary root, or radical, breaks out of the seed coat.

B. Patterns of Early Growth

    1. Patterns of germination and development have a heritable basis dictated by a plant's genes.

2. Growth refers to an increase in the number, size, and volume of cells.
   a. Some meristematic cells never differentiate, continuing to divide and make more cells.
   b. Others are the basis for development, the process by which gene expression causes cell differentiation.
3. Development in plants relies on extensive coordination among cells just as it does in animals.
   a. Transcription of master genes guides the formation of body details.
   b. Plant cells communicate with one another—primarily using hormones.
   c. The production of hormones is highly influenced by environmental cues such as temperature, water, day length, and gravity.

27.7 Plant Hormones and Other Signaling Molecules

A. Plant Hormones
   1. Plant hormones are signaling molecules that bind to receptor molecules to affect gene expression, enzyme activity, or ion concentrations in a target cell. In plants, five major classes of hormones interact to stimulate growth and development at specific times: gibberellins, auxins, abscisic acid, cytokinins, and ethylene.
   2. Gibberellins promote cell division and stem elongation.
      a. They also help buds and seeds break dormancy and resume growth in the spring.
      b. In some species, they influence the flowering process.
   3. Auxins affect cell division and elongation. Their effect depends upon the target tissue.
      a. Auxins produced in the apical meristems result in elongation of shoots.
      b. They induce cell division and differentiation in vacular cambium, fruit development in ovaries, and lateral root formation in roots.
      c. Auxins also inhibit abscission, the dropping of leaves, flowers, and fruits from the plants.
   4. Abscisic acid (ABA) inhibits cell growth, helps prevent water loss (by promoting stomata closure), and promotes seed and bud dormancy.
   5. Cytokinins stimulate cell division in root and shoot meristems, where they are most abundant; they are used commercially to prolong the life of stored vegetables and cut flowers.
   6. Ethylene is the only gaseous hormone; it stimulates the ripening of fruit and is used commercially for this purpose.

B. Other signaling molecules include brassinolides, jasmonates, salicylic acid, and systemin.

27.8 Adjusting the Direction and Rate of Growth

A. Tropisms are plant responses to environmental stimuli, and are typically mediated by hormones.

B. Responses to Gravity
   1. Gravitropism is the growth response to Earth's gravity.
   2. No matter which way the plant is oriented to the Earth's surface, shoots grow up, and roots grow down.
   3. Plant statoliths are modified plastids that settle downward in root cap cells, where they may cause auxin redistribution inside the cells to initiate a gravitropic response.

C. Responses to Light
   1. Phototropism is a growth response to light, particularly blue light.
   2. The adjustments place the plant parts in positions where they can better capture light for photosynthesis.

3. Bending toward the light is caused by elongation of cells (auxin stimulation) on the side of the plant *not* exposed to light.
4. Solar tracking describes plant parts changing position in response to the sun's changing angle throughout the day.

   D. Responses to Contact
1. Thigmotropism is unequal growth triggered by physical contact; it is found in climbing vines and tendrils.
2. Plant cells that are in contact with the support stop elongating and bend around it.
3. Mechanical stress, such as wind forces or damage from browsing animals, inhibits growth in a response related to thigmotropism.

27.9 Sensing Recurring Environmental Changes

   A. Biological Clocks
1. Most organisms have an internal biological clock that governs the timing of rhythmic cycles of activity. Those on a 24-hour cycle are termed circadian rhythm.

   B. Setting the Clock
1. Biological clocks can be reset.
   a. Phytochromes are photosensors in plants that are sensitive to red and far red light.
   b. The perception of red light or far red light alters plant tropisms.

   C. When to Flower?
1. Photoperiodism is a biological response to a change in relative length of daylight and darkness in a 24-hour cycle.
2. The flowering process is keyed to changes in day length throughout the year.
   a. "Short-day plants" flower in late summer or early autumn when day length becomes shorter (e.g., chrysanthemums).
   b. "Long-day plants" flower in the spring as day length becomes longer (e.g., irises).
   c. "Day-neutral plants" flower when they are mature enough to do so (e.g., sunflowers).
3. Vernalization is the stimulation of flowering in spring by low winter temperatures.

27.10 Plant Defenses

   A. Plant defenses include thorns or bad-tasting chemicals that directly deter herbivores.

   B. Plants also have a variety of chemical signals that protect them from pathogens, a response called systemic acquired resistance.

   C. Senescence
1. The dropping of leaves, flowers, fruits, and so on is called abscission. This process may be a response to stress or a part of the normal plant life cycle.
2. Senescence is the phase in a life cycle from maturity to death.

   D. Dormancy
1. Dormancy is a period of arrested growth caused by and ended by environmental cues.
   a. Strong cues for dormancy include short days, cold nights, and dry, nitrogen-deficient soil.
   b. Dormancy has great adaptive value in preventing plant growth on occasional warm autumn days for plants that would only be killed by later frost.
2. Dormancy is broken by milder temperatures, rains, and nutrients; it probably involves gibberellins, abscisic acid, and environmental cues.

Suggestions for Presenting the Material

♦ Take the time to present flower anatomy and the introduction of terms students will still be less familiar with. The animated figure 27.2 will help students with understanding how the anatomy relates to gamete production.

♦ Give examples of a sporophyte and a gametophyte in the life cycles of some common plants. Explain the difference between a spore and a gamete. It may be necessary to briefly review meiosis I and II and terms such as haploid and diploid, especially if it has been some time since the students studied mitosis and meiosis.

♦ Make extensive use of animated Figure 27.5 that illustrates the life cycle of a flowering plant. This visual summary will assist students with all the material presented in this chapter.

♦ Students will find it easier to comprehend the development of male and female gametophytes if they have dissected a flower before this is discussed. If students wonder why the events of gamete formation and fertilization are so complicated, remind them that these are very advanced plants; plant evolution and diversity will be discussed later.

♦ Discuss with your students once again how growth in plants differs from growth in animals.

♦ Introduce the term hormone and discuss the need for growth-regulating hormones. There are many lab experiments designed to investigate the role of hormones in plant growth and development; many of them are available from biological supply houses in the form of kits. These can be prepared ahead of time and used as demonstrations or performed by the students.

♦ **Common Student Misconceptions**

  o Once again, students are exposed to the concept of alternation of generations in plant reproductive processes—which more often than not is very confusing for them. Stress that this chapter deals with angiosperm reproduction, where this process is transparent in the production of pollen and egg.

  o Many students will still fail to grasp that seeds contain embryonic plants.

Classroom and Laboratory Enrichment

♦ Show line drawings or pictures of any angiosperm in flower, and ask students to point out the gametophyte and sporophyte portions of the plant.

♦ Introduce models, photos, and diagrams to illustrate floral structure and to reinforce new terms. Have students dissect at least one type of flower, preferably one with large parts, in lab or lecture.

♦ Show time-lapse films of flower and fruit formation.

♦ Have students learn the parts of a seed by dissecting bean and corn seeds after they have been softened in water for several hours. Reinforce with color pictures that more clearly show the internal structure of seeds—students will have difficulty seeing these structures.

♦ Use microscope slides and/or pictures of a lily to discuss microspore and megaspore development.

♦ Prepare a demonstration of different kinds of fruits, or ask students to bring fruits to class or lab. Students will be fascinated to see the relationship between the parts of the flower before fertilization and the subsequent fruit parts.

- Use techniques of vegetative propagation or tissue culture to grow new plants. This can be done by the students in lab or can be prepared ahead of time, ideally with different stages of growth represented, as a demonstration.

- Show scanning electron micrographs of the pollen grains of some familiar plants.

- Show close-up photos of bees and the pollen-carrying devices on their legs. Or if your group is small, place actual specimens of these insects under stereomicroscopes.

- Locate photos of flowers that are formed in various ways to lure insects to alight and feed.

- For a demonstration of germination processes and early growth at apical meristems, mark the root tips or shoot apical meristems of sturdy just-sprouted seedlings (beans or peas are fine) at measured intervals. Keep the seeds moist in a Petri dish lined with paper toweling. Measure the rates of growth after one week. Exactly where along the root or shoot is the increase in length occurring?

- Determine if the food stored in sprouting seeds is starch or sugar by treating the seeds with tetrazolium solution and Lugol's solution.

- Design and implement experiments involving seed germination. Vary conditions such as temperature or light, and examine the effects on germination rate.

- In species with hard seed coats, examine the effects of seed scarification (the removal or breakage of seed coats) on germination rate. Students can use a seed scarifier, if available, or gently rub seeds between blocks covered with a fine grade of sandpaper. Compare germination rates between seeds that have been scarified and those left unscarified.

- How does soaking seeds in water overnight before sowing affect germination rate? Compare germination rates between presoaked seeds and unsoaked seeds.

- Compare the cotyledons of monocots and eudicots by examining recently sprouted corn and bean seedlings.

- How does complete darkness affect seedling growth? Compare the lengths and weights of bean or pea seedlings raised in light with those raised in complete darkness.

- Examine the effects of auxins, gibberellins, and cytokinins on plant growth and development.

- Investigate the role of the intact shoot tip in inhibiting lateral bud development in *Coleus*. What happens to lateral buds if the shoot tip is removed?

- Discover the effects of different wavelengths of light on phototropism.

- Examine the effects of ethylene on fruit ripening or abscission; bananas are an excellent fruit to use in this illustration because they react so quickly.

- Locate and show a segment of a video depicting growth and development of a seedling.

Plight of the Honeybee (revisited)

- What are the differences among messenger, ribosomal, and transfer RNA molecules? Have students discuss how these terms relate to gene transcription and gene translation. Challenge students to understand the connection among molecular cellular events, protein production, and the overall health of an organism.

- Discuss how the honeybees are exposed to picorna-like viruses. This will lead to discussions of parasites as vectors for disease. Referencing the fact that disease is also spread in humans via parasite vectors.

♦ Based upon the new research results regarding colony collapse disorder, propose potential strategies for combating this problem. Consider treatments for the honeybees, and those targeting the mites and virus.

Additional Ideas for Classroom Discussion

♦ Why do botanists use flowers rather than leaves or stems as indicators of species identity?

♦ Have students discuss why it is so hard to determine tissue origin in fruits sold in stores.

♦ Distinguish between megaspores and microspores.

♦ What is included in an ovule of a flowering plant? What events take place inside the ovule? What are some of the changes that take place inside an ovule after fertilization has occurred?

♦ Is a pollen grain analogous to a human sperm cell? Why or why not?

♦ Discuss floral diversity. Ask students to name different kinds of flowers, and then discuss the shapes, types of parts, and pollination of each.

♦ What is double fertilization?

♦ Cut open apples, pears, green beans, strawberries, oranges, pineapples, and any other fruits or vegetables you have on hand in class or lab. Identify the floral origin of as many parts as you can. For example, which part of the fruit was the ovary wall? The carpel? The integument? The sepal? The stigma and style?

♦ Define the terms fruit and vegetable. What is the difference between these two terms? Why do we use the term fruit when we are talking about tomatoes and green beans?

♦ Why do many fruits change from green to red, yellow, or orange as they ripen? Of what adaptive value is the sweet smell produced by most fruits?

♦ Is there any truth to the disgusting allegation that honey is actually "bee vomit"?

♦ Why do you think there are poisonous seeds, berries, leaves, and stems in the plant kingdom?

♦ How does growth in plants differ from growth in humans? Why can growth in plants be seen as a counterpart to movement in animals?

♦ How does hormone production and activity differ in plants and animals? What are some similarities shared by plants and animals? What are some differences?

♦ What is the evolutionary adaptive value of seed dormancy?

♦ Why do grasses keep growing even after being repeatedly trimmed by lawn mowers or grazing animals? Where is the meristem located in shoots of grasses?

♦ What is the biological reasoning behind the old saying "one bad apple spoils the whole bunch"? Discuss the role of ethylene in hastening fruit ripening.

♦ How could a sap-feeding insect actually stimulate plant growth? (answer: plant works harder to replace lost sap)

♦ How could a foliage-feeding insect increase growth of understory plants? (answer: increased light penetration)

♦ How could irrigation of cotton plants increase insect damage? (answer: more green leaves support more larvae)

How Would You Vote? Classroom Discussion Ideas

♦ Have students complete class polling using the JoinIn clickers. Systemic pesticides are easy to apply and effective for long periods. They also get into plant nectar and pollen eaten by honeybees. To protect bees and other pollinators, should the use of these pesticides on flowering plants be restricted? Wow! What a dilemma. Here is a new, safer way to deliver pesticides that are needed to ensure our crops, but it imperils the pollinators we need to ensure the development of our crops. Obviously much research needs to be done before we place such a load of these chemicals in the environment that we wipe out the vital little bees.

Term Paper Topics, Library Activities, and Special Projects

♦ Examine diversity among flowers. Describe the coevolution of flowering plants and insects.

♦ Identify as many of the flowering plants on campus as you can. If flowers are available, collect them, identify them, and bring them back to class or lab. One group of students could prepare a map of campus trees and plants and lead other groups in a campus plant walk.

♦ Select a well-known flowering plant species, and prepare a timetable showing when the reproductive events leading up to seed formation occur.

♦ Learn more about some of the reproductive isolating mechanisms that discourage self-pollination among many flowering plant species.

♦ Using Thomson's InfoTrac College Edition, have students research articles related to crop production, pollination, and pollinators. Have them complete a one-page paper that summarizes their findings.

♦ Have students research and construct a position paper related to the How Would You Vote topic of systemic pesticides. Should they be banned, highly regulated, studied more?

♦ Describe commercial uses of asexual reproduction in flowering plants.

♦ Describe the different uses of each part of the wheat grain. What is wheat germ? Wheat bran? How does white flour differ from whole wheat flour?

♦ Why are commercial bananas and many commercial varieties of grapes seedless? How are seedless varieties of normally "seedy" fruits such as watermelons created?

♦ Discuss the role of evolution in floral diversity. What is an example of a primitive flower? An advanced flower?

♦ Learn more about the role of pollen in human allergy. Collect daily and monthly information on the types and amounts of pollen found in your area. What species have the most pollen? What months of the year have the highest pollen counts? Should we regulate the planting of nonnative ornamental vegetation in cities and towns in states such as Arizona where people have moved seeking low pollen counts?

♦ Discuss the use of pollen grains as indicators of the past vegetation history of an area.

♦ Describe different seed dispersal mechanisms used by flowering plants. Make a list of dispersal mechanisms found among local plants or plants on campus.

♦ Research the process by which bees make and store honey.

♦ Document the role of animals in seed dispersal and the extent to which this helps plants.

♦ Describe how insect infestations or plant diseases can affect plant growth.

- How long can most seeds remain viable? Learn more about documented cases of extreme seed longevity. What steps can be taken to increase seed viability? What are some of the actions taken by seed companies to ensure maximum seed viability?

- Why are seedlings raised in complete darkness white or yellow instead of green? Describe the role played by sunlight in chlorophyll synthesis.

- What are some species whose seeds require stratification (cold, moist conditions for several weeks prior to sowing) for successful germination? What is the survival value of such a requirement?

- How are auxins, gibberellins, cytokinins, and abscisic acid used by commercial growers? How is ethylene used to hasten fruit ripening?

- Look up the geographic distributions of several long-day plants, short-day plants, and day-neutral plants. How is the effect of day length on flowering related to the geographic range of a particular plant species?

- Describe synthetic auxins used as herbicides. How do these compounds actually work? How are these compounds manufactured? What is their impact on the environment?

Responses to *Data Analysis Activities*

1. Twelve of the captured rodents showed some evidence of pollen.
2. This evidence is not sufficient to conclude that rodents are the main pollinators of this plant, as insects may have a more significant effect.
3. The average number of seeds produced by caged plants (1.95) was significantly lower than control plants (20.0).
4. These data support the hypothesis that rodents are required from pollination of *M. depressa* because the percent of plant that set fruit, the average number of fruits per plant, and the average number of seeds per plant was much greater in the uncaged plants as compared to the caged plants. Also, evidence of pollen was found on the majority of the rodents examined in the analysis.

Possible Responses to *Critical Thinking* Questions

1. The oat seedlings labeled B and D will bend toward a directional light source since their coleoptiles are intact and exposed to the light source. The oat seedlings labeled A and C will not bend toward a directional light source since their coleoptiles has been removed (A) or covered with a light-blocking tube (C).

2. Excessive auxin production will affect the plant's phenotype in the following manner: excessive grow, extensive lateral roots, lack of lateral buds, excessive differentiation of the xylem, lack of abscission, and rapid fruit development.

28

ANIMAL TISSUES AND ORGAN SYSTEMS

Chapter Outline

Objectives

1. Describe the various levels of animal organization.
2. Know the characteristics of the four main tissues, noting their structure, function, and examples of each.
3. Know the types of cells that compose each tissue type, and cite examples of organs that contain significant amounts of each tissue type.
4. Characterize each of the major organ systems of the human body.
5. Describe how the four principal tissue types are organized into an organ such as the skin.

Key Terms

stem cells

extracellular fluid (ECF)

interstitial fluid

plasma

epithelium, -lia

basement membrane

microvilli

exocrine glands

endocrine glands

connective tissue

loose connective tissue

dense, irregular

  connective tissue

dense, regular

  connective tissue

cartilage

adipose tissue

bone tissue

blood

skeletal muscle tissue

cardiac muscle tissue

smooth muscle tissue

nervous tissue

neurons

epidermis

dermis

sensory receptor

negative feedback

apoptosis

Lecture Outline

28.1 Stem Cells

  A. Stem cells may lead hold keys to many medical therapies and treatments.

    1. Stem cells are self renewing and can be induced to differentiate into different cell lines in the body.

  B. There are two main types of stem cells.

    1. Embryonic stem cells, which form after fertilization, can develop into any of the bodies cell and tissue types.

    2. Adult stem cells can only differential into a limited range of cells.

  C. Despite the promise of stem cells, their use is limited and there are many ethical debates surrounding their use.

    1. Embryonic stem cells are harvested from pre-implantation human embryos.

    2. Some students suggest that adult stem cells can be rejuvenated in order to make them more like embryonic stem cells.

28.2 Organization of Animal Bodies

  A. Levels of Organization

    1. Animal development produces a body with many cell types that are connected by cell junctions and are often surrounded by an extracellular matrix.

    2. Animal body plans are made of 4 basic tissue types:

      a. Epithelial tissue serves as coverings and linings for the body.

      b. Connective tissue provides integrative and structural support for the body.

      c. Muscle tissue is used for movement.

      d. Nervous tissue is used for stimulus detection and information processing.

    3. Animal tissues are organized into organs that carry out specific tasks.

    4. Two or more organs that work together are an organ system.

  B. The Internal Environment

    1. Most of the body weight of an organism is fluid that consists of water and solutes like salts.

      a. Extracellular fluid (ECF) surrounds internal tissues and aides nutrient transmission.

      b. ECF is divided into two portions: interstitial fluid (the fluid between cells) and plasma (the fluid portion of the blood).

    2. Organisms regulate their internal environment and maintain conditions within a narrow range through a process called homeostasis.

C. Evolution of Animal Structure
   1. Animal structure has evolved, or changed over time, in response to requisites for function.
   2. Evolution does not create new structure; evolution remodels existing structures so the result, however functional, is usually not perfect.

28.3 Epithelial Tissue
   A. General Characteristics
      1. In this tissue, one surface is free and the other adheres to a basement membrane.
      2. In order to maintain structural integrity, many tight junctions have formed in order to withstand mechanical stress.
   B. Types of Epithelium
      1. Simple epithelium is one-cell thick and may have flat (squamous), cuboidal, or columnar cells.
      2. Stratified epithelium has many layers—as in human skin.
      3. Glands are secretory organs derived from epithelium.
      4. Exocrine glands often secrete through ducts to free surfaces; they secrete mucus, saliva, wax, milk, and so on.
      5. Endocrine glands secrete hormones directly into intercellular fluid for distribution by the blood.
   C. Carcinomas – Epithelial Cell Cancers
      1. Human skin is constantly replenishing itself; because of this there is a great potential for DNA replication errors that lead to cancer.

28.4 Connective Tissues
   A. Most connective tissue contains cells and fibers (collagen and/or elastin) secreted by fibroblasts, all scattered in a ground substance.
   B. Soft Connective Tissues
      1. Loose connective tissue supports epithelia and organs, and surrounds blood vessels and nerves; it contains fibroblast cells and fibers plus macrophages.
      2. Dense, irregular connective tissue has thicker fibers and more of them, but fewer cells; it forms protective capsules around organs.
      3. Dense, regular connective tissue has its fibers in parallel; this is the arrangement found in tendons (muscle to bone) and ligaments (bone to bone).
   C. Specialized Connective Tissue
      1. Cartilage contains a dense array of fibers in a jellylike ground substance.
         a. It cushions and maintains the shape of body parts; it resists compression and is resilient.
         b. Locations include the ends of bones, parts of the nose, external ear, and disks between vertebrae.
      2. Adipose tissue cells are specialized for the storage of fat, which can be used as an energy reserve and as cushions to pad organs.
      3. Bone tissue stores mineral salts, produces blood cells, and provides support and protection to the body and its organ systems. Bones also work with muscles to perform movement.
      4. Blood transports oxygen, wastes, hormones, and enzymes; it also contains clotting factors to protect against bleeding and components to protect against disease-causing agents.

28.5   Muscle Tissues

A. Muscle tissue contracts in response to stimulation, then passively lengthens.

B. There are three types of muscle defined by their appearance, location, and function.
    1. Skeletal muscle tissue attaches to bones for voluntary movement; it contains striated, multinucleated, long cells.
    2. Cardiac (heart) muscle is composed of short, striated cells that can function in units.
    3. Smooth muscle tissue contains spindle-shaped cells; it lines the gut, blood vessels, and glands; its operation is involuntary.

28.6   Nervous Tissue

A. Nervous tissue exerts the greatest control over the body's responsiveness to changing conditions.
    1. Neurons are excitable cells, organized as lines of communication throughout the body.
    2. Neuroglia are diverse cells that protect and metabolically support the neurons.

B. Sensory neurons detect stimuli; interneurons coordinate the body's responses; motor neurons relay signals to muscles and glands for response.

28.7   Organs and Organ Systems

A. Organs in Body Cavities
    1. Many human organs are located inside of internal cavities that develop from coelom in the embryo.

B. Vertebrate Organ Systems
    1. Organ systems perform specialized functions.
    2. Figure 28.13 briefly describes each of the organ systems (integumentary, muscular, skeletal, nervous, endocrine, circulatory, lymphatic, respiratory, digestive, urinary, and reproductive) that contribute to the survival of the living cells of the vertebrate body.
    3. The formation and function of the organs are outcomes of a long-term program of growth and development.

28.8   Closer Look at an Organ Human Skin

A. The outer covering of human bodies interfaces with the environment and is called the integument.
    1. The skin consists of an outer epidermis and an underlying dermis.
    2. The skin has several functions.
        a. The skin covers and protects the body from abrasion, bacterial attack, ultraviolet radiation, and dehydration.
        b. Its receptors are essential in detecting environmental stimuli.
        c. It helps control internal temperature.
        d. In humans, the skin produces vitamin D.

B. Structure of the Skin
    1. The dermis lies beneath the epidermis and is mostly a dense connective tissue with elastin and collagen fibers.
        a. Its dense connective tissue cushions the body against everyday stretching and mechanical stresses.
        b. Adipose tissue and loose connective tissue insulate or cushion some body parts.
        c. Blood vessels, lymph vessels, and receptors of sensory nerves are embedded in the tissue.
        d. Sweat glands help dissipate heat, and oil glands lubricate and soften the skin, plus they produce secretions that reduce bacterial populations on the skin.

2. Epidermis is a stratified squamous epithelium.
   a. The epidermis varies among vertebrates.
   b. As animals evolved from life in water to life on land, their outer layer adapted. The epidermis has keritanocytes that make a tough, waterproof layer.
   c. Keritanocytes also became specialized to claws, nails, beaks, fur, and hair.
3. Epidermis contains melanocytes and dendritic cells.
   a. Melanocyte cells produce melanin pigment that darkens the skin and protects against the sun's rays; hemoglobin and carotene also contribute to skin color.
   b. Dendritic cells alert the immune system to threats from viruses and bacteria.
      1) These cells are phagocytes and engulf viruses and bacteria that they encounter in the skin.
      2) UV radiation damages these cells, making them more vulnerable to cold sores—a Herpes simplex infection.

D. Sun and the Skin
   1. UV light stimulates melanocytes to make more melanin, resulting in a tan.
   2. Continued exposure to the sun's rays causes loss of elasticity and the dwindling of glandular secretions—in short, aging.
   3. UV also harms DNA, which can result in skin cancer.
   4. UV radiation stimulates the body to make vitamin D, but it also causes the breakdown of folate, which is often deficient in the diet.
   5. One hypothesis regarding the variation of skin color among people in different parts of the world considers the amount of sun exposure in each environment.
      a. People with high exposure to sun produce more melanin as protection from UV radiation.
      b. People with low sun exposure have fewer melanocytes.

E. Effects of Age
   1. Aging skin is marked by the slowing of cell division, loss of elasticity, and wrinkling.
   2. Tanning and sun exposure accelerates aging in the skin.

F. Farming Skin
   1. Skin is cultured from cells taken from circumcised foreskin.

28.9 Integrating Activities
   A. Detecting and Responding to Change
      1. Sensory receptors monitor body conditions in order to detect changes.
   B. Negative Feedback Control of Body Temperature
      1. Negative feedback is a mechanism that organisms use to monitor homeostatic conditions.
      2. Human skin uses a negative feedback mechanism to control body temperature.
         a. When the temperature increases, your body shifts blood flow to your skin which helps dissipate your heat into the environment.
         b. When the temperature cools, your body shifts blood flow away from your skin to preserve body temperature.
   C. Intercellular Communication
      1. Intercellular communication can occur between cells using gap junctions or over longer distances using hormones.
      2. Signaling usually occurs in three step: 1) a signaling molecule binds to a receptor, 2) the signal is transduced in the cell, 3) the cell responds to the signal.
      3. Apoptosis is programmed cell death, which is an important part in the lifespan of a cell.

Suggestions for Presenting the Material

♦ Although this chapter includes brief discussions of cell functions and human organ systems, the main topic is *tissues*. There is really no need for details of body systems listed in this chapter because each will be discussed in later chapters.

♦ The presentation of tissues will be more meaningful if slides are shown during your lecture.

♦ Function is related to form, make a point of showing how each tissue has developed to serve a certain function.

♦ Create a guideline for students for each of the four main tissue types. Have students find details for each tissue type including: drawings, functions, examples, etc.

♦ Use one of videos on the Multimedia Manager to introduce this chapter. These are helpful in grabbing the interest of students.

♦ Save discussions of organ systems other than the skin until you reach that chapter in the text.

♦ Start discussing the idea that the human systems are integrated. Figure 28.14, for example, shows how the circulatory system functions effectively when the digestive and respiratory systems bring materials in and the urinary system eliminates waste.

Classroom and Laboratory Enrichment

♦ Select slides of various types of tissues for projection onto a large screen. Ask the students to identify the type of tissue and where it is found in the body.

♦ Invite an athlete who has suffered a knee injury and has had corrective surgery to describe the damage and reconstructive process.

♦ During the discussion of bone, pass a cleaned bone (from a meat market) around the classroom. Comment on the nonliving and living composition of the bone. Another option is to demonstrate that bone has both organic and mineral components by soaking one chicken bone in acetic acid (to remove minerals) and by heating another in an oven at a high temperature (to remove organic material).

♦ After discussing the basic tissue types, have the students view real microscopic structures in order to identify the tissue types as they exist in a real organ.

♦ Use a model of the various tissues to illustrate their structure.

♦ Exhibit a vertebrate embryonic or fetal skeleton that is specially stained to show the cartilage.

♦ Take the opportunity to educate this young audience on skin care—causes, prevention, and the statistics of the disease. Several companies offer comprehensive posters on skin cancer.

♦ Explore stem research further. Hold a stem cell forum and debate.

♦ In lab groups, have each group examine different organisms, i.e. a fish, a pig, a nematode, a planaria, etc. Have each group identify how their organism has incorporated variations of the tissue types or variations in the organization of the in the bodies of the different animals.

♦ Have each student or lab group select an organ and report on the organ system it belongs to, and the various tissue and types that make up that organ.

♦ This is a good chapter to start reinforcing how evolution works to select for favorable, but not perfect outcomes. Introduce the concept of comparative anatomy; use comparative anatomy and physiology to demonstrate variations and adaptation that have appeared in many animal lineages.

Stem Cells (revisited)

♦ Why are stem cells so valuable and sought after in embryological research?

♦ What are the characteristics of stem cells? What can stem cells be used for?

♦ How would the use of stem cells be different than any other medical intervention used to save lives?

♦ Why do some groups label stem cell research as unethical?

♦ Would the use of rejuvenated stem cells (adult stem cells induced to be more like embryonic stem cells) end the ethical debate about the use of stem cells?

♦ How do you feel about stem cell research? In your mind is there a difference between adult stem cell research and embryonic stem cell research?

Additional Ideas for Classroom Discussion

♦ Why is blood—a liquid—considered a *connective* tissue?

♦ Is there any validity to the cynic's observation that "beauty queens are just exposing a lot of well-placed dead cells"?

♦ Is using a tanning bed any safer than exposure to the sun?

♦ Rising blood sugar levels after a meal normally trigger insulin secretion, which in turn causes glucose to be converted to glycogen for storage. How is this similar to the response of an air conditioner thermostat to rising room temperature?

♦ What is liposuction? Does it permanently remove adipose tissue from the treated areas? Why is there a limit to the amount of adipose tissue that can be safely removed from the body at one time?

♦ Astronauts who orbited the Earth early in the space program experienced considerable loss of bone mass under gravity-free conditions. How was this remedied in subsequent flights?

How Would You Vote? Classroom Discussion Ideas

♦ Monitor the voting for the online question. This question of what source can, or cannot, be used for stem cell research is unfortunately clouded by political and religious stances. From a purely biological research standpoint, the value of these cells to the advancement of science outweighs the question of their source. Also, a common response against stem cell use is that humans shouldn't "play god." An important thing to consider, for those students, is how is the use of stem cells to save someone's life different than any other medical intervention?

♦ Have students complete classroom polling using the JoinIn clickers.

Term Paper Topics, Library Activities, and Special Projects

♦ Osteoporosis is a topic of current interest, especially to women. Research osteoporosis and present ways the disease can be prevented.

♦ What roles, if any, do estrogen replacement therapy and exercise play in the prevention of osteoporosis?

Animal Tissues and Organ Systems   **231**

- We are warned to protect our skin from the sun by using sun-block preparations. What chemical substances are effective in these preparations, and how do they work?

- Describe the differences between exposure in tanning booths with exposure to the sun in terms of skin cancer rates.

- Define and describe other essential functions of the skin.

- Consider the pros and cons of stem cell research. With your research, state a definitive position on your support or rejection of stem cell research.

Responses to *Data Analysis Activities*

1. 25% - Standard Method, 45% - Cultured Skin

2. 40% - Standard Method, 65% - Cultured Skin

3. The difference was evident as early as 4 weeks after treatment.

Possible Responses to *Critical Thinking* Questions

1. There are advantages and disadvantages to the use of cell cultures when testing cosmetics. The best advantage is that no animals have to be harmed in the testing. Also, because the cells are human, they may react in a manner that more accurately represents how human tissues might respond. The disadvantage of using cells is that there is no overall organism to respond to the stimulus. There is no immune system, no brain, no other systems that might respond negatively to the stimulus. For example, if a person is going to be allergic to the cosmetics that be caused by a response for the entire immune system.

2. If radiation or chemotherapy works by stopping cell division, it will also cause hair to fall out. This is because hair is grown as the follicle divides rapidly (every 24-72 hours) and pushes out the growing, keratinized cells. As the cell division stop, no more new cells are produced from the follicle and the hair falls out.

3. Tissues and organs show emergent functions. For example, an individual epithelial cell cannot function as a barrier. However, because of their morphology and because they form strong junctions between cells, epithelial tissues work well as a barrier. Similarly, the stomach works break down food in several different ways, but it is a combination of functions of the tissues that makeup the stomach. There are three muscular layers that mash food up and control movement through the organ. The stomach is lined with epithelial cells that contain glands that produce mucus, enzymes, and hydrochloric acid that aid in digestion. Connective tissue holds the stomach together as it expands to allow more food into the stomach.

4. The tissue that is pictured is epithelial tissue. There are several reasons that indicate that this is epithelial tissue. For example, the cells are lined with cilia which are indicative of this being a lining. Also, secretory glands are present; glands are only found in epithelial tissue.

29

NEURAL CONTROL

Chapter Outline

Objectives

1. Compare and contrast invertebrate and vertebrate nervous systems.
2. Describe the visible structure of neurons, neuroglia, nerves, and ganglia, both separately and together as a system.
3. Understand the distribution of the invisible array of proteins, ions, and other molecules in a neuron, both at rest and as a neuron experiences a change in potential.
4. Understand how a nerve impulse is received by a neuron, conducted along a neuron, and transmitted across a synapse to a neighboring neuron, muscle, or gland.
5. List several ways by which information flow is regulated and integrated in the human body.
6. Describe the organization of peripheral versus central nervous systems.
7. Identify the parts of primitive brains, and explain how the human brain is more advanced.

Key Terms

neuron	axon	endorphins	blood–brain barrier
neuroglia	membrane potential	myelin	medulla oblongata
nerve net	resting membrane	somatic nerves	cerebellum
sensory neurons	potential	autonomic nerves	cerebrum
interneurons	action potential	sympathetic neurons	thalamus
motor neurons	threshold level	parasympathetic	hypothalamus
ganglion	positive feedback	neurons	cerebral cortex
nerve cord	synapse	meninges	primary motor cortex
central nervous system	neuromuscular junction	cerebrospinal fluid	limbic system
peripheral nervous	neurotransmitters	white matter	
system	acetylcholine	gray matter	
dendrites	synaptic integration	reflex	

Lecture Outline

29.1 In Pursuit of Ecstasy

A. Ecstasy is a drug that gives a mild high, making you feel really socially accepted, less anxious, and more aware of your surroundings.
  1. The active ingredient is MDMA, which disrupts controls over serotonin in the brain, causing neurons to release too much.
  2. Excess serotonin can over stimulate cells causing feelings of empathy, energy, and euphoria, and can cause the body's internal temperature controls to break down.
  3. Lower serotonin levels contribute to a loss of concentration, memory problems, and depression.

B. The nervous system evolved as a way to sense and respond fast to changing conditions inside and outside the body.

29.2 Evolution of Nervous Systems

A. The neuron, or nerve cell, is the basic unit of communication in all nervous systems. There are three kinds of neurons.
  1. Sensory neurons are receptors for specific sensory stimuli.
  2. Interneurons in the brain and spinal cord integrate input and output signals.

3. Motor neurons send information from integrator to muscle or gland cells (effectors).

4. Neuroglia cells structurally and metabolically support neurons.

B. The Cnidarian Nerve Net

1. Animals evolved in the seas, and animals with the simplest nervous systems still live in water.

2. Radial animals such as hydra, jellyfish, and cnidarians have a nerve net.

3. The nerve net is a mesh of neurons that extends through the body that detects stimuli and controls contractile cells.

4. Instead, it allows for simple, stereotyped movements that provide the basic operating machinery of nervous systems.

C. Bilateral, Cephalized Systems

1. Evolution of bilateral body plans was accompanied by cephalization.

2. Planarians and flatworms are the simplest animals with a bilateral, cephalized nervous system with nerves and ganglia.

3. Annelids and arthropods have a simple brain with paired ganglia.

4. Chordates have one dorsal nerve cord. Vertebrates have a complex brain at one end of the nerve cord.

5. Selection favored expansion of sensory structures and brain centers capable of coordinating, processing, and directing the body's responses to new stimuli, as found in the vertebrates.

D. The Vertebrate Nervous System

1. The central nervous system of vertebrates includes the brain and spinal cord.

2. The peripheral nervous system includes all of the nerves carrying signals to and from the brain and spinal cord.

   a. Afferent axons deliver signals into the brain and spinal cord.

   b. Efferent axons carry signals away from the central nervous system.

29.3 Neurons—The Communicators

A. Neurons and Their Functional Zones

1. Each neuron consists of three main parts.

   a. The cell body contains the nucleus and other organelles.

   b. Dendrites are short extensions that receive stimuli and conduct them toward the cell body. Sensory neurons typically have one dendrite, while motor neurons and interneurons have many dendrites.

   c. Axons are long extensions that conduct signals away from the cell body. Most neurons have only one axon.

2. The neuron is organized into an input zone, trigger zone, conducting zone, and output zone.

29.4 Membrane Potentials

A. Resting Potentials

1. A neuron at rest maintains a steady voltage difference across its plasma membrane.

   a. The inside is more negatively charged than the outside.

   b. This is called the resting membrane potential.

2. When a neuron receives signals, an abrupt, temporary reversal in the polarity—the inside becomes more positive—is generated by the sodium ions rushing inward (an action potential).

3. Two properties of the neuron membrane permit a resting potential.

   a. The lipid bilayer bars the free passage of potassium ions and sodium ions.

   b. Ions can flow from one side to the other through channels in transport proteins.

4. There are more potassium ions inside and more sodium ions outside the resting neuron membrane.
   a. Sodium-potassium pumps move two potassium ions in and three sodium ions out to maintain the resting potential.
   b. Potassium ions have a tendency to passively leak out.
   c. This ion gradient is critical in signal propagation.
B. Neurons are excitable because of their ability to generate an action potential, a reversal of the resting potential that generates electricity.

29.5   A Closer Look at Action Potentials

A. Approaching Threshold
   1. When a stimulus reaches a certain minimum—a threshold—gated channels open, and sodium rushes in.
   2. In an accelerating way, more and more gates open.
   3. At threshold, the opening of more gates no longer depends on the stimulus but is self-propagating; this is an example of positive feedback.

B. An All-Or-Nothing Spike
   1. The charge reversal makes the sodium gates close and potassium gates open.
   2. The sodium–potassium membrane pumps also become operational to fully restore the resting potential.

C. Propagation Along the Axon
   1. The action potential is self-propagating and moves away from the stimulation site toward axon endings.
   2. A brief inactivation period follows after each action potential where sodium gates shut and potassium gates open restoring the ion gradient.

29.6   Chemical Communication at Synapses

A. Sending Signals at Synapses
   1. A synapse is a junction between a neuron and an adjacent cell, separated by a synaptic cleft into which a neurotransmitter substance is released.
      a. The neuron that releases the neurotransmitter molecules into the cleft is called the presynaptic cell.
      b. The neurotransmitter binds to receptors on the membrane of the postsynaptic cell.
   2. Acetylcholine (Ach) as an example.
      a. Acetylcholine is the transmitter at neuromuscular junctions.
      b. An action potential induces the motor neuron to release Ach, which binds to receptors on skeletal muscle fibers.
      c. Sodium channels open in the muscle fiber's plasma membrane and the muscle excites.
      d. The resulting action potentials stimulate muscle contractions.
      e. Some neurotransmitters bind more than one type of postsynaptic cell. ACh stimulates skeletal muscle contraction but it slows cardiac muscle contractions.

B. Cleaning the Cleft
   1. After their work is done, signaling molecules must be removed from the synaptic clefts to make way for new signals.
   2. Diffuse enzyme degradation and membrane pumps are some of the mechanisms that clear the cleft.

C. Synaptic Integration
   1. Neurons receive messages from many neurons simultaneously.
   2. In synaptic integration, a neuron sums all inhibitory and excitatory signals arriving at the input zone.

D. Neurotransmitter and Receptor Diversity
1. Some neurotransmitters and their effects.
    a. Norepinephrine and epinephrine prime the body to respond to stress or to excitement.
    b. Dopamine plays roles in memory, learning, and fine motor control.
    c. Serotonin acts on brain cells to govern mood and memory.
    d. GABA inhibits the release of other neurotransmitters.

29.7 Disrupted Signaling – Disorders and Drugs
A. Neurological Disorders often involve a disruption of signaling at synapses.
1. Parkinson's Disease is a result of damage to dopamine secreting neurons that results in motor and speech problems.
2. Attention Deficit Hyperactivity Disorder is also linked to lower than normal levels of dopamine.
3. Alzheimer's Disease, the leading cause of dementia, is linked to lower than normal levels of acetylcholine.
4. Mood disorders, like depression, can be cause by abnormal interactions between dopamine, serotonin, and norepinephrine.

B. Effects of Psychoactive Drugs
1. Stimulants increase alertness and anxiousness.
    a. Nicotine and caffeine block Ach receptors.
    b. Cocaine increases the sense of pleasure by blocking reabsorption of norepinephrine, dopamine, and serotonin.
    c. Amphetamines increase dopamine, serotonin, and norepinephrine reducing appetite and energizing users.
    d. MDMA (ecstasy) and crystal "meth" are amphetamines.
2. Analgesics
    a. Analgesics mimic endorphins — the natural pain killers secreted by the brain.
    b. Morphine, codeine, oxycontin, and heroin are the common addictive pain killers.
3. Depressants slow motor responses by inhibiting Ach output.
    a. Alcohol and barbiturates are depressants.
    b. Alcohol stimulates the release of endorphins and GABA, so users experience a brief euphoria followed by depression.
4. Hallucinogens
    a. These drugs skew sensory perception by interfering with acetylcholine, norepinephrine, and serotonin.
    b. Marijuana acts like a mild depressant and gives mild euphoria, but it can also cause disorientation, anxiety, and hallucinations.
    c. LSD, mescaline, and psilocybin are also examples of hallucinogens.

29.8 The Peripheral Nervous System
A. Axons Bundled as Nerves
1. Signals between brain or spinal cord and body regions travel by nerves.
    a. Axons of sensory neurons, motor neurons, or both are bundled together inside connective tissues.
    b. Many axons are covered by a myelin sheath derived in part from Schwann cells.
    c. Each section of the sheath is separated from adjacent ones by a node where the axon membrane (plentiful in gated sodium channels) is exposed.
    d. The action potentials jump from node to node, which is fast and efficient.

B. Somatic and Autonomic Systems
1. The human peripheral system has two types of nerves based on location.
    a. Spinal nerves (31 pairs) connect with the spinal cord and innervate most areas of the body.
    b. Cranial nerves (12 pairs) connect vital organs directly to the brain.
2. Spinal and cranial nerves can also be classified on the basis of function.
    a. The *somatic* nerves relay sensory information from receptors in the skin and muscles, and motor commands to skeletal muscles (voluntary control).
    b. The *autonomic* nerves send signals to and from smooth muscles, cardiac muscle, and glands (involuntary control).
C. Sympathetic and Parasympathetic Nerves
1. Sympathetic nerves increase overall body activity during times of stress, excitement, or danger; they also call on the hormone epinephrine to increase the "fight-flight" response.
2. Parasympathetic nerves tend to slow down body activity when the body is not under stress.
3. Opposing sympathetic and parasympathetic signals control most organs.

29.9 The Spinal Cord

A. Spinal Cord
1. The spinal cord is a pathway for signal travel between the peripheral nervous system and the brain.
    a. The cord is also the center for controlling some reflex actions.
    b. The spinal cord (and also the brain) is covered with tough membranes—the meninges—and resides within the protection of the stacked vertebrae.
    c. Gray matter contains the cell bodies, dendrites, unsheathed axons, and neuroglia.
    d. White matter contains myelin sheathed axons and neuroglia.
2. Signals move up and down the spinal cord in bundles of sheathed axons.
B. Reflex Arcs
1. Reflexes are simple paths of information flow in automatic response to sensory stimuli.
2. In the simplest reflex, the reflex arc, sensory neurons directly synapse on motor neurons.
3. In the stretch reflex, receptors of sensory neurons (muscle spindles) transmit impulses to the spinal cord where direct synapses with motor neurons occur.
C. Spinal Cord Injury and Multiple Sclerosis
1. Spinal cord injuries are a permanent disruption of spinal cord nerves that can lead to paralysis.
    a. Spinal cord injuries are permanent because central nervous tissue does not regenerate.
2. Multiple Sclerosis is an autoimmune disease that attacks a person's myelin reducing the effectiveness of their nervous communication.

29.10 The Vertebrate Brain

A. Brain Development and Evolution
1. The forebrain, midbrain, and hindbrain form from three successive portions of the neural tube.
2. The most primitive of the tissue is the brain stem, which contains simple, basic reflex centers.

B. Protection at the Blood–Brain Barrier
   1. The brain and spinal cord are bathed with cerebrospinal fluid that exists within a system of cavities and canals.
   2. The fluid cushions vital nervous tissue from sudden, jarring movements.
   3. The blood–brain barrier operates at the plasma membranes of cells forming the capillaries that service the brain.
      a. Tight junctions fuse the capillary cells together, forcing substances to move through the cells to reach the brain.
      b. Membrane transport proteins allow essential nutrients to move through but bar wastes and certain toxins.

C. The Human Brain
   1. An average-sized human brain weighs about three pounds and has about 100 billion interneurons.
   2. The medulla oblongata has influence over respiration, blood circulation, motor response coordination, and sleep/wake responses.
   3. The cerebellum acts as reflex center for maintaining posture and coordinating limbs.
   4. The pons ("bridge") possesses bands of axons that pass between brain centers.
   5. The midbrain originally coordinated reflex responses to visual input.
   6. The cerebrum integrates sensory input and selected motor responses.
   7. The thalamus relays and coordinates sensory signals.
   8. The hypothalamus monitors internal organs and influences responses to thirst, hunger, and sex.

29.11 The Human Cerebrum

A. Functions of the Cerebral Cortex
   1. The left hemisphere deals with speech, math, and analytical skills; the right half controls nonverbal skills, such as music.
   2. Motor areas control voluntary motor activity.
      a. The *frontal* lobe includes the motor cortex, which coordinates instructions for motor responses.
      b. The frontal lobe also includes the premotor cortex (learned patterns of motor skills), Broca's area (speech), and the frontal eye field (voluntary eye movements).
   3. Sensory areas deal with the meaning of sensations.
      a. The *parietal* lobe contains the somatosensory cortex—the main receiving area for signals from the skin and joints.
      b. The *occipital* lobe, which is located in the rear, has centers for vision.
      c. The *temporal* lobe, near each temple, is a processing center for hearing and houses centers for influencing emotional behavior.
   4. Association areas—occupying all parts of the cortex except primary and sensory areas—integrate, analyze, and respond to many inputs.

B. Connections with the Limbic System
   1. The limbic system, located at the middle of the cerebral hemispheres, governs out emotions and has roles in memory.
   2. Connections from the cerebral cortex pass through the limbic system, allowing us to correlate organ activities with self-gratifying behavior, such as eating and sex.
   3. It is distantly related to olfactory lobes and still deals with the sense of smell, especially as it relates to memory.

C. Making Memories
1. "Memory" is the storage and retrieval of information about previous experiences.
2. Information becomes stored in "memory traces"—chemical and structural changes in brain regions.
   a. Short-term memory lasts from seconds to hours and is limited to small bits of information.
   b. Long-term memory is more permanent and seems to be limitless.
   c. Declarative memory stores facts and impressions of events.
3. Emotions influence memory retention.

Suggestions for Presenting the Material

♦ To grab the students' attention start the lecture with any of the ABC videos available from the Multimedia Manager.

♦ An effective comparison for individual nerves is a light switch where the dendrites and cell body are the switch, the axon sends the electricity like a wire to the synapse, which is like a light bulb.

♦ The nervous system is one of the most difficult to comprehend at any level. Therefore, extra time and thorough explanations are especially needed in this chapter.

♦ The function of the neuron membrane in permitting passage of Na^+ and K^+ ions is confusing. Initially, you may wish to focus on sodium only, then expand to the role of potassium.

♦ A good analogy for the resting potential is a battery. Just about all of your students should recognize that all batteries need a positive and negative terminal. Sodium provides the positive terminal while large negatively charged proteins serve as the negative terminal. Be sure to clarify the role of potassium as many students have the misconception that potassium is the negative terminal.

♦ The changes in the neuron membrane can be demonstrated using Figure 29.9 (a–d) and the words *polarized*, *depolarized*, and *repolarized*, which are conventional terms but are not used in this edition of the text. The Multimedia Manager provide an animation as well.

♦ The concept of "all-or-nothing events" and "thresholds" can be illustrated by describing the use of a firearm. When the trigger is pulled and reaches the critical point (threshold) at which the hammer is released, the bullet leaves the barrel and travels the expected distance. Of course, the bullet either goes or stays (all or nothing), and the manner in which the trigger is activated (slowly or quickly) should not influence the speed of bullet travel.

♦ Emphasize the temporary nature of the acetylcholine bridge across the synapse by comparing it to a pontoon bridge used by the military to cross small streams and rivers.

♦ If the students can recite the sequence of structures through which an impulse passes during a *reflex arc*, they have a good grasp of the nerve conduction pathways. Add the ion flow across the membranes, and the story is pretty well complete!

♦ Emphasize the continuity of fiber tracts between the brain and spinal cord. Stress the primary functions of the spinal cord as a reflex center versus the brain as a sense-interpretation and directed-response center.

♦ Work with the psychology department and have guest lecturers come in and trade talking about how psychologists study the brain versus how neuroscientists study the brain.

♦ Students generally find it easier to distinguish between the sympathetic and parasympathetic divisions of the autonomic nervous system if they are told that the sympathetic division is involved in mobilizing "fight-or-flight" reaction while the parasympathetic division produces a general "slowing-down" and "business as usual" response.

♦ **Common Student Misconceptions:**

  o Students often confuse *neurons* and *nerves*. Be sure to emphasize the difference between these two terms.

  o Some students may not be able to distinguish the backbone (vertebral, or spinal, column) from the spinal cord. Be sure to assist them with this by using appropriate diagrams in the text.

Classroom and Laboratory Enrichment

♦ The concept of thresholds and all-or-nothing events can be demonstrated by using dominoes (or for large classes, several audiocassette cases). Line up about 20 dominoes placed on end and spaced about one inch apart. Ask a student to gently touch one end domino to begin the progressive fall. Emphasize that the student's touch (threshold stimulus) caused a standing row (polarized) to begin falling (depolarization) at a constant speed (all-or-nothing event). Pose the following question (and demonstrate the answer): Would a greater and faster stimulus cause more rapid falling? To demonstrate *repolarization*, a second student could begin resetting the dominoes even before the falling is complete.

♦ Arrange with a physics student or instructor for a demonstration of an action potential as recorded on an oscilloscope screen.

♦ Permit students to demonstrate the knee jerk reflex arc by using percussion hammers. It is important to ask the subjects to close their eyes to prevent "cheating."

♦ Show a film or video of an animation of nerve impulse transmission.

♦ Have microscope slides of neurons available for laboratory demonstration.

♦ Work with students to dissect sheep brains and spinal cord.

♦ Have students compare brain models from several different species comparing how the brain has adapted differently.

♦ Using live *Hydra* and *Dugesia* (planaria), test for nervous response to touch, vibration, light, mild acid or alkali, and heat. Are there differences between the two species with respect to degree and speed of response?

♦ Use dissectible models of neurons, neuroglial cells and the brain to illustrate the location of parts.

♦ Exhibit a vertebral column/spinal cord/herniated disc model to demonstrate why so much pain and functional loss are associated with herniated discs.

♦ Use a spinal cord/vertebral column cross-sectional model to illustrate the relation between the two structures.

♦ Find a simulation that allows students to change several variables that affect resting and action potentials and/or neurotransmitters.

♦ Have students do presentation of the effects of various psychoactive drugs.

In Pursuit of Ecstasy (revisited)

♦ Why are teenagers and young adults so susceptible to taking recreational drugs such as ecstasy?

♦ Do you think persons at a "rave" even know what drugs they might be taking?

- What are the long term effects of MDMA?

- What is the history of the development of MDMA?

- How would you plan an ecstasy awareness campaign that effectively targets teenagers and young adults?

Additional Ideas for Classroom Discussion

- What would be the result of demyelination of axons such as occurs in multiple sclerosis?

- Upon hearing that salt was not good for him, a freshman college student began a fanatical program to eliminate all sodium chloride from his diet. By cooking his own meals, he was able to eliminate virtually all sodium. What complications could he expect as a result of his brash action?

- If neurons operate under the all-or-nothing principle, how are we able to distinguish soft sounds from loud sounds, or a gentle touch from a crushing blow?

- To most amateur musicians, the playing of sixteenth notes is a challenge, but to trumpet virtuoso Wynton Marsalis, thirty-second and sixty-fourth notes are a breeze. Describe the action of nerves and tongue muscles that regulate the air flow through the mouthpiece.

- Why does a physician's tapping of the knee or elbow reveal the general status of the nervous system *in general*, not just the condition of those two joints?

- Why does conduction in myelinated "afford the best possible conduction speed with the least metabolic effort by the cell"?

- Why does drinking large amounts of coffee or other caffeine-containing beverages tend to make a person "nervous" or "jittery"?

- Do invertebrates, such as the cockroach, feel pain?

- What is the importance of the role of neurotransmitter receptors?

- Pain is the result of certain neurotransmitters affecting a certain neural pathways. Why is pain so different between individuals?

- The central nervous system and closely associated ganglia house the cell bodies of neurons. As opposed to the peripheral axons and dendrites, the cell bodies are not regenerated after traumatic injury. What advantages and disadvantages does this structural arrangement pose for humans?

- Why does a small speck of food stuck between your teeth feel like a large chunk when rubbed with your tongue?

- The exact mode of action of the famous, and now banned, insecticide DDT has never been elucidated (after nearly 50 years of research). However, textbooks describe it as a "central nervous system" poison. What does this imply?

- Explain why elderly people may be unable to remember what they ate for breakfast but can relate the details of a teenage romance.

- Discuss the characteristics of brain disorders such as Parkinson's disease and Alzheimer's disease. Show examples of people with these disorders with videos.

How Would You Vote? Classroom Discussion Ideas

- Monitor the voting for the online question. In the United States, there is tendency on the part of the general public to see jail as the solution for all of society's offenders. However, we cannot lock up everyone, and even if we could, is it a reasonable solution? Rehab programs for nonviolent drug offenders should be the first course of treatment. Jail-time should be considered on subsequent offenses.

♦ Have students complete poling using the JoinIn clickers.

Term Paper Topics, Library Activities, and Special Projects

♦ The neurons of the human body can communicate one with the other much the same as telephones in your city can intercommunicate. In the telephone system, wires touch wires to pass the impulse, but neurons are not directly "wired." Investigate the effects on the body of the elimination of synapse function such as would be caused by organophosphate pesticides, which inhibit acetylcholinesterase.

♦ One of the most effective antidotes for the organophosphate poisoning referred to above is *atropine*. Investigate its mechanism of action. Based on what you find, could administration of atropine be harmful if OP poisoning *has not* occurred?

♦ Prepare a list of neurological disorders in which you focus on the specific cause of the difficulty in each case.

♦ Investigate the consequences of central nervous system damage as opposed to peripheral damage.

♦ Investigate some of the factors that determine the speed at which an impulse is conducted in a neuron.

♦ Why are injuries to the central nervous system, such as gunshot wounds, more permanently debilitating than those to the peripheral system?

♦ What is the importance and the role of pain in our everyday life?

♦ Examine people who do not sense pain. Describe what it would be like to not be able to sense any pain.

♦ What is the basis for "healing" accomplished by the practice of chiropractic medicine? What are its strengths and weaknesses?

♦ Using the mode of action of organophosphate insecticides as a tool, delve into the similarities and differences between the physiology of insect and human nerve function.

♦ Prepare an argument for the suppression of a presently readily available drug, say, alcohol, or prepare an argument for the legalization of marijuana.

♦ Examine depression. Describe what causes depression and how antidepressants work to treat depression.

♦ Explore the research relating dreams to actual events—past and future. What do dreams tell us about ourselves?

♦ Investigate the use of biofeedback for controlling pain, heart rate, and other autonomic functions.

♦ Research and report on any neurotoxin, disorder, or drug and report on its effects on the nervous system.

♦ Botox is a neurotoxin used to make skin look younger. Investigate where Botox comes from and how it works, and formulate an opinion on how you feel regarding this cosmetic procedure.

Possible Responses to *Data Analysis Activities*

1. The control rats moved the most during the first 5 minutes.
2. There were 76 photobeam breaks in the MDMA rats from 5-10 minutes.
3. The MDMA rats moved the most in the last 5 minutes.
4. There is obviously some difference in the MDMA rats that causes a delayed and excessive response.

Possible Responses to *Critical Thinking* Questions

1. All too often we think of babies as miniature adults, but they are not. The undeveloped blood–brain barrier is one good example. The adult body can perfectly process normal hormones, amino acids, ions, etc. even if their concentrations vary somewhat on the high side. Even alcohol, caffeine, and nicotine can be detoxified. But to the susceptible fetus and newborn, any of these substances could enter the brain in concentrations capable of causing damage. Thus, in addition to paying careful attention to her newborn's diet, a conscientious mother would limit her indulgences for the health of her unborn baby. Both parents should continue to be careful in the foods they provide to their baby as he or she develops.

2. Botox inhibits the action of acetylcholine, the neurotransmitter that is most associated with movement.

30

SENSORY PERCEPTION

Chapter Outline

Objectives

1. Describe and note examples of each of the six general categories of sensory receptors.
2. Contrast the mechanism by which the chemical and somatic senses work.
3. Understand how the senses of balance and hearing function.
4. Identify and describe the function of each of the parts of the human ear.
5. Describe how the sense of vision has evolved through time.
6. Identify and describe the function of each of the parts of the human eye.

Key Terms

stimulus	perception	cornea	vomeronasal organ
mechanoreceptors	somatic sensations	pupil	organs of equilibrium
pain receptors	visceral sensations	visual accommodation	vestibular apparatus
thermoreceptors	pain	rod cells	hair cells
chemoreceptors	lens	cone cells	outer ear
photoreceptors	compound eyes	fovea	middle ear
sensory adaptation	camera eyes	olfactory receptors	inner ear
sensation	retina	pheromones	cochlea

Lecture Outline

30.1 A Whale of a Dilemma

    A. Whales move using acoustical cues.

        1. Sound moves five times faster in water than air.

        2. Whales have more neurons to collect auditory information.

        3. Jaws pick up the vibrations, which travel through a layer of fat to the middle ear.

    B. Whales use echolocation.

        1. They emit high-pitched sounds that bounce off objects.

        2. Noise from human endeavors, like new military sonar systems, may be raising havoc with whale acoustical systems.

30.2 Detecting Stimuli and Forming Perceptions

    A. Excitation of Sensory Neurons

        1. In vertebrates sensory neurons detect stimuli.

        2. The brain processes the stimuli giving rise to a sensation.

        3. Each stimulus is a form of energy that activates sensory receptors.

            a. *Mechanoreceptors* detect forms of mechanical energy (pressure, position, and acceleration).

            b. *Pain receptors* detect tissue damage.

            c. *Thermoreceptors* detect heat energy.

            d. *Chemoreceptors* detect chemical energy in specific substances dissolved in fluid.

            e. *Osmoreceptors* detect changes in solute concentration (water volume).

            f. *Photoreceptors* detect visible and UV light.

    B. Sources of Information About a Stimulus

        1. Sensory receptors transduce stimulus energy into action potentials, which are assessed by the brain using three factors.

            a. Genetically determined *pathways* of neurons in the brain can interpret incoming action potentials only in specific ways; for example, receptors from eyes "see" only light.

            b. Strong stimulation of a receptor causes a greater *frequency* of action potentials.

            c. Strong stimulation causes a greater *number* of neurons to fire.

        2. In sensory adaptation the frequency of action potentials decreases or stops even when the stimulus is maintained; for example, clothing is no longer felt once it is put on for the day.

    C. Sensation and Perception

        1. Sensation is the detection of sensory stimuli.

        2. Perception is deciding what sensory input mean.

30.3 Somatic and Visceral Sensations

    A. The somatic sensations arise from sensory receptors located in tissues throughout the body; visceral senses arise from the internal organs.

    B. The Somatosensory Cortex

        1. Information about touch, pain, temperature, and body position are sent from the skin and joints to the somatosensory cortex in the cerebral cortex.

C. Pain
1. Pain is the perception of injury to some region of the body.
   a. Sensations of somatic pain come from receptors in the skin, skeletal muscles, joints, and tendons.
   b. Sensations of visceral pain, which is associated with internal organs, are related to excessive chemical stimulation, muscle spasms and fatigue, and inadequate blood flow.

30.4 Do You See What I See?
A. Requirements for Vision
1. Vision requires eyes (photoreceptors) and a neural program in the brain that can interpret the patterns of action potentials.
2. Photoreceptors contain pigment molecules that absorb photon energy, which can be converted to excitation energy in the sensory neuron.
3. A visual field is the part of the outside world that an animal sees, made easier with a lens.
4. Invertebrate eyes are less complex.
   a. Many invertebrates have photoreceptor cells that detect changes in light intensity but do not form images.
   b. Insects and crustaceans have compound eyes with numerous photosensitive units, each capable of sampling a portion of the visual field to assemble a visual mosaic.
   c. Squids and octopuses have camera eyes, each with a lens, cornea, and retina.
B. The Human Eye
1. The outer layer consists of a sclera ("white" of the eye), which covers most of the eye; the cornea covers the front.
2. The middle layer consists of choroids, ciliary body, iris, and pupil.
3. The pigmented iris controls the amount of light entering through the pupil.
4. The cornea and lens bend the light rays so that the image is in focus on the retina.
C. Focus Mechanisms
1. Because of the bending of the light rays by the cornea, accommodation must be made by the lens so that the image is in focus on the retina.
   a. In fish and reptiles, the lens is moved forward and back (like a camera lens) to focus.
   b. In birds and mammals, the ciliary muscle changes the shape of the lens to focus.
2. To focus light on close objects, the ciliary muscle contracts so that the lens is rounder. This is why it is important to take breaks when reading or looking at a computer screen.

30.5 The Human Retina
A. Photoreceptors, linked to neurons, are located in the retina.
1. Rods are sensitive to dim light and detect changes in light intensity.
2. Cones respond to high-intensity light, contribute to sharp daytime vision, and detect colors.
   a. Each rod cell contains molecules that can be altered by light, resulting in voltage changes in membranes.
   b. Cone cells each carry a different pigment for red, green, and blue colors; cone cells at the fovea (center of retina) provide the greatest visual acuity.

B. The sense of vision is the result of processing the information through levels of synapsing neurons.
   1. Stimulation begins in the rods and cones, then moves to bipolar sensory neurons, then to ganglion cells whose axons form the optic nerves that lead to the brain's visual cortex.
   2. Signals travel along the optic nerve to the lateral geniculate nucleus of the brain, where the positions of the receptive fields correspond to those of the retina; final interpretation of sight occurs in the visual cortex.

30.6   Visual Disorders
   A. Color Blindness
      1. Red-green colorblindness is an X-linked, recessive abnormality.
      2. Some or all of the cone cells that detect red or green wavelengths are missing.
   B. Lack of Focus
      1. Astigmatism is a curvature of the cornea that results in improper focusing.
      2. In nearsightedness, the eyeball is too long or the ciliary muscle contracts too strongly and the object focuses in front of the retina.
      3. In farsightedness, the eyeball is not long enough or the lens is lazy and the object focuses behind the retina.
      4. Glasses, contacts, or surgery can correct most of these focusing problems.
   C. Age-Related Disorders
      1. *Macular degeneration* is a loss of the photoreceptor cells in the macula and fovea, the areas of most precise image focus.
      2. *Glaucoma* results from too much aqueous humor inside the eyeball, causing damage to the blood vessels and ganglion cells, affecting vision.
      3. A *cataract* is a gradual clouding of the lens reducing the amount of light entering the eye.

30.7   The Chemical Senses
   A. Sense of Smell
      1. The sensory pathways of olfaction and taste begin with chemoreceptors.
      2. Olfactory receptors detect water-soluble or volatile substances.
         a. Some receptors respond to pheromones, which are molecules released outside the body to elicit a social response in a member of the same species (for example, bombykol in silkworm moths).
         c. Reptiles and most mammals have a vomeronasal organ that responds to pheromones.
   B. Sense of Taste
      1. Taste receptors are chemoreceptors that enable animals to distinguish nutritious from noxious substances.
         a. Receptors of some animals are located on antennae, legs, tentacles, or fins.
         b. In humans, taste receptors are often components of taste buds distributed mostly on the tongue.
         c. The five main tastes include sweet, sour, salty, bitter, and umami.

30.8   Keeping the Body Balanced
   A. The sense of balance depends on the organs of equilibrium located in the inner ear.
      1. The vestibular apparatus (utricle, saccule, and semicircular canals) is a closed system of fluid-filled sacs and canals inside the ear.
         a. Inside the semicircular canals changing movements are detected (dynamic equilibrium) when fluid bends hair cells attached to sensory neurons.

   b. Organs in the saccule and utricle detect linear movements of the head (static equilibrium).

  2. The brain evaluates input from all receptors and integrates the information to maintain awareness of body position.

 B. Mismatched signals between, or overstimulation of, the hair cells of the vestibular apparatus can result in motion sickness.

31.5 Detecting Sounds

 A. Properties of Sound

  1. Sounds are traveling vibrations of mechanical energy.

  2. Hearing is the perception of sound.

  3. The wavelike forms of mechanical energy show amplitude (loudness) and frequency (pitch).

 B. Vertebrate Hearing

  1. The outer ear in mammals has a pinna for gathering sounds.

  2. The middle ear picks up vibrations from the eardrum and passes them to three small bones (hammer, anvil, and stirrup), which amplify the sounds before transmittal to the inner ear.

  3. The inner ear has a vestibular apparatus and the cochlea. The transduction of sound waves into action potentials takes place in the cochlea. Receptors in the form of hair cells respond to pressure waves transmitted through the surrounding fluid.

   a. Impulses are sent along the auditory nerve to the brain for interpretation.

   b. The hair cells in the organ of Corti of the human ear can be permanently damaged by prolonged exposure to intense sounds.

 C. Hearing Loss

  1. Hearing loss can occur as result of damage to the cilia that sense sound waves.

  2. Prolonged exposure to high sounds levels or exposure to some antibiotics can cause permanent hearing damage.

Suggestions for Presenting the Material

♦ The information on sensory systems may be more familiar to your students because of previous exposure to the material. Most junior and senior high school health and biology classes provide a fair introduction to the sensory organs.

♦ "If a tree falls in the woods and no one is there to hear it, does it make a sound?" The most unique portion of the brain is that all of perception is based on the ability to decode senses using our basic sensory receptors. Have a discussion about potential sensory stimuli that humans are unable to detect compared to other animals.

♦ Assuming your students *do* possess basic knowledge of the senses, it remains for you to emphasize two areas. The first is to relate the sense receptor and its interpretation within the brain. This is the subject of the initial portion of the chapter. The second is to provide some depth to the students' understanding of sensory receptor mechanisms.

♦ To demonstrate the difference between sensation and perception, show the students several examples of optical illusions. This helps to identify between what the eyes are actually taking in versus how the brain is seeing each image.

♦ Two of the more difficult questions beginning students pose are: "How do I distinguish, say, sight from sound?" and "How do I perceive varying intensities of a stimulus?" Emphasize the role of the brain as an interpreter of impulses directed to specific regions by specialized receptors. Also point out that the frequency of action potentials and the number of axons that "fire" provide the quality we call "intensity" of stimulus.

♦ Start lecture by turning on a CD with classical music. About 10 minutes into the lecture, see how many students are still paying attention to the music. Have a discussion about accommodation of the senses.

♦ Each of the senses provides unique input. Try to draw distinctions between those that operate rather independently (for example, sight) and cooperatively (for example, taste and smell).

♦ As you describe each sense, you should describe the structure of the sense organ, the mechanism of stimulus reception, and the interpretation of that stimulus. For example, the eye perceives light by reaction with chemicals on the retina to give the sensation of degrees of light and color.

♦ Be sure to point out to the students that incoming light must pass through several neuronal layers before it reaches the rods and cones. This seems backwards, but it works! Refer them to Figure 30.9.

Classroom and Laboratory Enrichment

♦ Have the students measure receptor field density. Have one student apply a two pointed compass to several areas on another student (back of neck, lip, trunk, forearm, finger), the student with the compass decreases the distance between the two points until the other person only feels one point. What areas are more sensitive? Why might that be?

♦ The simple detection of taste by a blindfolded person is still a favorite activity. Ask volunteers to hold their nose and close their eyes while drops of various liquids (vinegar, onion juice, lemon juice, and so on) are placed on the tongue. Ask them to identify the substances, but don't respond until you have repeated the experiment with the students using *both* smell and taste receptors.

♦ Try doing the taste experiment while the student holds their nose.

♦ If your lecture room or laboratory can be sufficiently darkened, you can demonstrate the abilities of rods and cones by a simple demonstration. Pull the shades and turn out the lights, quickly pull a red cloth from your pocket, and ask students to identify the color. Substitute other colors, change the light intensity, and wait for iris accommodation as variations in the protocol.

♦ One of the usual practices in optometrists' offices is to take instant photos of the retina. Ask for permission to present several photos, perhaps some exhibiting defects, and show them to the class. If the doctor will speak to the class, even better!

♦ Dissect a sheep eyeball.

♦ Use dissectible models of the ear and eye to illustrate their structure.

♦ Use a Snellen chart to demonstrate the visual acuity test.

♦ Use the Ishihara color charts for color blindness.

♦ Demonstrate the use of the ophthalmoscope for viewing the retina.

♦ Demonstrate the use of the otoscope for viewing the tympanic membrane.

♦ Using the five primary sensations have students make a map of their taste buds.

♦ Make up several animals that live in extreme environments. Have students brainstorm what sensory adaptations these animals may have to survive in their environment.

- There are several videos available commercially or via youtube that demonstrate individuals with sensory perception problems. Use these as demonstrations in your class.
- Be careful trying this; have a student spin around 10 times fast and try and walk straight forward. Discuss why the individual wants to move in one direction.

A Whale of a Dilemma (revisited)

- If neurons operate under the all-or-nothing principle, how are we able to distinguish soft sounds from loud sounds, or a gentle touch from a crushing blow?
- What responsibility do humans have to protect other species by curtailing sensory stimulation that may cause harm, like with the wail situation?
- What action should governments take to ensure the preservation of a particular sense, say hearing? What responsibility rests on the individual?
- How is the exposure to intense, unwanted sound different from say exposure to unwanted light or smells?

Additional Ideas for Classroom Discussion

- Do invertebrates, such as the cockroach, feel pain?
- Does pain exists in the area where you feel the pain or as a perception of pain in the brain?
- Sometimes musicians are said to have a "trained ear." What does this expression really mean?
- What is the advantage to an insect of having a compound eye?
- Why do many persons in their mid-forties need to use bifocal lenses?
- Is there any scientific basis to that "carrots are good for your eyes" slogan?
- What is "motion sickness"? How can it be controlled?
- Why is it difficult to orient your body in space?
- How can you tell where your body is in the space around you if your eyes are closed?
- In our "civilized" world, many people experience hearing loss as a result of aging, a condition called presbycusis. A study revealed that this condition did not exist in a primitive Sudanese tribe, the Mebans. This study suggests that some environmental factor of the civilized world is responsible for this type of deafness. What is that factor?
- It's trivia quiz time; name the sense that:
  a. Is most easily fatigued (thank goodness!)
  b. Can be dulled by smoking
  c. Cannot be shut out easily
  d. Has more receptors in more places than any other
  e. Uses small bones
  f. Operates like a camera

How Would You Vote? Classroom Discussion Ideas

- Monitor the voting for the online question. It would be highly desirable to limit the underwater noise that large ships make, but is it reasonable? Could we expect government officials to deny citizens the oil and other goods these ships carry in exchange for peace and quiet for whales? I doubt it.

- Have students complete classroom polling using the JoinIn clickers.

Term Paper Topics, Library Activities, and Special Projects

- Investigate the use of biofeedback for controlling pain, heart rate, and other autonomic functions.

- Scientists are gathering increasing amounts of evidence from laboratory studies and human testing that show gradual hearing loss caused by exposure to highly amplified music. Report on the dangers—are they real or imagined?

- One of the most intriguing subjects is the phenomenon of "phantom" pain. Explore its manifestations.

- One critique of evolution is that something like the human eye could not be produced through small successive changes. However, the evolution of the eye is well documented; report on the evolution of the eye.

- The fovea is an anatomical blind spot. Describe why that is the case and why humans do not have a blind spot in their vision.

- Many animals are incorrectly labeled as color blind; however many animals have varying densities of rods and cones. Describe several different animals rod and cone density and why evolution would have selected for those densities

- Based on your library research, prepare an "awards" list for the animal group that exhibits the keenest of each of the five major senses (sight, hearing, smell, taste, and touch).

- How do local anesthetics block the sensation of pain?

- Human do not rely on their sense of smell as much as other animals. Whay evolutionary changes may account for that?

- Describe the various problems associated with vision that are correctable with lenses, surgery, drugs, or other means.

- How can animals such as fly larvae (maggots) respond to and move away from light when they have no eyes of any kind?

- How does a detector device that checks blood vessel patterns in the eye and compares them to known records provide a better security system for military installations than do fingerprints?

- Radial keratotomy, a surgical procedure for correcting myopia, is controversial. What does this procedure involve, and what are the pros and cons of its use?

- Investigate the differences between nerve deafness and conductive deafness.

- Have students explore some of the websites to better appreciate and understand the complexity of the senses.

Possible Responses to *Data Analysis Activities*

1. The frequency that was most easily detected by all three was around 500 Hz.
2. The 1000 Hz sound had to be 10 dB for the 50 year old carpenter to hear.
3. The 25 year old carpenter had the best hear from the 4000-6000 Hz range.
4. Based on the data provided, it seems that the hearing loss in the 50 year old carpenter was caused by exposure on the job.

Possible Responses to *Critical Thinking* Questions

1. It is unlikely that humans have a magnetic sense, if we consider all the people who have gotten lost in the woods and not been able to determine which direction to proceed. On the other hand, there are those persons who seem to have an uncanny sense of direction even in new environments. Perhaps experiments could be devised in which persons are placed in unfamiliar locations and the hits and misses at determining the correct direction of the compass are recorded.

2. Evidently birds of prey, such as owls and hawks, are better at seeing prey beneath them when flying because of the arrangement of the retina in the eye. Hummingbirds would have a different arrangement because they have to hover in front of the flowers that they are feeding from, leading to an arrangement somewhere in middle back of the retina.

31

ENDOCRINE CONTROL

Chapter Outline

Objectives

1. Know the general mechanisms by which molecules integrate and control the various metabolic activities in both vertebrate and invertebrate animals.
2. Understand how the neuroendocrine center controls secretion rates of other endocrine glands and responses in nerves and muscles.
3. Know the major endocrine glands and their secretions.
4. Be familiar with other endocrine glands and their role in the body.
5. Know how sugar levels are regulated by hormones.
6. Differentiate the modes of action of steroid and nonsteroid hormones.

Key Terms

endocrine disruptors	second messengers	parathyroid glands	type 1 diabetes
local signaling	hypothalamus	adrenal glands	type 2 diabetes
molecules	pituitary gland	adrenal cortex	gonads
animal hormones	releasing hormones	adrenal medulla	pineal gland
endocrine system	inhibiting hormones	cortisol	thymus gland
steroid hormones	thyroid gland	pancreas	

Lecture Outline

31.1   Hormones in the Balance

   A. Pesticides may be endocrine disrupters.

      1. The herbicide atrazine caused tadpoles to develop both male and female reproductive organs and is feminizing zebrafish.

   B. It is very controversial, but some investigators believe that chemicals in the environment are contributing to earlier onset of puberty and low sperm counts in humans.

31.2   The Vertebrate Endocrine System

   A. Mechanisms of Intercellular Signaling

      1. Signaling molecules are hormones and secretions that can bind to target cells and elicit in them a response.

      2. There are several types of signaling molecules.

         a. *Neurotransmitters* are secreted from neurons and act on immediately adjacent target cells for a short time.

         b. *Local signaling molecules* are secreted from cells of many different tissues; they act locally and are swiftly degraded.

         c. *Animal hormones* are secreted from endocrine sources and some neurons, and are then transported by the blood to target cells.

   B. Discovery of Hormones

      1. In the early 1900s, Bayliss and Starling first demonstrated that a hormone (later named secretin) released into the blood triggers secretion of pancreatic juices.

      2. Starling coined the word *hormone* for internal secretions released into the bloodstream that influence the activities of other tissues and organs.

      3. The sources of hormones may be collectively called the "endocrine system," which shows intimate connections with the nervous system.

   C. Neuroendocrine Interactions

      1. Nervous and endocrine function is closely tied together.

      2. Hormones can affect brain function, i.e. sleep/wake cycles.

      3. The nervous system can affect hormone release.

32.2   The Nature of Hormone Action

   A. Signal Reception, Transduction, and Response

      1. Cell communication has three steps.

         a. A signal activates a target cell receptor.

         b. It is transduced to a molecular form that acts in the receiving cell.

         c. The cell may undertake a functional response.

2. Enzymes make hormones from a variety of sources.
   a. Steroid hormones are derived from cholesterol.
   b. Amine hormones are modified amino acids.
   c. Peptide hormones are short chains of amino acids.
3. Intracellular Receptors
   a. Lipids form a hormone-receptor complex by binding to a receptor in the cytoplasm or nucleus.
   b. Most often, it binds to a promoter near a hormonally regulated gene.
   c. Transcription and translation result in a protein product that carries out the target cell's response to the signal.
4. Receptors at the Plasma Membrane
   a. The peptide/protein hormone-receptor complex activates transport proteins or triggers the opening of gated channel proteins that span the cell membrane.
   b. The hormone-receptor complex may stimulate the production of cyclic AMP, a "second messenger," which amplifies the signal by activating numerous enzymes.

B. Receptor Function and Diversity
   1. Cells do not always switch some activity on or off in response to hormones. Their sensitivity is affected by other factors.
      a. First, cells ignore any hormone unless they have receptor for it.
      b. Second, different hormones often interact. The binding of one may have an effect on another.
      c. Third, the concentration of a hormone in a tissue affects the chance that a target cell will respond.
      d. Fourth, a target cell's health influences response.
      e. Fifth, environmental cues such as temperature or day length can influence a cell's response.

31.4 The Hypothalamus and Pituitary Gland

A. The hypothalamus and pituitary gland work jointly as the neural-endocrine control center.
   1. The hypothalamus is a portion of the brain that monitors internal conditions and emotional states.
   2. The pituitary is a pea-sized gland connected to the hypothalamus by a stalk.
      a. The posterior lobe of the pituitary consists of nervous tissue and releases two neurohormones made in the hypothalamus.
      b. The anterior lobe consists of glandular tissue and secretes six hormones and controls the release of others.

B. Posterior Lobe Function
   1. The axons of neuron cell bodies in the hypothalamus extend down into the posterior lobe of the pituitary.
   2. Two hormones are released into the capillary bed.
      a. Antidiuretic hormone (ADH) acts on the walls of kidney tubules to control the body's water and solute levels.
      b. Oxytocin (OT) triggers uterine muscle contractions to expel the fetus and acts on mammary glands to release milk.

C. Anterior Pituitary Function
   1. The hypothalamus produces releasing and inhibiting hormones that target the anterior pituitary.
      a. Most of the hypothalamic hormones are releasers that call for secretion of hormones by target cells.
      b. Others are inhibitors that discourage target cell secretions.

2. The anterior lobe regulates secretion by many other endocrine glands.
   a. ACTH stimulates the adrenal cortex.
   b. TSH stimulates the thyroid gland.
   c. FSH stimulates egg formation in females and sperm formation in males.
   d. LH also acts on the ovary to release an egg and on the testes to release sperm.
   e. GH, or growth hormone, triggers secretions from liver cells that promote growth in bone and soft tissues in the young.
      1) Oversecretion of GH in adulthood causes a thickening of skin and bones called acromegaly.
   f. *Prolactin* acts on the mammary glands to sustain milk production.

31.5 Sources and Effects of Other Vertebrate Hormones

   A. In addition to the major endocrine organs, several other areas are capable of endocrine action.
      1. The gut secretes hormones that affect digestion.
      2. Adipose cells secrete leptin which suppresses appetite.
      3. The kidneys secrete erythropoietin which stimulates red blood cell production.
      4. The heart secretes atrial natriuretic peptide which stimulates the kidneys to excrete water and salt.

31.6 Thyroid and Parathyroid Glands

   A. Feedback Control of Thyroid Function
      1. The human thyroid gland is at the base of the neck; it secretes calcitonin and thyroid hormone.
         a. In humans, calcitonin affects calcium levels slightly.
         b. Thyroid hormone is central to metabolism and development.
      2. The anterior pituitary and hypothalamus control thyroid hormone secretion by negative feedback loops.
         a. A hormone's blood level above a set point slows its secretion.
         b. A low level of thyroid hormone causes the hypothalamus to secret more.
      3. The synthesis of thyroid hormone requires iodine, a nutrient we get from food. Deficiency leads to a lack of thyroid hormone and an enlarged thyroid.

   B. Parathyroid Glands and Calcium Levels
      1. Four parathyroid glands on the posterior surface of the thyroid secrete parathyroid hormone (PTH), the main control over the calcium in blood.
      2. Vitamin D deficiency lowers the calcium level in blood, which leads to over secretion of PTH and bone breakdown.

31.7 The Adrenal Glands

   A. The Adrenal Cortex
      1. One adrenal gland is located on top of each kidney.
         a. The outermost part of each gland, the adrenal cortex, releases steroid hormones.
         b. One controls sodium and water reabsorption in the kidneys.
         c. The adrenal cortex also produces and secretes small amounts of sex hormones.
      2. Among the secretions of the outer portion is cortisol, which helps control blood glucose levels.
         a. Cortisol secretion is an example of a homeostatic feedback loop.
         b. When blood levels of glucose fall (as in hypoglycemia), the hypothalamus releases CRH → anterior pituitary → ACTH → adrenal cortex → cortisol, which prevents muscle cells from withdrawing glucose from the blood.

     c. When the body is stressed, as in painful injury, the nervous system provides an override mechanism in which the levels of cortisol remain high to promote healing—this is called the cortisol stress response.

B. The Adrenal Medulla
1. Stress, excitement, or danger also triggers hormone secretion by the adrenal medulla, the inner part of the adrenal gland.
2. Sympathetic signals elicit the secretion of norepinephrine and epinephrine, which bring about the fight or flight response.

C. Stress, Elevated Cortisol, and Health
1. Ongoing stress can lead to health problems.
2. Elevated cortisol levels disrupt the production and release of other hormones.
3. The long-term use of synthetic corticosteroids has similar effects. These compounds are often prescribed to relieve pain and suppress inflammation.

D. Adrenal Insufficiency
1. Autoimmune disorders, like Addison's Disease, can lead to suppression of cortisol.

31.8 Pancreatic Hormones

A. The pancreas is a dual function gland; its exocrine function is to secrete digestive enzymes.

B. Certain cells within the pancreas have an endocrine function.
1. Alpha cells secrete *glucagon*, which causes glycogen stored in the liver to be converted to glucose, raising its levels in the blood.
2. Beta cells secrete *insulin*, which stimulates the uptake of glucose by liver, muscle, and adipose to reduce glucose levels in the blood, especially after a meal.
3. Delta cells secrete somatostatin, a hormone that helps control digestion and nutrient absorption. It can also inhibit the secretion of insulin and glucagon.

31.9 Diabetes

A. Diabetes mellitus is a metabolic disorder in which cells do not take up glucose as they should.
1. As a result, sugar accumulates in blood and in urine.
2. Complications develop throughout the body.
3. Uncontrolled diabetes damages blood vessels and nerves, especially in the arms, hands, legs, and feet.

B. Type 1 Diabetes
1. In type 1 diabetes, insulin is no longer produced because the beta cells have been destroyed by an autoimmune response; treatment is by insulin injection.
2. Type 1 diabetes accounts for only 5 to 10 percent of all reported cases, but it is the most dangerous.

C. Type 2 Diabetes
1. In type 2 diabetes, the insulin levels are near normal but the target cells cannot respond to the hormone; controlling diet is an effective treatment.
2. Worldwide, this type of diabetes is soaring; there is an association with western eating habits and sedentary lifestyles.

D. Hypoglycemia
1. Hypoglycemia blood glucose levels fall low enough to disrupt normal body functions.
2. While some tumors can cause this, it is usually attributed to diabetics who over-inject insulin—causing insulin shock.

31.10 The Gonads, Pineal Gland, and Thymus

   A. The Gonads
      1. Gonads are the primary reproductive organs, such as the male testes and female ovaries in humans.
         a. Gonads produce gametes.
         b. Gonads also secrete sex hormones, including estrogens and testosterone.
      2. Puberty is the post-embryonic stage of development when the reproductive organs and structures mature.

   B. The Pineal Gland
      1. Deep inside the vertebrate brain is the pineal gland, which secretes the hormone melatonin.
         a. Melatonin functions in the biological clock.
         b. Its secretions declines when the brain responds to signals about light that are sent from the retina. Production varies seasonally just as light levels do.
      2. Variations in melatonin levels affect the gonads in many species.
         a. In male songbirds, long winter nights result in higher melatonin levels and a dampened sexual activity.
         b. In spring, with longer days, melatonin levels drop and sexual activity increases.

   C. The Thymus
      1. The thymus gland lies beneath the breastbone and secretes hormones that help infection-fighting white blood cells, called T cells, to mature.
      2. The thymus grows until a person reaches puberty, following which it shrinks in size.

31.11 Invertebrate Hormones

   A. Evolution of Receptor Cells
      1. Molecular evidence points to gene duplication and subsequent divergences as a source for the diverse hormones and hormone receptors in vertebrates.
      2. Studies of sea anemones have shown similar receptor and other signaling molecules in the plasma membrane.

   B. Control of Molting
      1. Molting is the period of shedding of body coverings.
      2. Molting is primarily under the control of ecdysone, a steroid hormone.
      3. Chemicals that mimic or interfere with ecdysone and other hormones can be used as insecticides.

Suggestions for Presenting the Material

♦ The core of this chapter is the section describing the various endocrine glands, and their secretions and functions. Focus on the role of hormones and carefully reinforce terminology that you deem important and appropriate for your class.

♦ After suitable introductions have been made, there is no practical way to escape a presentation of the major glands and their secretions. Shift the work to the students, have the students work in small groups to prepare presentations about each gland, its hormones and targets.

♦ When discussing signaling mechanisms (Animated Figure 31.2), emphasize the chemical nature of steroids (lipid-bilayer soluble) versus proteins (not lipid soluble) and the need for a second messenger, namely cyclic AMP. Playing this animation will go a long way to providing visual context for the array of new terms.

- This chapter contains excellent figures and tables; these can be used to great advantage. One seasoned instructor asks students to bring their texts to class and invites them to follow along. You may choose to prepare your own overhead transparencies of the tables to help everyone keep up the pace.

- This chapter presents an array of new words—hormone names that are long and unfamiliar. As an aid to learning, subdivide the name and give the literal meaning of each portion, for example, adreno (adrenals)—cortico (cortex)—tropic (stimulate).

- Alternatively, select a few key hormones and actions that may be more familiar with students. For example, spend some time discussing the pancreatic hormones and their relationship with diabetes.

- "Antagonism" was mentioned in connection with the autonomic nervous system. Take this opportunity to point out antagonistic hormone pairs: calcitonin/parathyroid hormone; insulin/glucagon.

- Emphasize the necessity of learning both the hormone name and its abbreviation, which is often more commonly used than the name itself.

- Trace the path that synthetic chemicals could take through our food or water supply.

- Notice that even though the gonadal hormones are introduced, they are not discussed thoroughly until Chapter 38.

- Discuss the impact of diabetes on humans and the role our diet and lifestyles play in the perpetuation of this disease.

- Have some students that have type I diabetes discuss their experience managing diabetes. Find some people with type II diabetes to share their experiences.

- Type II diabetes is quickly becoming one of the leading health care problems in the US. Have a panel discussion with doctors, nurses, nutritionists, and patients that reoutinely deal with type II diabetes.

- Point out that some organs function as both endocrine and exocrine glands.

- **Common Student Misconceptions**
  - Students struggle most with the array of new terms; typically they have some idea about the release of hormones and their impact but little about the true complex role that hormones play in animal physiology.

Classroom and Laboratory Enrichment

- Human nature is such that students are very interested in the abnormalities that hyper- and hyposecretion of human hormones cause. You can stimulate interest in the total area of hormone control by showing pictures of the physical manifestations of such imbalances.

- Organic foods make a claim that they are produced in chemical free environments, design an inquiry to test this claim versus non-organic foods.

- Ask a local health scientist or practitioner to report on his/her experiences with hormone therapy.

- Seek evidence of a class member who has experienced or witnessed an epinephrine-mediated emergency response. Ask him/her to report.

260 Chapter Thirty-One

- Survey local grocery stores to determine the relative stocks of iodized and noniodized salt. Are there implications for the unwary consumer?

- Use a dissectible mannequin or a dissected fetal pig to show the location of the various endocrine glands.

Hormones in Balance (revisited)

- What responsibilities do humans have to regulate the use of endocrine disruptors in the environment?

- Why might it be important to protect frogs and fish regardless of whether the chemicals act as endocrine disruptors in humans?

- What do you think the potential is for endocrine disruptors to make their way into our food and water supplies?

- What are some examples of chemicals that might make their way into our food and water supplies?

Additional Ideas for Classroom Discussion

- Do hormones occur only in vertebrates? Have you ever heard of "ecdysone" in insects?

- Why does insulin have to be administered by injection rather than orally?

- If hormones are released to the entire body, why do they have effects only in specific areas?

- The effects of hormones take longer to act but last longer in duration than nervous responses. Why is that the case?

- Using knowledge gained in a freshman biology class, an athlete decided he might be able to raise his blood sugar quickly by injecting glucagon. This attempt is doomed for what reasons?

- What is the possible connection between the pineal gland and puberty?

- Some hormones seem to be doing another's duties; for example, sex hormones from the adrenals, blood sugar control by epinephrine, and thyroxine regulation of growth. Why is this so?

- What are anabolic steroids? Why do some athletes use them? What are the dangers associated with their use?

- Why do anabolic steroids cause long term complications for people who abuse them?

- Oxytocin is commonly used to induce labor. How does it work?

- Why do certain hypoglycemics, who regularly ingest excessive amounts of sugar, frequently develop diabetes later in life?

- What are some of the problems associated with hormone replacement therapy?

- People with untreated diabetes type I tend to be very thirsty and yet produce large volumes of urine. Why is this so?

- What are the differences between diabetes type I and type II? Why is diabetes types II so difficult to manage compared to type I?

How Would You Vote? Classroom Discussion Ideas

- Have students complete class polling using the JoinIn clickers. Use The regulation of chemicals used in food production that may disrupt hormone function in untargeted species can have devastating impacts on populations locally and regionally. While it is difficult to wait for scientific studies to fully investigate all aspects of potential chemical interactions, it may prove ecologically judicious to seek answers before such chemicals are released into our ecosystems.

Term Paper Topics, Library Activities, and Special Projects

- Have students research endocrine disruptors or suspected endocrine disruptors and present reports to the class about their findings.

- Have individual students or small groups work on a position paper related to the How Would You Vote topic on the release of chemicals that disrupt hormone actions in animals but increase human food supplies.

- Discuss the ethical issues of administering somatotropin to persons of normal stature who wish to become super athletes.

- Investigate and report on the fascinating discovery of the role of insulin by researchers Banting and Best.

- Select a major hormone and prepare an in-depth report on the abnormalities that may result from hypo- and hypersecretion.

- The role of hormones in insect development has been elucidated in only the past 40 years. Check an insect physiology text, and prepare a chronology of this research.

- Investigate stem cell research designed to correct type I diabetes, which is the result of autoimmune responses.

- Do a report that discusses the differences between endocrine disorders that are based on problems with the hormone versus problems with a receptor.

- Investigate which human hormones are now being produced using genetic engineering methods.

- Describe why endocrine disorders might be difficult to treat.

- Have students research the use of hormones in animal feed or injections that influence growth rates. How are these chemicals passed into and through the human portion of the food chain?

- Research the differences between diabetes type I and diabetes type II.

- As children, many of us were told that "sleeping makes you grow." Is there any scientific basis for this statement?

Possible Responses to *Data Analysis Activities*

1. The city with the highest sperm count was New York while Columbia, MO had the lowest sperm count.
2. The city with the sperm motility was New York while Columbia, MO had the sperm motility.

3. Smoking, age, and STD exposure all adversely affect sperm counts. However, that does not seem to make a difference in this regional data. For example, the oldest population with the most exposure to STDs, NY, has the highest sperm count.
4. Based on this data, the area that is most exposed to farmland has the lowest sperm count. This supports the hypothesis that agricultural runoff is having an effect on sperm count.

Possible Responses to *Critical Thinking* Questions

1. If a woman were to produce milk when she was not pregnant that would indicate an injury to the anterior pituitary gland and increase in levels of prolactin release.

2. Melatonin is a hormone that is released based on the amount of light an individual is exposed to; less light and darkness increase melatonin while bright light or long exposures to light suppress melatonin. A person who is blind and does not detect light would secrete more melatonin at a more constant level than sighted people. If blind women go through puberty and have reduced cancer rates because of melatonin, it would be due to an increased level of melatonin.

32

STRUCTURAL SUPPORT AND MOVEMENT

Chapter Outline

Objectives

1. Compare invertebrate and vertebrate motor systems in terms of skeletal and muscular components and their interactions.
2. Describe the details of bone construction.
3. Explain in detail the structure of muscles, from the molecular level to the organ systems level.
4. Explain how biochemical events occur in muscle contractions and how antagonistic muscle action refines movements.
5. Describe the impact of exercise, disease, and aging on bone and muscles.

Key Terms

hydrostatic skeleton	axial skeleton	joint	actin
exoskeleton	appendicular skeleton	ligaments	myosin
endoskeleton	compact bone	tendon	sliding-filament model
vertebral column	spongy bone	skeletal muscle fibers	sarcoplasmic reticulum
vertebrae	red marrow	myofibrils	motor unit
intervertebral disks	yellow marrow	sarcomeres	muscle tension

Lecture Outline

32.1 Muscles and Myostatin

    A. Like neurons, muscles cells generally do not divide after birth, rather they grow larger by building internal protein mass.

        1. Testosterone and human growth hormone both increase the mass of proteins inside of muscle cells.

        2. Synthetic hormones can lead to performance enhancement, which is why many governing bodies punish the use of such chemicals.

    B. Myostatin is a regulatory protein that limits protein growth in muscle cells.

        1. Inhibition of myostatin leads to increased muscle mass, strength, and decreased fat deposition.

        2. Drugs that inhibit myostatin may help treat muscle wasting diseases like muscular dystrophy but may lead to abuse by people who wish to attain inhuman muscle mass.

32.2 Animal Skeletons

    A. Types of Skeletons

        1. Animals move by the action of muscles, which need some medium or structural element against which the force of contraction can be applied

        2. There are three main types of skeletons in animals.

            a. In *hydrostatic skeletons,* the force of contraction is applied against internal fluids; examples are sea anemones and earthworms.

            b. In an *exoskeleton,* the force is against rigid external body parts, such as shells or plates; an example is arthropods.

            c. In an *endoskeleton,* the force is applied against rigid internal cartilage and bones; for example, vertebrates.

    B. Features of the Vertebrate Endoskeleton

        1. The skeleton of sharks and some other fish are made of cartilage while most endoskeletons consist of less cartilage with a bone matrix.

        2. Vertebrate refers to the vertebral column, backbone, common to vertebrates.

            a. Vertebrae are individual boney segments that make up the protective backbone.

            b. Intervertebral discs are made of cartilage and separate vertebrae in order to absorb shock and allow flexibility in the backbone.

        3. Vertebrate skeletons are divided into two major portions.

            a. The *appendicular skeleton* consists of the pectoral girdle with attached upper limbs, and the pelvic girdle with lower limbs.

            b. The *axial skeleton* includes the skull, vertebral column (individual bones separated by cartilaginous intervertebral disks), ribs, and sternum.

C. The Human Skeleton
   1. The human skeleton has typical vertebrate features as well special adaptations to standing upright.
      a. The cranium consists of several flattened, fused bones.
      b. Twelve paired ribs fuse with the sternum to from a protective case.
      c. The vertebral column extends from fused pelvic bones in an S shape to the cranium.
      d. The pectoral girdle is very flexible and consists of the scapula and clavicle and attaches to the bones of the arm.
      e. The pelvic girdle is much less flexible and consists of several fused bones that can support the weight of the upper body.

32.3   Bones and Joints
   A. Bones Structure and Function
      1. Bone tissue serves 5 key functions.
         a. Bones interact with muscles to maintain or change the position of body parts.
         b. Bones support the skin and soft organs.
         c. Bones form compartments that enclose and protect soft internal organs.
         d. Bone tissue acts as a depository for calcium, phosphorus, and other ions.
         e. Parts of some bones are sites of blood cell production.
      2. Bone is a connective tissue with living cells (osteocytes) and collagen fibers distributed throughout a ground substance that is hardened by calcium salts.
      3. Compact bone tissue forms the bone's shaft and the outer portion of its two ends.
         a. Concentric layers form around canals that contain blood vessels and nerves.
         b. The living bone cells reside in the ground substance.
      3. Spongy bone tissue has areas of red marrow that produce blood cells; cavities in most mature bones contain yellow marrow, which can be converted to red marrow if blood cell production needs to be increased.
   B. Bone Formation and Turnover
      1. Bones are constantly being remodeled.
      2. Bone turnover helps to maintain calcium levels for the entire body; enzymes from bone cells dissolve bone tissue and release calcium to the interstitial fluid and blood.
         a. Calcitonin from the thyroid causes levels to decline by storing the excess calcium in bones.
         b. Parathyroid hormone detects low levels of calcium and pulls sufficient quantities out of storage.
      3. Osteoporosis (decreased bone density) is associated with decreases in osteoblast activity, sex hormone production, exercise, and calcium uptake.
   C. Where Bones Meet — Skeletal Joints
      1. Joints are areas of contact or near-contact between bones.
         a. Fibrous joints are fixed in place, like the skull bones.
         b. Cartilaginous joints, such as between the ribs, permit slight movement.
         c. Synovial joints are freely-movable joints that are stabilized by ligaments — straps of dense connective tissue that attach bone to bone. These joints are found in places like your knee, ankle, and elbow.
      2. Joints are vulnerable to stress.
         a. Stretching or twisting a joint may result in a strain; tearing ligaments or tendons is a sprain; a dislocation occurs when the bones in a joint move out of place.
         b. In osteoarthritis, the cartilage at the end of the bone has worn away.
         c. In rheumatoid arthritis, the membranes in the joints become inflamed, the cartilage degenerates, and bone is deposited into the joint.

33.3 Skeletal–Muscular Systems
  A. Skeletal muscles are functional partners of bones.
    1. Each skeletal muscle contains several bundles of perhaps hundreds or thousands of muscle cells (fibers).
      a. Skeletal muscles, often arranged in antagonistic pairs, interact with one another and with bones.
      b. Tendons, cordlike straps of dense connective tissue, attach muscle to bone.
    2. Because most muscle attachments are located close to joints, only a small contraction is needed to produce considerable movement of some body part.
    3. There are three types of muscle in the human body.
      a. Only skeletal muscle is the functional partner of bone.
      b. Smooth muscle is found in soft internal organs such as the digestive tract.
      c. Cardiac muscle is found only in the heart wall.
  B. Tender or Torn Tendon
    1. Overuse of tendons can cause tendonitis, or inflammation, in tendons and can be treated with anti-inflammatory drugs.
    2. Chronic overuse can change the shape of a tendon leading to tendonosis which can only be treated with rest and physical therapy.
    3. When a tendon tears is can only be treated with surgery.

32.5 How Skeletal Muscle Contracts
  A. Structure of Skeletal Muscle
    1. Muscle cells (fibers) are composed of myofibrils, which are composed of two kinds of parallel filaments: actin and myosin.
      a. Actin is a thin filament composed of two beaded strands twisted together.
      b. Myosin is thicker; each molecule has a bulbous head and long tail making it resemble a golf club.
    2. The actin filaments are anchored at each end by the Z band (or disk), surrounded by the myosin filaments.
    3. All of the sarcomeres and their component myofibrils contract in parallel.
  B. Sliding-Filament Model
    1. Muscles shorten because the sarcomeres shorten within each cell by the sliding-filament model.
    2. The mechanism "pulls" the Z disks of each sarcomere toward each other.
      a. By forming cross-bridges, the myosin filaments slide along and pull the actin filaments toward the center of the sarcomere.
      b. The cross-bridges are formed when the local concentration of calcium exposes binding sites.
      c. ATP supplies the energy for both attachment and detachment.

32.6 From Signal to Responses
  A. Nervous Control of Contraction
    1. Signals from motor neurons result in action potentials in muscle fibers, causing the release of calcium stored in the sarcoplasmic reticulum.
    2. Actin and myosin interact and muscle contraction begins.
    3. Calcium balance is restored so that the muscle is ready for the next contraction.

B. Motor Units and Muscle Tension
    1. A motor neuron and all the muscle cells under its control are a *motor unit*.
        a. A single, brief stimulus to a motor unit causes a brief contraction called a muscle twitch.
        b. Repeated stimulation without a sufficient interval causes a sustained contraction called tetanus.
    2. When muscle tension is greater than the forces opposing it, contracting muscle cells shorten; when opposing forces are stronger, muscle cells lengthen.
        a. Isotonically contracting muscles shorten and move a load.
        b. Isometrically contracting muscles develop tension but do not shorten.
C. Energy for Contraction
    1. During brief periods of intense muscle activity, creatine phosphate is the source of phosphate to remake ATP.
    2. When muscle action is moderate, most of the ATP is provided by aerobic electron transport phosphorylation, which is dependent on oxygen supply and the number of mitochondria present.
    3. Anaerobic pathways, such as the conversion of pyruvate to lactate, also provide muscles energy.
D. Types of Muscle Fibers
    1. Red muscle fibers have high myoglobin content and an abundance of mitochondria allowing for efficient aerobic function.
    2. White Muscle fibers lack myoglobin, large reserves of glycogen, and metabolize using lactic acid fermentation.
    3. Fast twitch muscles have a faster ATPase on the myosin head so the muscle twitch is faster than slow twitch fibers.
        a. All white fibers are fast twitch.
        b. Red fibers are either fast or slow twitch.
    4. An individual's composition of muscle fibers depends on genetics.

32.7 Muscles and Health
    A. Effects of Exercise
        1. Aerobic exercise at low intensity and for a long duration makes muscles more resistant to fatigue by increasing their blood supply and the number of mitochondria.
        2. Anaerobic exercise increases actin, myosin, and glycolyitc enzymes but not endurance.
        3. Muscle tension decreases as adult humans age, but exercise remains beneficial in improving blood circulation and preventing loss of muscle tissue.
    B. Muscular Dystrophies
        1. Muscular dystrophies are a class of genetic disorders in which muscles progressively weaken and degenerate.
        2. A mutation on the X chromosome disrupts the normal action of dystrophin, one of the proteins in the plasma membrane of muscle fibers. This mutant form allows foreign material to enter a muscle fiber, and the fiber deteriorates.
    C. Motor Neuron Disorders
        1. Muscular weakness or paralysis can occur when motor neurons cannot signal muscles to contract.
            a. Survivors of polio were often left with this paralysis post infection.
            b. ALS, also known as Lou Gehrig 's disease, occurs when motor neurons die.

D. Botulism and Tetanus
   1. *Clostridium botulinum* is an anaerobic soil bacterium that can cause botulism.
      a. The toxin enters motor neurons and stops the production of acetylcholine.
      b. Affected persons must be treated immediately to prevent cessation of heart beating and breathing.
      c. *C. tetani* endospores can live in the soil for years.
         i. After entering the body, the spores germinate and release a toxin.
         ii. The muscles remain in contraction (tetanus) and gradually weaken over several days.

Suggestions for Presenting the Material

♦ Although this chapter's title may imply that the content will be about muscles only, remind the students that muscles can move the body *only* in conjunction with the bones.

♦ The extent to which you require your students to learn the names of bones is your choice. However, with today's emphasis on the human body, the use of the anatomical names for body parts, including bones, is becoming more common.

♦ Try to find some common ground with your students in respect to learning about the muscle and bone relationships in the body. Know the majors of the students in your class. Dancers may be keen on understanding movement; athletes may be more interested in injury or training.

♦ This is a topic that is familiar to many people, but there are many myths about muscle training and the use of dietary supplements. Invite athletic trainers or sports physiologists into your class to discuss training and the use of supplements responsibly.

♦ The formation, development, and replacement of bone can also be presented by referring briefly to the material on tissues in Chapter 28.

♦ Figure 32.12 and animation of muscle contraction are helpful in presenting the ultrastructure of muscle. Using the analogy of a rope (see the Enrichment section below) is also very helpful.

♦ Don't miss the opportunity when discussing the sliding-filament model to emphasize the molecular explanation for the fact that individual muscles can only pull, not push. Again, the rope analogy is helpful.

♦ The dual role of calcium as the provider of bone hardness and as muscle facilitator should be made clear; the role of calcium (and it's interaction with troponin and tropomyosin) is omitted from this edition. Be careful and provide references if you bring this relationship up in class.

♦ Emphasize all the points that ATP would be required for a muscle contraction: active transport in neurons and sarcoplasmic reticulum, and in the recharging of myosin heads, but not for the actual power stroke of the myosin. This leads to a discussion of rigor mortis; why do the muscles become rigid after all of the ATP is used up?

Classroom and Laboratory Enrichment

♦ Ask a forensic pathologist to tell the class about the wealth of information that the skeletal remains can reveal about one's health and medical history at the time of death.

♦ Demonstrate the action of muscle by using a "muscle contraction kit" available from biological supply houses.

♦ For a cheaper demonstration of muscle/tendon actions, find a butcher or chicken/turkey farm and procure several chicken or turkey feet (most places will give them to you for free). You can use pliers to pull on tendons and see their actions. The legs can also be dissected to examine the tendon relationships. This is better than using preserved materials because of the effect that preservatives have on the proteins in the muscles.

♦ If you have one available, the use of a real human skeleton will better stimulate student interest and present a three-dimensional aspect to your lecture.

♦ Arrange for a body builder to appear before the class (more effective if unannounced). Describe the origin, insertion, and function of some major muscles as they are flexed.

♦ Obtain case studies where skeletal remains have been used to solve crimes or identify information about victims.

♦ Have students prepare presentations on individual weight lifting exercises and how that specific exercise effects individual muscles preferentially.

♦ Students can visualize the ultrastructure of muscles more readily if the comparison to a large rope is made. The best is one used for boat anchorage because it is made of many subunits.

♦ Show a video of arthroscopic surgery. Many orthopedic surgeons routinely produce such videos and give them to their patients.

♦ Use models of freely-movable joints to illustrate their structure.

♦ Obtain a fresh beef knee joint to demonstrate the structure and tissues of that joint.

♦ If available, use a model of a sarcomere to facilitate the students' comprehension of that microscopic structure.

♦ Take this opportunity to educate your students about osteoporosis and how to prevent it. Several companies have comprehensive posters detailing osteoporosis to use as visual aides.

Muscles and Myostatin (revisited)

♦ How do people normally increase muscle mass?

♦ Why does inhibition of myostatin lead to muscle growth?

♦ Why would myostatin inhibitors help to treat both obesity and muscular dystrophy?

♦ What ethical dilemmas might arise if an effective myostatin inhibitor existed?

Additional Ideas for Classroom Discussion

- Distinguish between hydrostatic skeleton, endoskeleton, and exoskeleton.

- The exoskeleton and muscle arrangement of ants allow them to accomplish extraordinary feats for their small size. Why are there not larger animals with similar motor system arrangements?

- What are the benefits and drawbacks of a hydrostatic skeleton? An exoskeleton? An endoskeleton?

- What are the effects of moderate strength training on the *skeletal* system?

- Consider the present evolutionary state of the human knee. Is it sufficient for the punishment modern athletic activity places on it?

- Why is bone considered "nonliving" by those unfamiliar with its structure? Why is considered living by biologists?

- What technological and research developments allowed the sliding-filament *theory* of the 1960s to become the sliding-filament *model* of the 1980s?

- Evaluate this statement: Muscles only pull. If this is true, how can you *push* a door open?

- Which muscles are collectively called the "hamstrings"? In which sports are they most likely to be injured and why?

- What are effective ways to train a muscle?

- What are the differences between resistance training and weight lifting?

- What would be the difference in muscle composition between an elite sprinter and elite marathon runner?

- What is a "slipped" or herniated disk? What are its most common causes?

How Would You Vote? Classroom Discussion Ideas

- Monitor the voting for the online question. It is very unfortunate for the American consumer that dietary supplements are NOT regulated by the FDA. This "loophole" allows anyone to sell anything for any reason with no guarantee (by testing results) that the product is (1) *effective* for the purposes listing on the label, and (2) safe taken as directed. This oversight will have far reaching negative health repercussions in future years.

- Have students complete classroom polling with JoinIn clickers.

Term Paper Topics, Library Activities, and Special Projects

- A challenging task is the assembly of a disarticulated skeleton. If your department has one, attempt to lay the bones out on a lab table in their approximate position and articulation. This is a good group project.

- Investigate the difference(s) in the development of muscles for power (weight) lifting versus development for body sculpting and exhibition.

- Document the development of the sliding-filament theory of muscle contraction and the research evidence that supports it.

- Describe the additional proteins involved in muscle contractions: troponin and tropomyosin.

- Describe the role of sodium, calcium, creatine, creatine phosphate, and ATP in muscle contraction.
- Describe the effects of "muscle gain" supplements and research into their effectiveness.
- Report on the technique of arthroscopic surgery.
- Research the following spinal disorders: spina bifida, scoliosis, lordosis, and kyphosis.
- Investigate the use of electrical stimulation to accelerate the healing of bone fractures.
- Discuss the muscle disease called myasthenia gravis, its suspected cause, and the type of treatment currently used.
- Create a weight training plan to increase strength and a plan to increase endurance and describe the why each plan would work.
- Research osteoporosis. Report on the disease and several ways to prevent it.
- Contrast the difference between muscular dystrophies and multiple sclerosis.
- Investigate the use of Botox as a cosmetic procedure. How does it work? Where does the toxin come from? Is it something you would do?

Possible Responses to *Data Analysis Activities*

1. All nine children in the experimental group experienced bone growth while none of the children in the control group demonstrated bone growth.
2. The experimental group had roughly 1/3 of the fractures that the control group experienced.
3. Yes.

Possible Responses to *Critical Thinking* Questions

1. Creatine supplements are widely available in health food stores, a fact that most persons take as proof of their effectiveness and safety. Unfortunately, they have not been certified by the FDA as either. It *is* known that creatine is an intracellular source of phosphate for the regeneration of the ATP needed in muscle contraction. Research has shown that creatine will improve performance during brief, high-intensity exercise (marathons may not qualify here!). Some persons will accept this as reason enough to take the pills because "winning is everything." However, as with any exogenous compound taken into the body, the long-term effects must be evaluated. Again, because the FDA has not approved this "drug," the properly gathered data is not available. Lydia should be informed that she takes creatine "at her own risk."

2. Duchenne muscular dystrophy is caused by a single mutant gene on the X chromosome. It is an X-linked recessive condition. Therefore, if Zachary was carrying the mutation he would have the disease. Since he does not have it, then his offspring will not be likely to have it, since it does not run in his wife's family.

33

CIRCULATION

Chapter Outline

Objectives

1. Explain how the cardiovascular systems of vertebrates differ from those of invertebrates.
2. Describe the composition and functions of blood.
3. Trace the routes of blood flow in the human cardiovascular system, including pulmonary and systemic circuits.
4. Explain what is happening during each portion of the cardiac cycle.
5. Discuss the factors that cause blood to exist under different pressures.
6. Describe the composition and function of the lymphatic system.

Key Terms

circulatory system	veins	systole	vasoconstriction
heart	venules	sinoatrial node	blood pressure
blood	aorta	atrioventricular node	systolic pressure
open circulatory system	atrium, atria	cell count	diastolic pressure
closed circulatory	ventricle	red blood cells	lymph vascular system
system	superior vena cava	white blood cells	lymph
capillaries	inferior vena cava	platelets	lymph nodes
pulmonary circuit	pulmonary artery	hemostasis	spleen
systemic circuit	pulmonary vein	fibrin	
arteries	cardiac cycle	pulse	
arterioles	diastole	vasodilation	

Lecture Outline

33.1   And Then My Heart Stood Still

    A. The heart requires an electrical signal to function properly.

        1. The pacemaker in the heart wall causes the heart muscle to contract.

        2. Sudden cardiac arrest is the cessation of the beat.

    B. Normal heartbeat must be restored as quickly as possible.

        1. CPR is usually the quickest and requires no special equipment.

        2. Defibrillators are becoming more available, even in public places.

33.2   The Nature of Blood Circulation

    A. All organisms require transport mechanisms to get nutrients and oxygen to cells.

    B. Open and Closed Circulatory Systems

        1. The circulatory system moves substances to and from cells.

            a. Blood is a fluid tissue composed of water, solutes, and formed elements.

            b. The heart is a muscular pump that creates the pressure to move blood.

            c. Blood makes exchanges with interstitial fluid in tissue spaces between cells.

            d. Exchanges between interstitial fluid and blood keep the internal environment tolerable.

        2. Arthropods and most mollusks have an open system.

            a. Blood is pumped from a heart into large tissue spaces where organs are "bathed."

            b. Blood is returned to the heart at a leisurely rate.

        3. Vertebrates have a closed system.

            a. All the vessels and the heart are connected so that blood remains enclosed.

            b. Blood volume is constant and is equal to the heart's output at any time.

            c. Flow rate slows as blood moves through the fine capillaries of the capillary beds.

    C. Evolution of Vertebrate Circulation

        1. All vertebrates have a closed circulatory system, differing in their pumps and plumbing.

        2. In fishes, blood flows in a single circuit, passing through a heart of two chambers.

        3. In amphibians the heart is partitioned into right and left halves, permitting a partial separation into two circuits.

4. Birds and mammals have two separate circuits of blood flow.
    a. The right half of the heart receives deoxygenated blood and pumps it to the lungs of the pulmonary circuit.
    b. The left half receives blood from the lungs and pumps the oxygen-rich blood to all of the tissues and organs in the systemic circuit.
5. With two fully separate circuits, blood pressure can be regulated in each one.

33.2 The Human Cardiovascular System

A. The general route of blood circulation is: heart → arteries → arterioles → capillaries → venules → veins → heart.

B. Blood circulates through two circuits.
    1. The human heart is a double pump, propelling blood into the two cardiovascular circuits.
        a. In the *pulmonary circuit*, oxygen-poor blood is pumped to the lungs from the right side of the heart, and oxygen-rich blood is returned from the lungs to the left side.
        b. In the *systemic circuit*, oxygen-rich blood is pumped from the left side of the heart to all the body.
    2. Usually a given volume of blood in either circuit passes through only one capillary bed; an exception is blood from the digestive tract that passes through the liver before entering the general circulation.

33.3 The Heart Is a Lonely Pumper

A. Structure of the Heart
    1. The heart's durability arises from its layered structure.
        a. The outer covering of the heart is the pericardium, which is partially a fluid-filled sac and the outer part of the heart wall.
        b. The bulk of the heart wall is the heart muscle—myocardium—serviced by coronary circulation.
        c. The heart is lined with a smooth endothelium.
    2. The heart has four chambers and four valves.
        a. Each half of the heart consists of an atrium (receiving) and a ventricle (pumping) separated by an atrioventricular valve.
        b. Blood exits each ventricle through a semilunar valve.

B. Flow To, Through, and From the Heart
    1. Deoxygenated blood drains into the heart from the superior and inferior vena cava.
    2. Blood is transported to the lungs by pulmonary arteries to be oxygenated and back to the heart via pulmonary veins.

C. The Cardiac Cycle
    1. The cardiac cycle consists of a sequence of contraction (systole) and relaxation (diastole).
        a. As the atria fill, the ventricles are relaxed.
        b. Pressure of the blood in the atria forces the atrioventricular valves to open; the ventricles continue to fill as the atria contract.
        c. The ventricles contract, the atrioventricular valves close, and blood flows out through the semilunar valves.
        d. It is the contraction of the ventricles that is the driving force for blood circulation.

D. Setting the Pace for Contraction
    1. Cardiac muscle tissue is found only in the heart.
    2. Cardiac muscle has orderly arrays of sarcomeres, which contract by a sliding-filament mechanism.
    3. Because of the close junctions of cardiac muscle cells, they contract in unison.

4. The initiation and distribution of signals that tell other cardiac muscle cells to contract is a function of the cardiac conduction system.

5. Excitation for a heartbeat is initiated in the sinoatrial (SA) node (the cardiac pacemaker) then passes to the atrioventricular (AV) node for ventricular contraction; this is the cardiac conduction system.

33.5 Characteristics of Blood

A. Functions of Blood

1. It carries oxygen and nutrients to cells, and it carries secretions and wastes away from them.

2. It helps stabilize internal pH.

3. It is a highway for cells and proteins that protect and repair tissues.

4. It equalizes body temperature in birds and mammals.

B. Human Blood Composition and Volume

1. In humans, body size and the concentrations of water and solutes dictate blood volume.

   a. On average, humans have about five liters, about 6–8 percent of body weight.

   b. In vertebrates, blood is a viscous fluid, thicker than water and more slowly flowing.

   c. Blood's fluid portion is called plasma; the cellular portion consists of blood cells and platelets.

   d. Stem cells are unspecialized cells that retain the capacity for mitotic cell division.

2. Plasma (50–60 percent of blood volume)

   a. This fluid portion of the blood is mostly water, about 90 percent.

   b. Some plasma proteins transport lipids and vitamins; others function in immune responses and blood clotting.

   c. Plasma also contains ions, glucose, lipids, amino acids, vitamins, hormones, and dissolved gases. It also acts as a solvent for hundreds of different plasma proteins.

3. Red Blood Cells (RBCs)

   a. Red blood cells transport oxygen from lungs to aerobically respiring cells and carry carbon dioxide wastes from them.

   b. In mammals, when red blood cells mature the cells lose their nucleus. They are flexible disks with a depression at their center.

   c. Red blood cells contain hemoglobin—an iron-containing protein that binds with oxygen. Hemoglobin occupies about 98 percent of the interior of human red blood cells. It is what gives red blood cells their bright red color.

   d. They form from stem cells in bone marrow, lose their nuclei, and live about 120 days.

   e. The number of cells per microliter (about 5 million) is called the cell count.

4. White Blood Cells (WBCs)

   a. White blood cells function in daily housekeeping activities and in defense.

   b. Some remove dead or worn-out cells and protect us against invading microbes and foreign agents.

   c. White blood cells differ in size, nuclear shape, and staining traits.

      i. Numbers fluctuate with levels of activity and state of health.

      ii. Several types act as phagocytes with roles in inflammation.

      iii. Several act in specific immune defense.

5. Platelets and Hemostasis

   a. Megakaryocytes are 10 to 15 times bigger than other blood cells that form in bone marrow.

   b. They break up into platelets, membrane-bound fragments of cytoplasm that last five to nine days and function in blood clotting.

    c. Hemostasis is the process that stops blood loss during injury.
       i. When a vessel is injured it constricts to stop blood loss.
      ii. Platelets adhere to the site and activate fibrin to create a mesh network over the site.

33.6 Blood Vessel Structure and Function

A. Rapid Transport in Arteries
1. Arteries are large diameter vessels that present low resistance to flow as they conduct blood *away from* the heart.
2. Because of their elastic walls, arteries tend to "smooth out" the pulsations associated with the discontinuous pumping cycle of the heart.

B. Adjusting Flow at Arterioles
1. Blood flow to organs, except the brain, is a function of activity.
    a. The brain gets a constant supply.
    b. When you exercise, blood flow to the kidneys and gut slows.
2. Neural and endocrine signals cause changes in arteriole diameter by stimulating the muscle cells in the walls.
    a. If the blood pressure increases, the arterioles are instructed to relax (vasodilation).
    b. If the pressure decreases, the diameter of the arterioles decreases (vasoconstriction).
3. Arterioles serve as control points where adjustments can be made in blood volume distribution.

C. Exchange at Capillaries
1. Capillaries are one endothelial cell thick and have a narrow diameter that facilitates transport and exchange.

D. Return to the Heart
1. Veins and venules have valves to prevent backwards flow.

33.7 Blood Pressure

A. Controlling Blood Pressure
1. A special instrument with a cuff surrounding the upper arm is connected to a pressure-measuring device.
    a. The peak pressure (systolic) is recorded when the ventricles are contracting—120mm is typical.
    b. The lowest pressure (diastolic) is reached when the ventricles are relaxing—80mm.
2. Blood pressure is related to blood volume, constriction of the arterioles.
    a. Receptors on the aorta and in carotid arteries of the neck alert a control center in the brain when blood pressure drops or increases.
    b. In response, the brain calls for changes in cardiac output and arteriole diameter.

33.8 Capillaries Exchange

A. Slowdown at Capillaries
1. Flow of blood slows at capillaries because the cross-sectional area of capillaries is much larger than the flow from the arteries can supply; this slowdown makes exchange more effective.

B. How Substances Cross Capillaries Walls
2. Movement across the capillary is by several modes: diffusion (of oxygen and carbon dioxide), endocytosis and exocytosis (of proteins), between the cells (of ions), and bulk flow (of water).
    a. At the beginning of a capillary bed, there is a movement of plasma out into the interstitial fluid in a process known as ultrafiltration.

  b. Further on, some tissue fluid moves into the capillary through clefts between its endothelial walls in a process known as capillary reabsorption.

33.9 Vein Function

 A. Moving Blood to the Heart
  1. Capillaries merge into venules then into veins.
   a. Blood pressure and resistance to flow in veins are both low; valves prevent backflow.
   b. Veins are blood volume reservoirs (50–60 percent of blood volume) because their walls are elastic.
  2. The movement of skeletal muscles squeezes the veins and pushes the blood along against the forces of gravity.
 B. When Venous Flow Slows
  1. Damage to valves leads to blood pooling in veins; in peripheral veins this can cause varicose veins; in the rectum or anus this can cause hemorrhoids.

33.10 Cardiovascular Disorders

 A. Rhythms and Arrhythmias
  1. ECGs can reveal arrhythmias, an abnormal heartbeat.
   a. Bradycardia is a below average resting cardiac rate, which may be the result of ongoing exercise.
   b. Tachycardia, fast heartbeat, is caused by exercise or stress.
  2. Atrial and ventricular fibrillation are repeated contractions that disrupt the normal cardiac cycle.
 B. Atherosclerosis and Heart Disease
  1. In this condition, arteries thicken and lose elasticity. The condition worsens when lipids such as cholesterol build up in the arterial wall.
   a. Low-density lipoproteins (LDLs) infiltrate the walls, causing an atherosclerotic plaque to form.
   b. Platelets gather at the site and initiate clot formation.
  2. Enlarging plaques and blood clots narrow or block arteries.
   a. A clot that stays in place is a thrombus; a dislodged, traveling clot is an embolus.
   b. The tiny coronary arteries are the most vulnerable, leading to the familiar signs of a heart attack.
 C. Risk Factors
  1. Cardiovascular disorders are the leading cause of death in the U.S.
  2. Tobacco smoking tops the list of risk factors contributing to this problem.
  3. Others include genetics, hypertension, cholesterol, obesity, diabetes, age, physical inactivity, and gender.

33.11 Interactions with the Lymphatic System

 A. The lymphatic system returns water and solutes from interstitial fluid (lymph) to the bloodstream via transport tubes.
 B. Lymph Vascular System
  1. The lymph vascular system includes lymph capillaries and lymph vessels.
  2. It collects water and plasma proteins that leaked out of capillaries.
  3. It delivers fats absorbed from food in the small intestine to the blood.
  4. It transports cellular debris, pathogens, and foreign cells to lymph nodes for disposal.
 C. Lymphoid Organs and Tissues
  1. Lymph nodes are strategically located at intervals along lymph vessels.
   a. Before entering blood, lymph trickles through at least one node and gets filtered.

  b. Masses of white blood cells are located inside the nodes and attack nonself items.
2. The spleen is the largest lymphoid organ; it removes spent RBCs, holds macrophages, and produces red blood cells in human embryos.
3. The thymus secretes hormones that regulate the activity of lymphocytes and is a site where they multiply and mature.

Suggestions for Presenting the Material

♦ Begin your presentation of this chapter by showing the video introduction of Figure 33.1 This will help tie together students' understanding of the functional relationship between the circulatory system and the electrical conduction of signals in the nervous system.

♦ You may choose to vary the sequence of topics presented in the text and begin with the "plumbing" prior to the blood composition. The text lends itself well to this arrangement. Nearly all lectures on circulation conclude with the *lymphatic system*.

♦ There are a large number of blood vessels. Be aware of which ones you want to make important for your students to know.

♦ This chapter omits a discussion of ECGs. Students, however, may ne interested to know how they are recorded and what they are measuring.

♦ One of the strengths of this text is the inclusion of excellent summary tables such as the one found in Figure 33.9, which reviews the components of the blood. These tables should be called to the students' attention, perhaps by using an overhead reproduction.

♦ The animated figures in the chapter are worth the time to show in class to help place the unfamiliar or new concepts in context for your students.

♦ When discussing the functions of blood, it may be helpful to refer to other lectures that will expand on the topic. Such instances include: white blood cells and immunity (Chapter 34); red blood cells and respiration (Chapter 35); and nutrient transport (Chapter 36).

♦ Because of the complexity of the entire cardiovascular system, the simplified scheme in Figure 33.5 is useful for introducing the concepts of pulmonary and systemic circuits. The concept of oxygen-rich and oxygen-poor blood can be emphasized here. This can be followed by the heart pathways and contraction sequence.

♦ The heartbeat, pulse, and blood pressure are measurable quantities of interest to students; therefore, these deserve as much lecture time as is feasible.

♦ Capillary exchange is a topic that allows you to review previous lectures on diffusion and active transport.

♦ The mechanism of clotting, and the somewhat confusing term hemostasis (*not homeostasis*) used to describe it, may need special attention and/or simplification.

♦ **Common Student Misconceptions**

  o Usually students feel they have a fair grasp of circulation until the lymphatic system is introduced. Then it is a "What's this for?" expression. Stress the necessity for such a system and the *one-way return* of fluid to the general blood supply.

  o This chapter includes a discussion of closed and open circulatory systems. Students will be familiar with a closed system because that is the type in the human body; but the open concept implies a great deal of "hemorrhaging," which sounds *terminal*, but in this context, is *normal*.

Classroom and Laboratory Enrichment

♦ Ask a physician to demonstrate an artificial pacemaker; include comments on the limitations and usefulness of such an artificial device versus the natural SA node.

♦ Request a cow heart(s) from a local meat processor (be sure to ask them to leave the aorta on it) to use in a lab setting. Students are amazed at the size of the heart! Dissect both the atria and ventricles to show students the similarity in mammal heart structure and function. Show students the SA node and other key features of the exterior of the heart.

♦ In dissecting a fetal pig, take care to preserve and trace large blood vessels around the heart. Have the students practice observations by comparing and contrasting the gross anatomy of parallel arteries and veins.

♦ Make contact at a local pathology lab. Some pathologists maintain demonstration organs for use in classrooms. Have them bring in a diseased heart.

♦ To illustrate cardiovascular disorders, show a video of a heart bypass operation. Using a model, illustrate for students what is "bypassed" in the procedure.

♦ Use angiograms to demonstrate blood flow around the heart before and after bypass and/or catheterization procedures. Contact a local cardiologist to come and talk about the procedures.

♦ Discuss the role of cholesterol and its contribution to heart disease.

♦ Students love to see the animated Figure 34.11 as it includes both familiar information and introduces them to the less familiar. You may elect to use this video to both introduce the cardiovascular system and as a study or review tool.

♦ Conduct a panel discussion that includes physicians, pathologists, EMTs, and physical therapists to discuss problems associated with heart disease.

♦ Borrow a sphygmomanometer and ask a person skilled in its use to explain how blood pressure is determined, using members of the class as volunteers.

♦ Obtain a digital sphygmomanometer and have students track their blood pressure though the course of events in lab. Can you make any generalizations from your data?

♦ Conduct a simple experiment where students measure the effects of exercise on heart rate and blood pressure. This makes a good data analysis activity because you can generate a large amount of data in a short period of time.

♦ Obtain a recording of heart sounds as they would be heard through a stethoscope. Relate sounds to events of the normal and abnormal cardiac cycle.

♦ Have EMTs or a physician com to lab and demonstrate CPR and the use of AEDs.

And Then My Heart Stood Still (revisited)

♦ How can you explain the fact that persons who die of heart attack (lack of oxygen to heart muscle) have perfectly adequate amounts of oxygenated blood in their heart chambers?

♦ Ask students to reflect on heart disease or cardiac disorders in their own families.

♦ Should CPR training be a required skill to be learned in high school or college? Compare the value of knowing this technique versus a mastery of past participles.

Additional Ideas for Classroom Discussion

♦ What are indicators of heart disease?

♦ In the case of a heart attack, why is one of the initial treatments to give a drug like TPA that inhibits clotting?

♦ Who would have a bigger heart, an average individual, a couch potato, or a marathon runner? Why?

♦ Why does high blood pressure cause heart disease?

♦ Aerobic training lowers heart rate and blood pressure, why is that beneficial?

♦ Why are veins portrayed as blue? Is deoxygenated blood blue?

♦ The heart is really a "double pump." It is also, of course, divided into four chambers. Does this mean that one pump consists of atria, the other of ventricles, *or* does it mean the left and right sides are pumping to separate circulations? Explain your reasoning.

♦ Why is the lymph system such a "highway" for the spread of certain cancers?

♦ Why is hemophilia in *females* (although extremely rare) more often fatal than in males?

♦ Evaluate the truthfulness of the statement "I'm a blood relative." Is there a more accurate expression that could replace this one?

♦ Have students reflect on and discuss the ceaseless activity of their own heart. Have them complete the simple calculations for how many times per hour, day, month, and year their own heart beats.

♦ In small groups, have students compile a list of common activities of college-age students that are considered risk factors for heart disease.

How Would You Vote? Classroom Discussion Ideas

♦ Have students complete class polling using the JoinIn clickers. There are many good topics that high schools should add to their curricula, including lifestyle education (smoking, birth control, etc.). Most of these topics are concerned with maintaining the health and wellbeing of oneself. Learning CPR in preparation for helping someone else is always a worthy use of time. Knowing CPR may save a person's life—it may save yours someday.

Term Paper Topics, Library Activities, and Special Projects

♦ Have students research one type of cardiovascular disorder of interest. Have them report on their results in a short paper.

♦ Have students complete a position paper taking a pro or con position on the trend toward further regulation of activities and foods that are considered prime contributors to cardiovascular disease in the U.S.

♦ Research the causes of cardio vascular disorders. What types of indicators are preventable?

♦ Evaluate the effectiveness of various cardiovascular training programs on heart activity.

♦ Evaluate the reported links between lipids and cardiovascular diseases.

◆ Have students research blood contents. What are normal levels of materials in the blood? What is the difference between good and bad cholesterol? What are different types of anemia.

◆ Survey the various corrective surgical procedures that are routinely performed on the heart and its vessels. Select one or two for an in-depth report.

◆ It is often said that "the heart never rests." True, it does beat continuously from before birth until death, usually at old age. However, it does rest for 0.3 second after each beat. Assuming a steady pulse of 70 beats per minute, calculate the *total* amount of time the heart has rested in a person 75 years old.

Possible Responses to *Data Analysis Activities*

1. The death rate for blacks is about 20/100,000 higher than whites in the stroke belt.
2. The death rate for blacks in the stroke belt is about 60/100,000 higher than it is in New York State.
3. Whites is the stroke belt have a higher death rate than blacks in New York State.
4. Yes.

Possible Responses to *Critical Thinking* Questions

1. Moving the leg muscles during a long airplane flight or during any other time of prolonged inactivity is a good idea. Why? Because blood in the veins of the legs is under practically zero pressure and can be moved upward in the body toward the heart only by the squeezing pressure of the skeletal muscle on the vessels. Moving about the cabin would be a good idea, but in today's smaller jets, this may be impractical (especially with that damnable beverage cart blocking the way). Nevertheless, you can move your legs while seated and attempt to exercise the muscles at least a little bit.

2. Mitochondria provide energy for the cell to perform all its functions. The cardiac muscle cells never cease their activity under normal conditions, so they would need a continuous supply of energy, which the abundance of mitochondria can provide. Skeletal muscle cells, on the other hand, do have periods of rest where ATP provided by the mitochondria is not needed.

34

IMMUNITY

Chapter Outline

Objectives

1. Describe typical external barriers that organisms present to invading organisms.
2. Understand the process involved in the nonspecific inflammatory response.
3. Understand how vertebrates (especially mammals) recognize and discriminate between self and nonself tissues.
4. Distinguish between antibody-mediated and cell-mediated patterns of defense.
5. Explain the mechanisms of immunological specificity and memory.
6. Explain the basis for immunization.
7. Describe some examples of immune failures, and identify as specifically as you can which weapons in the immunity arsenal failed in each case.

Key Terms

immunity

complement

innate immunity

adaptive immunity

antigen

cytokines

neutrophils

macrophages

dendritic cells

eosinophils

basophils

mast cells

B cell

T Cell

cytotoxic T cell

NK cell

normal flora

plaque

lysozyme

inflammation

fever

T cell receptors

MHC markers

antibody

B cell receptor

self/nonself

 recognition

specificity

diversity

memory

effector cell

memory cell

antibody-mediated

 response

cell-mediated

 response

agglutination

allergy

allergen

immunization

vaccine

autoimmune

 response

AIDS

Lecture Outline

34.1   Frankie's Last Wish

    A.   Cervical cancer is caused by Human Papillomavirus (HPV).

        1.   As HPV infects cervical cells it can lead to transformation into cancerous cells.

        2.   About 10 strains of HPV are known to cause a lingering infection that leads to cervical cancer.

    B.   In 2006, Gardasil was approved as a vaccine that protects people from infection from four of the most common strains of HPV.

34.2   Integrated Responses to Threats

    A.   Evolution of the Body's Defenses

        1.   Immunity is the body's ability to resist and combat infections with a multitude of infectious invaders, most of which have coevolved with humans and every other animal.

        2.   Discriminating between self and nonself was a key innovation in the evolutionary history of animals, giving them the ability to detect antigens on viruses, bacteria, and other foreign cells, as well as tumor cells, toxins, and allergens.

        3.   Pattern receptors of early animals were functionally connected to chemical responses, causing the release of complement (circulating proteins that can tag or kill microbes) when anything was bound to the receptors.

            a.   Innate immunity offers immediate response to a fixed set of nonself cues.

            b.   Adaptive immunity evolved later, in order to tailor specific defense responses to specific pathogens and thus a diversity of threats.

    B.   Three Lines of Defense

        1.   Physical barriers such as intact skin and the linings of body cavities offer important protection.

        2.   Innate immunity is a second line of defense and begins after the tissue is damaged or after an antigen is recognized in the body.

        3.   The third line of defense is adaptive immunity in which white blood cells target and destroy specific antigens.

C. The Defenders
  1. White blood cells, produced from stem cells in bone marrow, not only circulate in blood and plasma, but also reside in lymph nodes, spleen, liver, kidneys, etc. where they stand ready to defend.
  2. Three kinds are swift to act but do not mount a sustained attack.
    a. *Neutrophils* are the most abundant and phagocytize bacteria.
    b. *Eosinophils* secrete enzymes that punch holes in parasitic worms.
    c. *Basophils* and *mast cells* secrete histamine, which sustains inflammation.
  3. Macrophages (formed from immature cells called monocytes) are slower to act but can engulf and digest just about any foreign agent, or damage tissue.
  4. Natural killer cells patrol the body looking for tumor cells, virus-infected cells, and bacterial cells; sometimes they punch holes in targeted cells to kill them.

35.2 Surface Barriers
  A. Vertebrate skin has tough surface layers made of dead, keratin-packed epithelial cells.
    1. Intact skin is an important barrier.
    2. Wounds or natural openings are portals for pathogen entry.

  B. Mucus provides a mechanical barrier by coating epithelial linings and trapping bacteria.
    1. Ciliated, mucous membranes in the respiratory tract sweep out bacteria and particles.
    2. Coughing is a mechanical barrier that expels bacteria.
    3. Lysozymes in the mucus act as a chemical barrier and degrade bacterial cell walls.
    4. The normal microbial inhabitants of the gut and vagina keep the growth of pathogens in check.
    5. Stomach and intestinal secretions can kill bacteria.
    6. Urine, with its low pH and flushing action, keeps pathogens from the urinary tract.

34.4 Innate Immune Response
  A. Phagocytes and Complement
    1. Macrophages patrolling interstitial fluid are the first to encounter a threat engulfing and digesting almost anything other than undamaged body cells; if their pattern receptors bind to a pathogen, they begin to secrete cytokines, which signal for more aid.
    2. Complement immediately binds to the antigen at a phagocyte's surface or to circulating microbes.
      a. These proteins are activated in a cascading fashion, yielding large concentrations of activated complement molecules in a localized tissue region.
      b. Activated complement proteins have many effects in aiding the elimination of invaders of the body.

  B. Inflammation
    1. Acute inflammation is a local response to tissue invasion or damage; redness, warmth, swelling, and pain occur at the site of damage or invasion.
    2. While complement proteins are being activated, basophils and mast cells secrete histamine, which promotes leakage of fluid out of capillaries.

  C. Fever
    1. Fever occurs when the body's core temperature exceeds the normal set point.
    2. Fevers of around 100°F can enhance immune functions.

34.5 Antigen Receptors in Adaptive Immunity
  A. Antibodies and Other Antigen Receptors
    1. T cell receptors (TCRs) recognize non-self antigens.
    2. TCRs also interact with human self markers called MHC markers.

3. Antibodies are a type of antigen receptor.
   a. An antibody molecule has four polypeptide chains—two identical "light" chains and two identical "heavy" chains.
   b. Each antibody has a variable region that is specific to an antigen.
4. There are five classes of antibodies, each serving different functions.
   a. IgM and IgD, the first to be secreted during immune response, trigger the complement cascade.
   b. IgG antibodies activate complement proteins and neutralize many toxins; they are long-lasting and can cross the placenta to protect the fetus.
   c. IgE antibodies stimulate basophils and mast cells to secrete histamine.
   d. IgA, present in saliva, tears, and mucus, helps repel invaders at the start of the respiratory system.
3. Each B cell is bristling with antibodies that all have the same kind of binding site for a specific antigen.

B. Antigen Receptor Diversity
1. Human can make billions of antigen receptors because the genes that encode for the receptors exist in separate locations that are spliced together.

C. Antigen Processing
1. Recognition of a specific antigen stimulates production of large populations of B and T cells ready for battle.
   a. When antigens enter the body, they are engulfed and destroyed by macrophages but not completely—the antigen becomes attached to the MHC marker to form an MHC-antigen complex, which is then displayed on the macrophage's surface.
   b. Any cell that displays antigen with a suitable MHC marker is known as an antigen-presenting cell and will be noticed by lymphocytes.

34.6 Overview of Adaptive Immune Responses

A. There are four characteristics of the innate, adaptive immune response.
1. The immune system is capable of *self/non-self recognition*.
2. The immune system has *specificity* in that it can respond to a specific antigen.
3. The immune system has *diversity* in that it can adapt to new antigens over time.
4. The immune system has *memory* in that it can remember antigens after an intial exposure.

B. First Step—The Antigen Alert
1. When a naive T cell binds to an antigen-MHC complex, the T cell secretes cytokines.
2. The cytokines signal other B and T cells to divide into two populations: effector and memory cells.
3. Effector cells are differentiated lymphocytes that act immediately against the antigen, and memory cells are long-lived B and T cells that develop during the first encounter.

C. Two Arms of Adaptive Immunity
1. Adaptive immunity has two separate arms for defense that work together to eliminate diverse threats.
   a. B cells and their progeny (effector cells) produce antibodies, which are specific substances that tag targets for destruction; this is called the antibody-mediated response.
   b. Cytotoxic T cells and natural killer cells (NK) destroy infected body cells and tumor cells, in cell-mediated immune responses.

D. Intercepting and Clearing Out Antigen
   1. T cells recognize antigen only if a macrophage, dendritic cell, or B cell presents it and then enters a lymph node after engulfing it; there the T cells are alerted to the threat.
   2. Daily, about 25 billion lymphocytes pass through each lymph node; lymph nodes trap most of free antigen that might be circulating.
   3. When effector cells have reduced the antigen-bearing agents in the body, the immune response slows and then stops.

34.7 The Antibody-Mediated Response
   B. An Antibody-Mediated Response
      1. When a pathogen enters the body, it is coated with complement and shunted to a lymph node where naive B cells await.
      2. The antigen binds with the antibody and is taken into the B cell only to reemerge activated as an MHC-antigen complex to be displayed on the cell surface.
      3. After an encounter with a helper T cell, the B cell undergoes mitosis to produce many B effector cells and memory cells.
      4. Effector cells produce enormous quantities of antibodies (primary immune response), which will seek out antigens (freely circulating in extracellular fluid) and mark them for disposal.

34.8 Blood Typing
   A. ABO blood typing is based upon surface markers on red blood cells.
   B. Type A has A markers; type B has B markers; type AB has both markers; type O has neither marker.
   C. Blood typing becomes important during blood transfusions; giving someone an incompatible transfusion leads to agglutination of the transfused blood.

34.9 The Cell-Mediated Response
   A. An antibody-mediated response is not effective against intracellular pathogens; the cell-mediated response targets sick or infected body cells.
   B. T cells recognize the antigen-MHC complexes on infected cells and kill them by punching holes in their cell membranes with proteins called perforins; they also can induce apoptosis.
   C. The main targets of cell-mediated responses are cells infected with intracellular pathogens, tumor cells, and cells of organ transplants.
   D. Natural killer cells are not activated by antigen-MHC complexes.
      1. NK cells appear to be lymphocytes (but not B or T) produced in the bone marrow.
      2. Natural killer (NK) cells kill tumor cells and virus-infected cells spontaneously, without the presence of antibodies.

34.10 Allergies
   A. An allergy is a secondary immune response to a normally harmless substance.
   B. Exposure triggers production of IgE antibodies, which cause the release of histamines and prostaglandins.
   C. A local inflammatory response results; death can even occur due to anaphylactic shock, a condition in which air passages leading to the lungs constrict, fluid escapes too rapidly from capillaries, and blood pressure drops.

34.11 Vaccines

A. Immunization is process designed to stimulate immunity in an individual.
    1. Active immunization involves a deliberate production of memory cells by a vaccine that is made from killed or weakened bacteria or viruses.
    2. Passive immunization occurs when someone is given antibodies purified from another individual.
    3. Vaccines are an important part of worldwide public health programs.

34.12 Antibodies Awry

A. The body has a built in detection for self-recognizing T cell receptors; when this fails an autoimmune disorder can occur.

B. Autoimmune Disorders
    1. In autoimmune disorders, lymphocytes turn against the body's own cells.
    2. Rheumatoid arthritis is an inflammation of the joints caused by antibody that treats the body's own IgG molecules as if they were antigens.
    3. Grave's disorder is an overproduction of thyroid hormones, which elevate metabolic rates, heart fibrillations, nervousness, and weight loss.
    4. Multiple sclerosis arises when autoreactive T cells trigger inflammation of myelin sheaths, disrupting nerve transmission.

C. Immunodeficiency
    1. When cell-mediated immunity is weakened, infections that would normally not be serious become life-threatening.
    2. In acquired immune deficiency syndrome (AIDS), the cause is the human immunodeficiency virus (HIV).

35.9 AIDS

A. AIDS is a group of disorders that follow infection by HIV.
    1. The virus cripples the immune system and makes the body highly susceptible to usually harmless infections.
    2. There is no cure for those already infected.

B. HIV Revisited
    1. HIV is am enveloped retrovirus.

C. A Titanic Struggle
    1. HIV is a retrovirus that primarily infects macrophages, dendritic cells, and helper T cells.
    2. The virus takes over the cell's machinery to produce massive quantities of new HIV particles.
    3. The first stage is mostly cleared by the body's adaptive response, but HIV particles continue to multiply in the lymph nodes and shed viral envelope proteins, which enter the blood; years or decades may pass with normal immune functioning.
    4. Glycoproteins shed from HIV envelopes bind to IgE, causing an inflammatory response and prompting more production of IgE instead of the needed IgG in a continuing cycle.
    5. Eventually, as the adaptive immunity mechanisms become less and less effective, the number of T cells destroyed exceeds the new T cells made, and the battle tilts in favor of the virus.

D. Transmission
    1. The most common mode of transmission is by unprotected sex with an infected partner.
    2. Infected mothers can pass it to a newborn during vaginal birth.
    3. Small amounts of blood on shared needles can be passed among drug users, or by patients in hospitals of poor countries.

E. Testing
    1. HIV is 99% detectable within three months of exposure.

F. Drugs and Vaccines
    1. Current drugs cannot cure HIV, but some can slow down its progression by interfering with viral replication.
    2. Vaccines have not been effective because the virus replicates in the immune system and mutates quickly.
    3. Education and prevention are key to slowing the spread of HIV.

Suggestions for Presenting the Material

♦   Do a quick review of pathogens so that students reactivate that information. In a two semester course, that information may have been covered in a previous semester.

♦   Discuss the difference between a disease and a disorder, and a pathogen, an infection, and a disease.

♦   Use current examples, there are unending outbreaks that spend time in the media that may help interest the students.

♦   Spend time discussing why a method for attacking both extracellular pathogens (antibody mediated response) and intracellular agents (cell mediated response) would be required.

♦   A quick glance at the figures in this chapter should convince anyone that the subject of body defense mechanisms is a difficult one, both to teach and to learn. However, with patience and explicit use of those same figures, the topics can be mastered.

♦   Spend some time clarifying the role of complement and cytokines to reduce the misconception that they are the same thing.

♦   The understanding of defense against foreign organisms by the human body is complicated by the fact that so many mechanisms and factors are operating at the same time. Remind students to use summary tables to help with this information.

♦   Spend time talking about the generalized steps in adaptive immunity (recognition which leads to stimulation of effectors and memory cells) and then make sure you reference those general steps when you discuss the antibody and cell mediated pathways. Use that to convey the similarities and then point out the differences.

♦   Have students role play the parts of the adaptive immune responses.

♦   It is unfortunate, but many people have misconceptions about vaccines. For example, despite numerous studies that discredit a link between the MMR vaccine and autism and despite the fact that the original researcher who made the claim was discredited by his coauthors and found to have committed fraud in his work, many people still harbor the feeling that MMR causes Autism. The unfortunate problem that this is leading to is the reemergence of measles, mumps, and rubella in Europe and North America in pockets where the disease were absent for many years. Do you best to dispel myths about vaccines and discuss what is known about the use and production of vaccines.

♦   The topics of *immunization* and *immune diseases* are always of interest to students and should be given sufficient time to allow for student discussion.

♦   **Common Student Misconceptions:**
    o   Students sometimes have difficulty distinguishing "antibody" from "antigen." This may help: Antigen is short for ***anti*body *gen*erator**.

Classroom and Laboratory Enrichment

♦ The dramatization of the suffering and death of a victim of AIDS (or a similar disease) will serve as an attention-getter for this topic—even more so if the victim was a personal acquaintance of the instructor.

♦ Tracking down the cause of an annoying allergy can involve some real detective work. Survey the class for such an experience, and ask for a brief oral report if the person is willing to share his/her experience.

♦ Watch clips of the Hollywood dramatization of Outbreak and compare that clips from The Coming Plague, a TBS documentary about real virus hunters.

♦ Use a simulated blood typing kit to do cross-matching tests in lab.

♦ The following link has a fun and interesting blood typing and transfusion activity: http://nobelprize.org/educational_games/medicine/landsteiner/landsteiner.html

♦ This chapter omits a discussion of methods of transmission, discuss ways that different pathogens travel.

♦ With the assistance of a microbiology student, prepare Petri dishes onto which smears from the human mouth, nose, hands, head, as well as commonly touched surfaces are made. Identify the microorganisms present in each location.

♦ Are insect bodies filth carriers? Attempt to answer this by letting different insects including a cockroach, house fly, and cricket crawl over the surface of an agar-filled Petri dish.

Frankie's Last Wish (revisited)

♦ Gardasil has been discussed as being made a requirement for school aged children, just like other vaccines. Why is it facing opposition from religious and parenting groups?

♦ There has been discussion in the scientific community that young boys should be vaccinated for HPV as well. Boys can carry and transmit the virus but be relatively asymptomatic. Should boys be vaccinated as well?

♦ HOV and HIV face a "public relations" battle because of the way that they are spread. In fact, HIV rates are increasing despite years of education and public health campaigns. Why do pathogens like HPV and HIV get treated differently than avian flu or H1N1 flu when they are potentially more of a health hazard?

Additional Ideas for Classroom Discussion

♦ What are the differences between how a bacterial and viral infection would affect a human body?

♦ How do antibiotics work?

♦ Why don't antibiotics work on viruses? What leads to antibiotic resistance?

♦ MRSA is an antibiotic resistant infection that was mentioned in the chapter. How is MRSA treated?

♦ During a recent outbreak of H1N1, the US Secretary of Health recommended limiting interpersonal contact to prevent the spread of the virus. Why would that work?

♦ Where does our term *vaccination* derive its meaning? Was it first used as a medical term as it now is?

- Why is the seasonal flu vaccine less effective than a more specific vaccine like the H1N1 flu vaccine?

- What are the potential side effects of vaccination? What is herd immunity?

- Thomas Malthus proposed three "grim reapers" that would restrain human population growth. One of these was "pestilence," or disease. How effective is disease as a population-limiting factor in the developed countries versus the underdeveloped countries?

- If there are so many infectious people as patients in hospitals, why aren't doctors and nurses continuously ill?

- Fever and inflammation are natural responses of our immune system. Is it wise to take over-the-counter medications to reduce these responses?

How Would You Vote? Classroom Discussion Ideas

- Monitor the voting for the online question. Our government has checks and balances in place for many reasons. If we go around these controls we are jeopardizing the entire system. On the flip side, there is certainly frustration in how long it takes for a drug to be approved by the FDA. Since the human condition is at stake, it is understandable to want to expedite the process and work in underdeveloped countries. However, these underdeveloped countries need to spend their resources elsewhere, rather than governing clinical trials. It is difficult to separate out emotion when trying to improve the human condition. My personal opinion is that the ethical standards in place in the United States should be followed by US companies. If the major developed countries were to come together to establish a standard for clinical trials that would be great, but not too realistic.

- Have students complete final polling using JoinIn clickers.

Term Paper Topics, Library Activities, and Special Projects

- Controversy still surrounds the polio vaccines—Salk and Sabin. Explore the details of how each of these vaccines is made and used. Include the advantages and disadvantages of each.

- Describe how vaccines are made.

- Describe how vaccines work.

- Research on the cause and treatment of AIDS has been rapid and continues to progress. Report on the latest strategies.

- Although vaccines are available throughout the world for the prevention of measles, diphtheria, and polio, there are about 20 other infectious diseases for which vaccines could be developed, but there seems to be little incentive to do so. Report on the reasons why this is so.

- Polio and smallpox have been conquered by effective vaccination programs. Prepare a report on the development of the vaccine for either of these diseases; be sure to include the chronology of events leading up to the marketing of the vaccine.

- Report on the H1N1 flu virus. Is there a vaccine for this virus?

- Research and report on Human Papillomavirus (HPV) and the vaccine available for the virus. What do you think of administering this vaccine to young children?

Possible Responses to *Data Analysis Activities*

1. One hundred and ten months into the study less than 1% of women with HPV type had cancer while 16-17% of women HPV 16 positive women had cervical cancer.
2. Women with both HPV 16 and HPV 18 would be in the HPV 16 group.
3. It is impossible to use this data to extrapolate overall risk for any one type of HPV because none of the HPV groups is mutually exclusive.

Possible Responses to *Critical Thinking* Questions

1. Antibodies produced by one's own immune system last longer than purified monoclonal antibodies used for passive immunization because while the monoclonal antibodies are used upon an immune response, a natural immune response produces B effector cells which will continue to produce antibodies.

35

RESPIRATION

Chapter Outline

Objectives

1. Understand the behavior of gases and the types of respiratory surfaces that participate in gas exchange.
2. Compare the mechanisms used in invertebrate and vertebrate respiration.
3. Understand how the human respiratory system is related to the circulatory system, to cellular respiration, and to the nervous system.
4. Understand how respiration can be disrupted by damage to respiratory centers in the brain, physical obstructions, infectious disease, and pollutants.
5. Explain how humans and other animals adapt to deal with high altitude and deep water conditions.

Key Terms

respiration

respiration surface

respiratory proteins

gills

tracheal system

countercurrent flow

lungs

alveolus, -oli

respiratory passageways

pharynx

larynx

glottis

epiglottis

trachea

bronchus, -chi

bronchioles

diaphragm

respiratory cycle

Heimlich maneuver

vital capacity

respiratory membrane

partial pressure

oxyhemoglobin, HbO_2

carbonic anhydrase

Lecture Outline

35.1 Impacts, Issues: Up in Smoke

    A. The body reacts to tobacco smoke.

        1. Immediately there is coughing, nausea, dizziness, and even headaches.

        2. Later, the cilia that line the respiratory tract are immobilized; white blood cells are killed; colds and bronchitis increase; and, of course, deadly cancer is a long-term reward.

    B. The "active ingredient" in this scenario is nicotine.

        1. It constricts the blood vessels, increasing blood pressure.

        2. It raises the level of "bad" LDL cholesterol and creates a decline in "good" HDL cholesterol.

        3. Females who start smoking as teenagers are about 70 percent more likely to develop breast cancer.

    C. Secondhand smoke also raises the risk of disease (lung cancer, asthma, respiratory problems) for nonsmokers.

35.2 The Process of Respiration

    A. Gas Exchanges

        1. Respiratory systems rely on the diffusion of gases down pressure gradients.

            a. Gases will diffuse down a pressure gradient across a membrane (respiratory surface) if it is permeable and moist.

        2. The amount of diffusion depends on the surface area of the membrane and the differences in partial pressure.

    B. Factors Influencing Gas Exchange

        1. Animals either must have a body design that keeps internal cells close to the surface or must have a system to move the gases inward.

        2. Concentrations of gases on either side of a membrane are important; the larger the gradient, the faster the rate of diffusion.

            a. Most animals have to keep moving gasses across their respiratory membranes in order to maintain steep gradients.

        3. Respiratory Proteins

            a. The main transport protein is hemoglobin, each molecule of which binds four molecules of oxygen in the lungs (high concentration) and releases them in the tissues where oxygen is low.

            b. Myoglobin is another iron-containing respiratory protein, which is a good storage molecule of oxygen because it has a higher affinity for oxygen.

35.3   Invertebrate Respiration

A.   Integumentary exchange, in which gases diffuse directly across a moist body surface (for example, earthworm), is adequate for small animals with a low metabolic rate.

B.   Gills, highly folded, thin-walled projections from the body, enhance exchange rates between the blood of aquatic invertebrates and their watery environment.

C.   Tracheal respiration in arthropods, such as insects and spiders, utilizes fine air-conducting tubules to provide gaseous exchange at the cellular level; very little participation by the circulatory system is needed.

35.4   Vertebrate Respiration

A.   Respiration in Fishes
   1.   A gill has a moist, thin, vascularized epidermis.
   2.   External gills project from the body surface of a few amphibians and some insects.
   3.   The internal gills of adult fishes are positioned where water can enter the mouth and then flow over them as it exits just behind the head.
      a.   Water flows *over* the gills and blood circulates *through* them in opposite directions.
      b.   This mechanism, called countercurrent flow, is highly efficient in extracting oxygen from water, whose oxygen content is lower than air.

B.   Evolution of Paired Lungs
   1.   Lungs contain internal respiratory surfaces shaped as a cavity or sac.
   2.   Lungs also participate in the production of sound, when air is exhaled past the vocal cords through the glottis opening.
   3.   Lungs provide a membrane for gaseous exchange with blood.
      a.   Air moves by bulk flow into and out of the lungs.
      b.   Gases diffuse across the inner respiratory surfaces of the lungs.
      c.   Pulmonary circulation enhances the diffusion of dissolved gases into and out of lung capillaries.
      d.   In body tissues, oxygen diffuses from blood → interstitial fluid → cells; carbon dioxide travels the route in reverse.
   4.   Various animals use different mechanisms for respiration.
      a.   Frogs in the larvae stage utilize gills and skin; as adults they use paired lungs and skin for respiration.
      b.   Amniotes have waterproof skin and no gills; they use well developed lungs for respiration.

35.5   Human Respiratory System

A.   The System's Many Functions
   1.   The lungs accomplish gas exchange via the alveoli.
   2.   Exhaled air permits vocalizations.
   3.   The system helps return venous blood to the heart and helps rid the body of excess heat and water.
   4.   Controls over breathing adjust the body's acid–base balance as well as the body's temperature.

B.   From Airways to Alveoli
   1.   The Respiratory Passageways
      a.   Air enters or leaves the respiratory system through nasal cavities where hair and cilia filter dust and particles from, blood vessels warm, and mucus moistens the air.

b. Air moves via this route: pharynx → larynx (route blocked by epiglottis during swallowing) → vocal cords (space between is glottis) → trachea → bronchi → bronchioles → alveoli.

c. The vocal cords lie at the entrance to the larynx.

d. When air is exhaled through the glottis, the folds of the cords vibrate to produce sounds, which are under regulation by nerve commands to the elastic ligaments that regulate the glottal opening.

2. The Paired Lungs

   a. Human lungs are located in the thoracic cavity, one on each side of the heart; the rib cage encloses and protects the lungs.

   b. Each lung is covered with a pleural membrane, which covers the lung's outer surface and lines the inside of the thoracic cavity.

   c. Inside the lungs, respiratory bronchioles bear outpouchings of their walls called alveoli, which are usually clustered as alveolar sacs.

   d. Alveoli provide a tremendous surface area for gaseous exchange with the blood located in the dense capillary network surrounding each alveolar sac.

3. Muscles and Respiration

   a. The diaphragm is a sheet of smooth muscle beneath the lungs; intercostal muscles are skeletal muscles between the ribs.

   b. The diaphragm and the intercostal muscles interact and exchange the volume of the thoracic cavity during breathing.

35.6 How You Breathe

A. The Respiratory Cycle

   1. The respiratory cycle includes on inhalation and one exhalation.

   2. In inhalation, the diaphragm contracts and flattens, muscles lift the rib cage upward and outward, the chest cavity volume increases, internal pressure decreases, and air rushes in.

   2. In exhalation, the actions listed above are reversed; the elastic lung tissue recoils passively.

   3. Pressure gradients between air inside and outside the respiratory tract change, causing air to flow into the airways.

   4. Using the Heimlich maneuver manually increases the intra-abdominal pressure to force the diaphragm up and force food out of the trachea.

B. Respiratory Volumes

   1. The maximum volume the lungs can hold is the total lung volume; total lung volume is 5.7 liters in men and 4.2 liters in females.

   2. Vital capacity is the maximum amount of air that can be moved in and out of the lungs in one breath.

   3. The tidal volume, about 0.5 liters, is the volume of air that moves into and out of the lungs in one respiratory cycle.

   4. The lungs never totally deflate during breathing.

C. Control of Breathing

   1. Respiratory centers in the brain control the rate and depth of breathing.

   2. When activity levels increase, chemoreceptors sense changes in the blood pH and signal the respiratory center to alter breathing levels.

   3. Reflexes, such as swallowing or coughing, and commands from the sympathetic nerves alter breathing patterns.

35.7   Gas Exchange and Transport
  A. The Respiratory Membrane
    1. The alveolar epithelium, the capillary epithelium, and their basement membranes form a respiratory membrane.
    2. Oxygen and carbon dioxide passively diffuse across the membrane in response to partial pressure gradients.
       a. Partial pressures are the amount of pressure an individual gas contributes to an overall mix of gasses; i.e. atmosphere contains nitrogen gas, oxygen, carbon dioxide, etc.
  B. Oxygen Transport and Storage
    1. Blood cannot carry sufficient oxygen and carbon dioxide in *dissolved form* to satisfy the body's demands; hemoglobin helps enhance its capacity.
    2. Oxygen diffuses down a pressure gradient into the blood plasma → red blood cells → binds to hemoglobin (four molecules per hemoglobin to form oxyhemoglobin).
    3. Hemoglobin gives up its oxygen in tissues where partial pressure of oxygen is low, blood is warmer, partial pressure of carbon dioxide is higher, and pH is lower; all four conditions occur in tissues with high metabolism.
    4. Myoglobin stores oxygen in cardiac muscle and in some skeletal muscles; when blood flow cannot keep up with the body's needs, myoglobin releases oxygen.
  C. Carbon Dioxide Transport
    1. Because carbon dioxide is higher in the body tissues, it diffuses into the blood.
    2. Ten percent is dissolved in plasma, 30 percent binds with hemoglobin to form carbaminohemoglobin, and 60 percent is in bicarbonate form.
    3. Bicarbonate and carbonic acid formation is enhanced by the enzyme carbonic anhydrase, which is located in the red blood cells.
  D. The Carbon Monoxide Threat
    1. Hemoglobin has a higher affinity for carbon monoxide than oxygen.
    2. Carbon monoxide prevents proper oxygen transport causing carbon monoxide poisoning.
  E. Effects of Altitude
    1. Even though the concentration of oxygen is the same at higher altitudes, the pressure is less.
       a. Less oxygen crosses the respiratory membrane.
       b. Less oxygen binds to hemoglobin.
       c. Altitude sickness can result; symptoms include shortness of breath, dizziness, and nausea.
    2. Over time, acclimatization leads to the production of more red blood cells to accommodate the change.

35.8   Common Respiratory Diseases and Disorders
  A. Interrupted Breathing
    1. Sleep apnea and sudden infant death syndrome (SIDS) are caused by a stop in breathing.
    2. Damage to the respiratory control center and weak signals (fewer serotonin receptors) may lead to these respiratory stresses.
  B. Tuberculosis
    1. About one-third of the human population carries the bacteria that cause tuberculosis; 10 percent of these carriers will develop the disease, which can be cured with long treatment courses of antibiotics.

2. Other viruses and bacteria can infect the lungs. Pneumonia is a general term for inflammation caused by an infectious organism.

C. Bronchitis, Asthma, and Emphysema
1. Chronic irritation of the lining of the bronchioles leads to bronchitis, in which there is an excess of mucus that may promote bacterial growth.
2. In asthma, and inhaled allergen or irritant triggers inflammation and constriction of airways.
3. In emphysema, the walls of the alveoli become fibrous and inefficient in exchanging of gases.

D. Smoking's Impact
1. Tobacco use kills millions and in the U.S. drains over $22 billion a year from the economy.
2. Secondhand smoke is a real danger to innocents who do not participate in the life-threatening habit themselves.
3. Smoking marijuana may also lead to chronic throat problems, bronchitis, and emphysema.

Suggestions for Presenting the Material

♦ The presentation of respiration can be effectively accomplished by following the sequence of the text. The outline begins with a survey of respiratory surfaces, then focuses on human respiratory organs and function, and concludes with mention of respiratory problems.

♦ When describing various respiratory surfaces, emphasize the one common feature they all share—moisture.

♦ Some students have a hard time making the jump from concentrations to partial pressures. Spend time breaking down atmospheric composition and describing how concentration is affecting pressures.

♦ Distinguish the arthropod *tracheas* from other respiratory surfaces by emphasizing their independence from the circulatory system.

♦ An effective way to present the human respiratory system is to use Figure 35.8 and follow the pathway of an inhaled and exhaled breath. This figure is also available as an animated feature.

♦ As you describe the *glottis* and *epiglottis*, include a note on the *Heimlich maneuver* (Figure 35.11).

♦ Use a bell jar model to demonstrate the how the diaphragm works to inflate and deflate the lungs. Don't have a bell jar model; put a balloon into an empty soda bottle.

♦ Bring some physics into the classroom; talk about how Fick's Law and Boyle's law are related to respiration.

♦ Be sure to stress the passivity of the lungs (compare to balloon) during respiration, and emphasize the role of the diaphragm and rib muscles.

♦ Highlight the differences between the ways oxygen and carbon dioxide are transported in the blood.

♦ Emphasize that the respiratory organs have some nonrespiratory functions such as coughing, sneezing, speech, yawning, regulation of pH, and sense of smell.

Classroom and Laboratory Enrichment

- Show how the measurement of oxygen consumption can be used to determine rate of metabolism by use of a simple spirometer (see a biological supply catalog). Alternatively, a computer simulation of the experiment may suffice.

- Ask for volunteers to debate "nonsmokers" versus "smokers" rights. Ask them to provide data, rather than emotional attacks.

- Have a person who has visited a high-altitude location report on the breathing discomforts he/she experienced.

- Do a comparative study of how different animals manage bulk gas intake.

- Dissect the respiratory system of a fetal pig.

- Construct or purchase a working model of the lungs, chest cavity, and diaphragm. If your university has an animal or meat lab you may be able to get unpreserved sheep's lungs to demonstrate how they expand by using a flexible pipe as a trachea and blowing into the lungs. Alternatively, display a freeze-dried preparation of a sheep's lungs.

- Demonstrate the Heimlich maneuver on a class volunteer; then ask classmates to demonstrate (gently!) on one another.

- Have the students use a spirometer to measure respiratory air volumes. Compare the results of smokers and nonsmokers, athletes and non-athletes, etc.

- Invite a scuba diver to discuss the special gas composition and gas exchange problems associated with deep dives.

- Have an exercise physiologist talk to the class about changes in respiration brought about by aerobic training.

- Use a chart or dissectible mannequin to locate major organs of the human respiratory system.

- Exhibit a model of a human larynx and trachea.

- Obtain preserved lung tissues of a smoker and non-smoker. Create a display of these lungs presenting statistics on the effects of smoking on the body.

- **Common Student Misconceptions**:
    o Many students do not realize the role that carbon dioxide plays in our breathing rates.
    o Be sure to emphasize that carbon dioxide is the factor that regulates the breathing by adjusting the pH of the blood.

Up In Smoke (revisited)

- Using cigarette ads gathered from magazines published during the past 40 years, show the change in public attitude toward smoking.

- How does the "smokeless" cigarette work? Why is the American Medical Association so adamantly opposed to its approval by the Food and Drug Administration?

- Why hasn't the message concerning the dangers of smoking effected teenagers and altered their taking-up of the habit?

- Should smokers be subject to higher insurance rates (medical and automobile) due to the higher costs they incur, forcing the insurance companies to pass on costs to everyone?

Additional Ideas for Classroom Discussion

♦ Which of the following *respiratory surfaces* does not require participation of the blood for delivery of oxygen to the tissues: (a) integument, (b) gills, (c) tracheas, or (d) lungs?

♦ What is happening in the condition we call "hiccups"? What causes it? What are the best short-term remedies? On what physiological principles (if any) are they based?

♦ Why is the best body position for public speaking and singing, a standing or "sitting tall" position?

♦ The air at high altitudes is sometimes described in everyday language as "thin." How does this translate in technical terms?

♦ The human respiratory system is adapted to intake air through the nose. What are the benefits of breathing in through our nose?

♦ Why is good posture important to good respiration?

♦ Why is CO lethal?

♦ Why do we yawn?

♦ Why do US Olympians train at higher altitudes?

♦ What are the drawbacks to training at higher altitudes?

♦ Can you die from holding your breath? Explain the neural mechanisms that are operating here.

♦ What are the functions of the sinuses?

♦ "Respiratory distress syndrome" (hyaline membrane disease) is the primary cause of respiratory difficulty in immature newborns. What are its symptoms and cause? How is it treated?

♦ What are the dangers of smoking beyond cancer?

How Would You Vote? Classroom Discussion Ideas

♦ Monitor the voting for the online question. Big money is made in the tobacco industry and in a declining domestic market, it makes sense that the business would look to international markets to continue the profit. Thus, international sales might become the marketing focus for American companies. International health agencies should be concerned about this shift. If the United States is concerned about global health as claimed, then the effort for tobacco reduction begun at home in the last few decades should continue abroad. The facts are clear about the health risks associated with smoking, and this should be made evident globally.

♦ Have students complete polling using JoinIn clickers.

Term Paper Topics, Library Activities, and Special Projects

♦ Vertebrate muscular activity is dependent on an oxygen supply carried by the blood (specifically, red cells). When demand exceeds supply, an *oxygen debt* is incurred, and activity slows or stops. Such is not the case with insects with their indefatigable flight muscles. Investigate why this difference exists.

- Certain woodwind musicians have perfected a breathing technique (circular breathing) that allows the production of continuous sound from the instrument. Investigate reports of this technique, and interview a practitioner. Arrange a demonstration, if possible.

- Report on different methods of animal ventilation and to do a comparative summary of different methods.

- Check a book of world records for the longest continuous bout of hiccups. What is the "ultimate" cure for a persistent case?

- How many people in the United States die of simple choking each year? What age is most affected? What is the most commonly lodged object?

- Do a regional comparison of respiratory irritants and incidents of respiratory illnesses.

- How might the anatomy and physiology of persons who were born and raised at very high altitudes be different from those who were born and raised in the lowlands and have only recently become acclimated to high elevations?

- How does the "smokeless" cigarette work? Why is the American Medical Association so adamantly opposed to its approval by the Food and Drug Administration?

- Investigate the effects of air pollution on respiratory functions.

- What is the singular advantage of the one-way flow of air in the *parabronchi* of the bird lung?

- Investigate asthma. Report on the statistics of the condition. What has happened to incidence rates over the past 30 years? Why is it changing? What can be done to prevent asthma?

- What is influenza? Why is H1N1 so much more problematic than normal flu strains?

Responses to *Data Analysis Activities*

1. 20
2. Over 10 pCi/L
3. A smoker in a home with 1.3 pCi/L is more likely to die from lung cancer than from an automobile accident.

Possible Responses to *Critical Thinking* Questions

1. Zinc is a coenzyme with carbonic anhydrase, the enzyme that converts CO_2 into carbonic acid and then bicarbonate in the blood stream. Reducing zinc in the diet leads to lower CO_2 output by an individual, this can be accounted for because while the enzyme, carbonic anhydrase, is still present, in lacking zinc it has a reduced efficiency.

2. The concentration of O_2 P_{O2} in the pulmonary veins and at the start of systemic arteries is the same. The concentration of the O_2 is what determines both the partial pressure of O_2 and the binding of O_2 to hemoglobin. As Oxygen enters the blood stream in the lungs, the high concentration of O_2 creates a high amount of binding between O_2 and hemoglobin. Because the arteries are thick and limit the contact of blood with the systemic tissues until the capillaries, the concentration of O_2 and the P_{O2} remains high. When the flow of blood slows through the capillaries and the red blood cells are exposed to the surrounding tissue, the concentration of O_2, and therefore the P_{O2}, drops and then the red blood cells release the oxygen.

3. Oxygen is used in the mitochondria during aerobic respiration of sugars (refer to chapter 7). In the mitochondria, glucose is "prepped" by the cells to produce H⁺ ion and electrons that will drive chemosmotic ATP formation. Oxygen is used as a final proton and electron acceptor in the mitochondria.

4. Fetal hemoglobin has a higher affinity for oxygen at a lower partial pressure. This is a crucial adaption for the fetal blood because all of the oxygen that the fetus receives is second hand. That means that the blood has to be transported from the mothers lungs to the placenta and then to the fetal capillaries. In a normal system there are two exchanges, on in the lungs and one at the tissue. In the fetus, there are three exchanges, one at the mothers lungs, one at the placenta, and then finally at the fetal tissue.

36

DIGESTION AND HUMAN NUTRITION

Chapter Outline

Objectives

1. Know the general way in which a digestive system is structured among different animals. Realize the behavioral limitations of organisms with incomplete digestive systems.
2. Understand the structure and function of the various organs of the human digestive system.
3. Know the path that a bite of food takes as it is digested in the body.
4. Understand which nutrients, vitamins, and minerals are necessary too support metabolism.
5. Explain how body weight is maintained by balancing caloric intake and physical activity.

Key Terms

incomplete digestive
  system
complete digestive
  system
esophagus
peristalsis
stomach

small intestine
colon
large intestine
rectum
anus
salivary glands
sphincter

gastric fluid
chyme
villi
microvilli
brush border cells
bile
gall bladder

feces
appendix
essential fatty acids
essential amino acids
vitamins
minerals

Lecture Outline

36.1   The Battle Against Bulge

   A. Eating food beyond energy required leads to storage of excess intake as fat.

      1. Evolutionarily this would have been beneficial as a method of having excess energy reserves in times of scarce food sources.

      2. Obesity creates several health related concerns: increase in type II diabetes incidence, cardiovascular disease, etc.

   B. Genetics and food portions have been used to explain some of the reasons why obesity is becoming more prevalent.

36.2   Animal Digestive Systems

   A. A digestive system mechanically and chemically reduces food to particles and molecules small enough to be absorbed into the internal environment.

   B. Incomplete and Complete Systems

      1. An incomplete digestive system (for example, in a flatworm) has one opening.

         a. Food enters and waste leaves through the same opening.

         b. Digestive products are absorbed directly to the needy tissues.

      2. A complete digestive system is a tube with two openings allowing food to move in one direction through the lumen; it performs five tasks.

         a. *Mechanical processing and motility* is the breaking up, mixing, and transporting of food material.

         b. *Secretion* is the release of needed enzymes and other substances into the lumen.

         c. *Digestion* is the chemical breakdown of food matter to molecules small enough to cross the gut lining.

         d. *Absorption* is the passage of digested nutrients into the blood and lymph.

         e. *Elimination* is the expulsion of undigested and unabsorbed residues at the end of the gut.

   C. Diet-Related Structural Adaptations

      1. Beaks and Bites

         a. Birds have a hard, keratin covered jaw that forms a beak for feeding.

         b. Mammals have different types of teeth depending on their diet: carnivores have specially adapted teeth for killing prey while herbivores tend to have teeth adapted for grinding plant material

      2. Gut Specializations

         a. Birds store meals in a stretchable crop and grind the food in a gizzard.

         b. Ruminants (for example, antelopes and cows) can eat grass almost continuously and have multiple stomachs to digest cellulose.

36.3   The Human Digestive System

A.   The human digestive system is a tube with two openings and many specialized regions.

   1.   Its overall extended length is 6.5–9 meters, comprising the mouth, pharynx, esophagus, stomach, small intestine, colon, rectum, and anus.

   2.   Accessory glands include the salivary glands, liver (with gallbladder), and pancreas.

   3.   Food processing begins in the mouth. Swallowing forces food into the pharynx and the food continues through the esophagus to the stomach.

   4.   From the stomach, food enters the small intestine where most digestion and absorption occur.

   5.   The final stage occurs in the colon, which absorbs most of the remaining water and ions, compacting the waste to feces. The feces pass through the rectum and exit the body through the anus.

36.4   Digestion in the Mouth

A.   Mechanical breakdown of food and its mixing with saliva begin in the mouth.

B.   Teeth chew the food.

   1.   Each has an enamel coat, a dentine core, and an inner pulp.

   2.   Incisors bite off chunks, canines tear, and premolars and molars grind food.

C.   Saliva (from salivary glands) contains salivary amylase to begin carbohydrate digestion, bicarbonate to neutralize acids, and mucins to lubricate.

36.5   Food Storage and Digestion in the Stomach

A.   Structure and Function of the Stomach

   1.   The stomach is a muscular sac that stores and mixes food, secretes substances that dissolve and degrade food, and controls the rate at which food enters the small intestine.

   2.   Gastric fluid includes hydrochloric acid, pepsinogens, and mucus.

      a.   HCl dissolves bits of food to form a soupy chyme; it also converts pepsinogen (inactive) to pepsin (active).

      b.   Pepsin begins the digestion of proteins.

      c.   Normally, mucus and bicarbonate ions protect the stomach lining; but if these are blocked, hydrogen ions stimulate the release of histamine, which in turn stimulates release of more HCl, which may result in a peptic ulcer.

   3.   Peristaltic contractions churn the chyme and keep the sphincter of the stomach's exit closed, but small amounts are released at regular intervals into the small intestine.

B.   Stomach Disorders

   1.   Gastroesophageal reflux occurs when the sphincter at the entrance to the stomach allows acids to splash back into the esophagus causing a burning sensation.

   2.   Stomach ulcers occur when H. pylori build up and cause an imbalance in acid secretion; this leads to erosion of the stomach lining.

36.6   Structure of the Small Intestine

A.   The small intestine has a diameter of 2.5 cm but extends for 5 to 7 m in most individuals.

B.   The small intestine has a very large surface area for absorption.

C.   The small intestine has a folded lining to increase surface area.

   1.   The surface of the small intestine is lined with villi, small folds.

   2.   The villi are lined with small, finger-like, microvilli which create the appearance of a brush border.

36.7   Digestion and Absorption in the Small Intestine

   A. Secretions from the liver, gallbladder, and pancreas enter via a common duct.

   B. Bicarbonate form the pancreas enters the small intestine in order to buffer the acidity of the stomach.

   C. Carbohydrate Digestion and Absorption
       1. Monosaccharides (glucose) and amino acids cross the gut lining by active transport and enter the bloodstream.

   D. Protein Digestion and Absorption
       1. Trypsin and chymotrypsin break down peptides into amino acids, which are actively transported into brush border cells.

   E. Fat Digestion and Absorption
       1. The liver aids in fat digestion by the emulsification action of bile; fatty acids combine with bile salts to increase the surface area of the fats.
       2. Diffusion gradients favor movement of fatty acids and triglycerides out of the small intestine and into the epithelial cells of the mucosa.

   F. Fluid Absorption
       1. Approximately 80 percent of the water in the digestive system enters and moves across the intestinal lining by osmosis.

   G. Disorders That Affect Digestion in the Small Intestines
       1. Lactose intolerance is caused by a decrease in effectiveness of the lactose digesting enzyme which leads to flatulence, bloating and gas.
       2. Gallstones occur when bilirubin or cholesterol accumulates in the gall bladder.
       3. Pancreatitis is an inflammation of the pancreas that can be caused by gall stones or by drug and alcohol abuse.

36.8   The Large Intestine

   A. The large intestine, which is abut 1.5 meters long, stores and concentrates feces—undigested and unabsorbed material, water, and bacteria.

   B. Structure and Function
       1. The large intestine begins as a cup-shaped pouch at its junction with the small intestine (appendix attached here).
       2. It is draped across the lower abdomen and ends in a rectum (feces storage) that opens to the outside through the anus.
       3. Smooth muscle contractions propel food through the colon.
       4. Gastrin and other signals cause the colon to contract and move the feces to the rectum, which activates a defecation reflex.

   C. Health and the Colon
       1. Several factors, including stress and a low-bulk diet, can delay defecation resulting in constipation.
       2. Fecal material lodged in the appendix can lead to the complications of appendicitis.
       3. Some people are genetically predisposed to develop colon polyps, which are mostly benign.
       4. Colon cancer is highly curable if detected early.

36.9 The Fate of Absorbed Compounds

A. Nutrient molecules are shuffled and reshuffled once they have been absorbed.

B. Shortly after a meal, the level of carbohydrates rises; some are converted to fat for storage, and others are converted to glycogen in the liver and muscle tissue.

D. Between meals, glucose levels are maintained by breakdown of glycogen reserves in the liver, and amino acids are converted to glucose; fatty acids from fats can be used directly by cells for energy.

E. The liver is a valuable organ for conversion of nutrients and detoxification of chemicals.

36.10 Human Nutritional Requirements

A. USDA Dietary Recommendations

1. The USDA has recently issued a set of nutritional guidelines to replace its earlier "food pyramid," based on extensive nutritional research.

2. The diet recommends lowering the intake of refined grains, saturated fats, trans-fatty acids, added sugars or caloric sweeteners, and no more than one teaspoon full of salt daily.

3. More fruits and vegetables with high potassium and fiber content are encouraged with fat-free or low-fat milk products and whole grains; 55 percent of daily caloric intake is to come from carbohydrates.

B. Energy-Rich Carbohydrates

1. Refined sugars and starches have a high-glycemic index.

2. They cause a surge in insulin for fast uptake of the ingested sugar, which later leads to increased hunger.

3. Excessive intake of high fructose corn syrup in soft drinks and other foods may be linked with obesity. Fructose may not satisfy hunger in the same way that glucose does and it can interfere with insulin's action and encourage fat storage.

C. Good Fat, Bad Fat

1. Phospholipids and cholesterol are important components of membranes; fats are energy reserves and provide insulation and cushioning.

2. The body needs very little polysaturated fat to supply the essential fatty acids, those not made by the body itself; consuming too much polysaturated fat increases risk for heart disease, stroke, and some cancers.

3. Trans fats are made from vegetable oils but are worse for the body than saturated fats.

D. Body-Building Proteins

1. Of the 20 different amino acids in proteins, eight are essential (that is, must be supplied in the diet).

2. Most proteins in animal tissues are complete; their amino acid ratios match human nutritional needs.

3. Nearly all plant proteins are incomplete in that they lack one or more amino acids that are essential for humans.

36.11 Vitamins and Minerals

A. Humans need small amounts of at least 13 organic molecules called vitamins to assist in cellular metabolism.

B. Inorganic substances called minerals (Ca, Mg, K, and Fe, for example) are also needed.

C. A balanced diet will normally meet all requirements for these substances; excessive intake is at least wasteful and at worst harmful.

36.12 Maintaining a Healthy Weight

    A. What Is a Healthy Weight?

        1. The BMI calculation is a widely accepted method for determining ideal body weight.

        2. BMI of 25 - 29.9 is considered overweight while BMI over 30 is obese.

        3. To lose weight, an individual has to both reduce caloric intake while increasing metabolic output.

    B. Why Is Obesity Unhealthy?

        1. Obesity can lead to diabetes, heart disease, gallstones, colon cancer, arthritis, and many other ailments.

    C. Eating Disorders

        1. Anorexia is an eating disorder when people reduce their caloric input to dangerously low numbers.

        2. Bulimia is an eating disorder where an individual binges on food and then induces vomiting to prevent caloric intake.

Suggestions for Presenting the Material

♦ The topics of *respiration, circulation,* and *excretion* can be correlated with *digestion,* especially by using an overall system diagram (Figure 36.5).

♦ The traditional method of presentation is to follow a mouthful of food as it passes from mouth to anus. Along the way, you can be as detailed as your course requires. For example, you may ask students to know structures, general secretions, and main functions as presented in Figure 36.5 but add only a few, all, or none of the enzymes.

♦ Similarly, you will need to inform students as to the amounts of material from Tables 36.2 (vitamins) and 36.3 (minerals) you require them to learn. These tables are provided for reference and completeness.

♦ The challenge of the digestive system is to break down food into its subcomponents to get as much nutrition as possible. Emphasize that when talking about the different functions of the digestive system.

♦ Students will enjoy your lectures more if you include brief notes on the various "problems along the way" that cause us minor, and occasionally major, distress.

♦ Nutrition is receiving increasingly more emphasis in our lives. You may wish to devote an entire lecture to this timely topic. This is also an excellent opportunity to review the contents of Chapter 3 and especially Table 3.1 (the molecules of life).

♦ In a discussion of nutrition, in addition to talking about the science of calories and intake, spend some time talking about the genetics and hormonal regulation that leads to obesity.

♦ Although it occupies only one page of the text, the discussion of "organic metabolism" and the accompanying Figure 36.12 present a wealth of information. You may need to streamline this material to accommodate the needs of your students.

♦ Discuss bariatric surgery and/or the ramifications of the loss of function of organs in the digestive system.

♦ This is an ideal time to discuss some of the fad weight-loss diets as well as the more legitimate ones. Students are extremely interested in this topic, and it is a beneficial one for them to discuss.

- When discussing obesity, introduce the concept of body mass index (BMI) as an indicator of the degree of obesity. Also include calculations of Basal Metabolic Rates (BMR) and energy expenditure. Consult a nutrition text for details.

- **Some Common Misconceptions:**
  - o Emphasize that *digestion* and *absorption* are inseparable in the total function of providing nutrition to body cells.
  - o If time allows, you may want to address the issues of malnourishment versus undernourishment.
  - o Many high schools do not provide nutrition classes. Students may not have as much information on this topic as you realize.

Classroom and Laboratory Enrichment

- Because the digestive organs lie cramped in a small space, one upon the other, drawings are not as useful as life-size models. If your department has a model, use it throughout your journey through the G-I tract.

- Dissect the digestive system of a fetal pig.

- Complete a comparative anatomical analysis of different animals.

- Demonstrate peristalsis by placing a ball of suitable size inside a flexible tube (such as a section of old bicycle tire inner tube) and squeezing to move it along.

- Mash up food and use enzymes and acids to digest the material as a demonstration.

- The action of a digestive enzyme (salivary amylase) can be demonstrated using the procedure outlined in the Enrichment section for Chapter 5 of this resource manual.

- Show a film depicting the consequences of vitamin and mineral deficiencies in the human diet.

- Ask if any volunteers from within the class, or outside, would be willing to tell the class about his/her digestive or eating disorder.

- Set up a panel discussion of doctors, exercise physiologists, and dieticians to discuss healthy diets.

- Use molecular models to demonstrate the process of digestion.

- Mix oil and water together in a flask to show their immiscibility. Then add soap to the mixture to illustrate emulsification.

The Battle Against Bulge (revisited)

- Will changing dietary regulations affect people decisions about dietary intake? (consider smoking)

- Diet plans for weight reduction are numerous and proliferating daily. How can the wary consumer recognize a plan that could be dangerous?

- How do you craft a fair legislative dietary policy? I.e. New York State is considering an "obesity" tax on sugary drinks. Is this a fair policy? What is the evidence that sugary drinks lead to obesity? How might legislation like this potentially and unfairly stigmatize obese people?

Additional Ideas for Classroom Discussion

♦ What is meant by "heartburn"? Is its use in television antacid advertising misleading, especially for young viewers? What would you propose as a better term?

♦ How is the stomach of a cow like the gut of a termite? How could antibiotics given a ruminant animal for a blood infection interfere with digestive function?

♦ What do you think of the programs that call for regimes of fasting and "purification of body fluids"? Are they biologically sound?

♦ Give some of the reasons that dietary fiber, such as bran, is so important in our diet.

♦ Why do some adults, who could drink milk as infants without difficulty, experience intestinal pain (due to gas) and/or dehydrating diarrhea when they drink milk?

♦ What are good dietary suggestions?

♦ What are all of the factors that lead to obesity?

♦ What are the risks of fad diets?

♦ How can you analyze the dietary information of the foods that you consume?

♦ Why can it be so difficult to lose weight?

♦ What are weight loss strategies?

♦ Why won't decreasing your caloric intake alone work to reduce an individual's weight?

How Would You Vote? Classroom Discussion Ideas

♦ Monitor the voting for the online question. Would a warning label on fast food really help make people aware that fast food is not a healthy choice? If the food was labeled, would anyone really read it? Even bigger question: Would anyone heed it? Americans have been warning-labeled to sleep. We need to address the problem of the unhealthy fast food meal at its source, namely, the *quality* and *quantity* of the food. Of course, consumers will object to healthier food in smaller portions because they have become so accustomed to what is unhealthy. It is much like other bad habits (smoking, alcohol consumption, etc.); we know the risks, but we crave the "forbidden fruit" anyway.

♦ Have students complete classroom polling with JoinIn clickers.

Term Paper Topics, Library Activities, and Special Projects

♦ Survey your class to collect data on height, weight, and BMI. Does the class fall within the ranges given in section 36.15?

♦ Monitor and record your caloric intake for a week. Prepare a report comparing calories burned versus caloric intake.

♦ Have each student create an account on MyPyramid.gov. Have them track their diet for a week and then use the reports in the website to analyze whether or not they are meeting the dietary guidelines.

♦ Compare and contrast different weight loss plans.

♦ *Anorexia* and *bulimia* seem to have appeared only recently as eating disorders. Trace the history of what is known about these conditions.

- The role of vitamins in human health is a fascinating story. Select one or two vitamins, and report on the history of discovery surrounding each.
- Investigate how the drug cimetidine (Zantac) suppresses the secretion of acid by the parietal cells of the stomach.
- Investigate recent findings concerning the cause of ulcers, namely the bacterium *Helicobacter pylori*.
- How were the effects of *H. pylori* discovered?
- Discuss why drinking coffee or other caffeinated beverages increases the sensation of hunger.
- Summarize the daily nutritional requirement of a 25-year-old man who works at a desk job and exercises very little.
- Describe several legislative measures undertaken in the name of nutrition (e.g. fat taxes, trans fat bans, high fructose corn syrup bans) and discuss their merits.

Possible Responses to *Data Analysis Activities*

1. Approximately 25-30% of the Hazda had fewer than 5 copies of the *AMY-1* gene.
2. None of the European Americans had more than 10 copies of the *AMY-1* genes.
3. These data support the hypothesis that a starchy diet favors duplications of the *AMY-1* gene. Populations with lower starch diets have fewer copies of the gene in their gene pool. Populations with higher starch diets have more genes in their gene pools.

Possible Responses to *Critical Thinking* Questions

1. If a snake eats only twice a year it has to maximize the efficiency of its digestive system. By having villi that expand 4-fold there is both the added room to fit more food in the intestines and allows for more surface area for absorption. By adjusting the stomach pH down to 1, the snake more effectively dissolves food in the stomach.

2. Starch and sugars have roughly the same number of calories per gram but vegetables that contain sugars and starches often have different numbers of calories per gram of food. For example, sweet potatoes have 1.2 cal/g wile kale has .3 cal/g. If the food weighs the same and the amount of calories are the same between starch and sugars, the density of the starches and sugars must be different between the different vegetables.

3. This will change per individual students.

37

THE INTERNAL ENVIRONMENT

Chapter Outline

Objectives

1. Explain how the chemical composition of extracellular fluid is maintained by mammals.
2. Describe the components of the human urinary system.
3. Understand the processes of urine formation and excretion and the hormonal controls involved in these processes.
4. Understand the degrees to which ectotherms, endotherms, and heterotherms can control their body temperatures.
5. Explain how heat gain and loss occur in birds and mammals and how these animals maintain a steady body temperature.

Key Terms

ammonia	nephrons	glomerular filtration	heterotherms
uric acid	Bowman's capsule	tubular reabsorption	shivering response
kidneys	proximal tubule	tubular secretion	brown adipose tissue
urine	loop of Henle	antidiuretic hormone	nonshivering heat
urea	distal tubule	(ADH)	production
ureter	collecting tubule	aldosterone	
urinary bladder	glomerulus	endotherms	
urethra	peritubular capillaries	ectotherms	

Lecture Outline

37.1   Truth in a Test Tube

    A.   Analysis of urine is a routine medical procedure.

        1.   The sugar level, pH, protein content, and solute concentration are checked.

        2.   Various home kits test for hormones in the urine indicating ovulation, pregnancy, or declining hormone levels (menopause).

    B.   Athletes have to undergo urine tests as a condition of their eligibility to perform.

    C.   Urine is an indicator of health, hormonal status, and drug use.

37.2   Maintaining the Volume and Composition of Body Fluids

    A.   The Internal Environment

        1.   By weight, the body is mostly water broken down into two basic parts: extracellular fluid between cells and plasma in the blood.

        2.   Maintaining the volume and composition of these fluids is a major aspect of homeostasis.

            a.   Water is lost in feces and urine, exhalation and secretions.

            b.   Metabolic reactions produce and introduce waste products, like CO_2 and urea into the body fluids.

            c.   Breakdown of amino acids produces ammonia, which can be toxic to cells.

    B.   Water-Solute Balance in Invertebrates

        1.   Marine invertebrates usually have the same water-solute concentration as the seawater so osmosis is negligible.

        2.   Planaria are freshwater invertebrates that have a higher solute concentration than the surrounding environment which causes water to diffuse into the organism.
        a. Excess water and metabolic wastes are removed by paired, tubular excretory organs.

        3.   Organisms with circulatory systems have to remove the metabolic wastes from their systems.

        4.   Arthropods do not excrete ammonia; instead an enzyme in their blood converts ammonia into uric acid which is emptied into the gut.

    C.   Water-Solute Balance in Vertebrates

        1.   In vertebrates, the extracellular fluid (ECF) is one-third as salty as seawater.

        2.   Freshwater fishes and amphibians gain water by osmosis and lose it in dilute urine.

        3.   Marine bony fishes have less salt than their surroundings; they lose water and make up for it by drinking seawater and pumping out excess solutes through gills.

4. As vertebrates evolved to land, they adapted novel mechanisms that could control the body's water-solute balance.
    a. A urinary system adjusts any shifts in composition or volume of extracellular fluid.
    b. Kidneys filter the blood, form urine, and maintain the body's water–solute balance.
    c. Urine is the fluid that rids the body of excess water and solutes.

37.3 Structure of the Urinary Systems
  A. Components of the System
    1. The human urinary system consists of two kidneys, each with a ureter leading to a urinary bladder (for storage), with an open channel (urethra) leading to the body surface.
    2. Each kidney is a bean-shaped structure about the size of a fist with cortex and medulla regions covered by a tough coat of connective tissue.
        a. Kidneys filter a variety of substances from the blood.
        b. Most of the filtrate is returned to the blood; about 1 percent ends up as urine.
        c. The kidneys regulate the volume and solute concentrations of extracellular fluid.
    3. Urine flows from each kidney through a ureter to a urinary bladder (for storage) and then out of the body through the urethra.
    4. Urination is a reflex response but can be controlled by nervous and muscular actions.
  B. Introducing the Nephrons
    1. Overview of Nephron Structure
        a. Nephrons filter and retain water and solutes, leaving concentrated urine to be collected in the central renal pelvis.
        b. Filtration occurs in the glomerulus—a ball of capillaries nestled in the Bowman's capsule.
        c. The Bowman's capsule collects the filtrate and directs it through the continuous nephron tubules: proximal → loop of Henle → distal → collecting duct.
    2. Blood Vessels Associated With Nephrons
        a. The peritubular capillaries exit the glomerulus, converge, and then branch again around the nephron tubules where they participate in reclaiming water and essential solutes.
        b. Urine forms constantly by glomerular filtration, tubular reabsorption, and tubular secretion; these processes involve all of the nephrons, glomerular capillaries, and peritubular capillaries.

37.4 Urine Formation
  A. Glomerular Filtration
    1. In glomerular filtration, blood pressure forces filtrate (water and small solutes) out of the glomerular capillaries. Blood enters the glomerulus under high pressure; arterioles here have wider diameters than most.
    2. Glomerular capillaries are highly "leaky" to water and small solutes.
        a. Blood cells, proteins, and other large solutes cannot pass the capillary wall into the capsule.
        b. Filtrate is collected by the Bowman's capsule and funneled into the proximal tubule.
  B. Tubular Reabsorption
    1. Tubular reabsorption takes place in the small tubules of the nephron.
    2. Water and solutes move across the tubular wall and out of the nephron and into the surrounding capillaries.

C. Tubular Secretion
   1. Tubular secretion moves substances from the capillaries into the nephron walls.
   2. Capillaries surrounding the nephrons secrete excess amounts of hydrogen ions and potassium ions into the nephron tubules.
   3. This process also rids the body of drugs, uric acid, hemoglobin breakdown products, and other wastes.

D. Concentrating the Urine
   1. Reabsorption mechanisms remove water from the glomerular filtrate.
      a. Sodium ions are pumped out of the proximal tubule (filtrate) and into the interstitial fluid surrounding the peritubular capillaries.
      b. Significant amounts of water follow passively down the gradient that has been created.
      c. In the descending limb of the loop of Henle, water moves out by osmosis, but in the ascending portion, sodium is pumped.
   2. This interaction of the limbs of the loop produces a very high solute concentration in the deeper parts of the kidney medulla and delivers a rather dilute urine to the distal tubule.

E. Hormonal Controls
   1. Two hormones and the hypothalamus signal adjustments in urine concentration.
      a. ADH (antidiuretic hormone) promotes water conservation.
         1) It is secreted from the hypothalamus via the pituitary.
         2) ADH makes the walls of distal tubules and collecting ducts more permeable to water, and thus the urine becomes more concentrated.
      b. Aldosterone enhances sodium reabsorption.
   2. Parathyroid hormone (PTH) promotes calcium reabsorption through its interactions with the kidneys.

37.5 Kidney Disease
   A. Causes of Kidney Failure
      1. Diabetes mellitus and high blood pressure are the main causes of kidney failure; genetic predispostion and toxins entering the body can also cause failure.
      2. High protein diets force the kidneys to work overtime in order to remove excess urea.
      3. Renal failure occurs when the rate of filtration through glomerular capillaries drops by half.

   B. Treating Kidney Failure
      1. Dialysis (hemo- or peritoneal) is a process that restores proper solute balances by using a machine to remove certain solutes in the blood.
      2. Dialysis is the removal of solutes across a semipermeable membrane.
      3. Dialysis is best as a short term treatment; long term problems require kidney transplants.

37.6 Heat Gains and Losses
   A. Changes to Core Temperature
      1. The core temperature of an animal body rises when heat from the surroundings or metabolism builds up.
      2. Four processes drive the exchanges of heat.
         a. Thermal radiation is the gain of heat from some source, or the loss of heat from the body to the surroundings depending on the temperatures of the environment.
         b. Conduction is the transfer of heat from one object to another when they are in direct contact, as when a human sits on cold (or hot!) concrete.

      c.   Convection is the transfer of heat by way of a moving fluid such as air or water.

      d.   Evaporation is a process whereby a heated substance changes from a liquid to a gaseous state with a loss of heat to the surroundings.

  B. Endotherm? Ectotherm? Heterotherm?

     1.   Ectotherms (such as lizards) have low metabolic rates; therefore, they must gain their heat from the environment in what we call behavioral temperature regulation.

     2.   Endotherms, such as birds and mammals, generate heat from metabolic activity and exercise controls over heat conservation and dissipation by means of adaptations such as feathers, fur, or fat, which reduce heat loss.

     3.   Heterotherms, such as the hummingbird, generate body heat during their active periods but resemble ectotherms during inactive times.

37.7   Temperature Regulation in Mammals

  A. Responses to Heat Stress

     1.   Peripheral vasodilation is the enlargement of the diameters of blood vessels to allow greater volumes of blood to reach the skin and dissipate the heat.

     2.   Evaporative heat loss by sweating is a common and obvious cooling mechanism.

       a.   Sweating to dissipate heat can only be effective when the external temperatures are high enough to cause evaporation.

       b.   Extreme sweating can lead to harmful loss of sodium as well as water.

     3.   Hyperthermia is a rise in core temperature, with devastating effects.

  B. Responses to Cold Stress

     1.   Mammals respond to cold by constricting the smooth muscles in the blood vessels of the skin (peripheral vasoconstriction), which retards heat loss.

     2.   In the pilomotor response, the hairs or feathers become more erect to create a layer of still air that reduces convective and radiative heat losses.

     3.   Rhythmic tremors (shivering) are a common response to cold but are not effective for very long and come at high metabolic cost.

     4.   Hypothermia is a condition in which the core temperature drops below normal; it may lead to brain damage and death. Frostbite is localized cell death due to freezing.

Suggestions for Presenting the Material

- Reference Figures 37.7 and 37.8 and their animations to help students understand nephron structure.

- Spend some time reviewing the concepts of homeostasis and cell transport. Do not assume that the students will be automatically on board if you start using terms like, osmosis, facilitated transport, active transport, and semipermeable membrane without some review.

- The discussion of fish in different aquatic environments provides a great point for a review of osmosis.

- To help prevent student confusion distinguish between structures carrying *blood* and those carrying *filtrate* in the various figures.

- Walk the students step by step through filtration, reabsorption, and secretion. The concepts are fairly simple, but the students often get confused as to what is happening and why.

- A good analogy for how the anatomy of glomerular filtration leads to a high hydrostatic pressure is a comparison of the afferent arteriole to a fire hose and the efferent to a garden hose; ask the students what would happen to the water pressure as the water from the fire hose tried to get into the garden hose.

- Review of ADH and aldosterone functions should be made during your presentation of kidney function.

- In your lecture, include some examples of larger desert mammals, such as the eland, and the special adaptations they have for conserving water and for regulating their body temperature.

- **Some Common Misconceptions:**

  o If you use the word *excretion* in your lectures, clearly distinguish it from the word *elimination*, which is the voiding of undigested waste via the anus. Also, students already have a difficult time with the difference between *excretion* and *secretion* and in this chapter they come up at the same time.

  o Be sure to explain the inadequacy of the layman's terms *warmblooded* and *coldblooded*.

Classroom and Laboratory Enrichment

- To aid the students' conceptualization of the nephron function, the following comparison to a drip-type coffee maker is made:

Nephron Part		Coffee Brewer Part	
a.	Afferent arteriole carrying blood in	a.	Hot water
b.	Blood with wastes	b.	Coffee grounds
c.	Glomerulus	c.	Filter paper
d.	Bowman's capsule	d.	Filter holder
e.	Proximal and distal ducts, Henle's loop, collecting ducts	e.	Carafe

- The storeroom-cleaning analogy reveals a possible explanation for why the kidney removes from the blood much more than it will eventually excrete. Pose this question based on the two scenarios that follow: Which of the following, (a) or (b), results in a more efficient cleaning of the storeroom?

  a. Carefully removing and disposing only those few selected items that are in plain view and identifiable as "no longer needed"

  b. Removing *all* items from the storeroom; then sweeping, dusting, and mopping; and finally replacing only those items selected as "still worth keeping"

- The complete analysis of urine can reveal a wealth of information concerning the status of body metabolism. Ask a clinical lab technician to speak on modern analysis techniques.

- Get a urinalysis kit. There are several available commercially or get test strips from a local pharmacy.

- If possible, invite a kidney transplant or dialysis patient to discuss his or her condition with the class. Some kidney centers have a speaker's bureau for just this purpose. They may also provide dialysis equipment for observation.

- Use a mannequin to show the locations of the urinary organs.

- Exhibit a model of a kidney to illustrate its parts and the blood vessels associated with it.

- Dissect a sheep kidney.

- Dissect the urinary system of a fetal pig.

- Display a model of a nephron.

- Use a model of a renal corpuscle to illustrate its structure.

- Provide microscope slides of the kidney for student viewing.

- This chapter talks about kidney failure; recent stem cell therapies have been employed to develop tissues that have been implanted in cows and have been demonstrated to effectively start filtering from the cow's blood. Discuss this technology in class; this is a good gateway to a discussion of DNA technology, medical ethics, stem cells, etc.

Impacts, Issues Classroom Discussion Ideas

- Name several conditions of the body that can be determined from the composition of one's urine.

- Why should athletes be singled out over the general public for drug screening tests? What other groups should be tested?

- Should a urine test be allowable as a condition of employment? What fields may be more likely to want to test potential employees?

Additional Ideas for Classroom Discussion

- Of these three processes—filtration, reabsorption, and secretion—which is(are) accomplished by a kidney dialysis machine? Explain any limitations of the device.

- Why do high-protein diet supplements for increasing muscle mass or losing weight include warnings saying that water intake must be increased when consuming the product?

- In the storeroom-cleaning analogy (see the Enrichment section), which scenario do you think results in a better cleaning of the storeroom? Do you think the same would apply to kidney function?

- When asked what the kidney does, most people would probably respond that it filters the blood. Why is this answer not a complete statement of kidney function?

- Obviously, humans can survive using only one kidney. Why then do we have two?

- If you were stranded in the middle of the ocean, why would it be dangerous to drink seawater?

- Is it possible to overload our kidneys' capacity by excessive intake of water?

- Why does eating salty foods make you thirsty?

- Why does eating salty foods make you temporarily gain weight?

- What are the benefits and drawbacks of maintaining a high body temperature? A low body temperature?

- What is the relationship that skin plays in maintaining body temperature? What would be the relationship between the skin, cardiovascular system, and water balance/urinary system in maintaining body temperature?

How Would You Vote? Classroom Discussion Ideas

- Monitor the voting for the online question. Certainly an argument could be made that drug testing of employees is an invasion of privacy. But the argument could also be made that **not** screening could be more problematic to more people. The reasoning would be bolstered by noting that one employee's reckless use of drugs could endanger many hundreds of lives, as in a bus driver or airline pilot.

♦ Have students complete polling by using JoinIn clickers.

Term Paper Topics, Library Activities, and Special Projects

♦ Investigate the workings of a kidney dialysis machine. Include historical perspectives and recent technological advances.

♦ Although Western cultures find the practice bizarre, the consumption of one's own urine is practiced in Eastern cultures (India, for example). Report on the supposed benefit of such actions and the possible dangers.

♦ What are kidney stones? What are some of the factors responsible for their formation?

♦ How are kidney stones treated?

♦ Investigate the reasons why humans cannot meet their water needs by drinking seawater exclusively.

♦ Popular wisdom reasons that because incidence of colds and flu increases in fall and winter, it is the drop in temperature and human exposure to it that are to blame. Find out if this is really true. Are there more compelling causes?

♦ Have students investigate the use of protein supplements or high protein diets and the impact they have on the kidneys.

♦ What is gout? Research the past history of gout. Is this condition still around today?

♦ Investigate deaths by water intoxication. What is it? Who is at risk? How often does someone die from water intoxication?

♦ Research the potential to engineer a human kidney using stem cells.

Possible Responses to *Data Analysis Activities*

1. The lowest amount of malathion metabolite was measured during the Organic phase.

2. The highest amount of chlopyrifos metabolite was measured during the first Nonorganic phase.

3. Switching to an organic diet reduced exposure of pesticides, as demonstrated by the amount of pesticide metabolites detected in the urine.

4. Yes.

Responses to *Critical Thinking* Questions

1. The longer loop of Henle provides for a longer distance over which the concentration gradients of the ions can be developed and thus provides for more reabsorption of water from the tubules into the peritubular capillaries.

2. Hyponatremia (water intoxication) occurs when too much salt is lost by sweating, along with water loss. The athlete drinks to replace the water from all the sweating, however, taking in too much water during excessive physical activity, like endurance athletes would experience, causes the sodium levels in their blood to drop even more. The low sodium level affects the production of nerve impulses, and impairs mental processes. Cells take on extra water and expand. As they swell, they put stress on the body's organs, particularly the brain, which has little room to expand within the skull. Eventually, fluid accumulates in the lungs, and athletes become breathless and nauseated. Athletes are not the only ones exposed to water intoxication. Water drinking contests have been used at fraternity hazings, causing death.

3. Polar bears are a good example of this relationship between body size and environment. They have large, compact bodies with relatively small surface areas from which they can lose their internally produced heat—an important asset in cold climates. The larger the animals, the more heat they will produce via metabolism. The amount of heat loss increases as the proportion of exposed surface area to body mass increases. Since that proportion is greater in small animals, they lose heat more quickly. An animal with long legs, ears, or a tail has more surface area than an animal of the same size that has shorter appendages. In extremely cold environments, a smaller body shape with short appendages would be more efficient at maintaining body heat because it would have relatively less surface area compared to body mass.

4. As alcohol inhibits ADH secretion Na reabsorption will slow down, as will water reabsorption. The overall result is that the body will lose water and Na in the urine, leading to dehydration (this effect is exacerbated in the blood as alcohol makes the bloodstream hypertonic).

38

REPRODUCTION AND DEVELOPMENT

Chapter Outline

Objectives

1. Understand how asexual reproduction differs from sexual reproduction. Know the advantages and problems associated with having separate sexes.
2. Describe early embryonic development and distinguish each: oogenesis, fertilization, cleavage, gastrulation, and organ formation.
3. Describe the structure and function of the human male and female reproductive systems.
4. Outline the principal events of prenatal development.
5. Know the principal means of controlling human fertility.
6. Understand human sexual behavior that may lead to pregnancy.

Key Terms

in vitro fertilization	semen	menstrual cycle	embryonic
asexual	seminiferous	menstruation	inductions
reproduction	tubules	PMS	apoptosis
sexual reproduction	ovaries	menopause	pattern formation
hermaphrodites	oocyte	cleavage	homeotic genes
external fertilization	estrogens	blastula	blastocyst
internal fertilization	progesterone	gastrulation	implantation
placenta	oviduct	gastrula	amnion
gonads	uterus	germ layers	chorion
testes (sing: testis)	endometrium	ectoderm	allantois
testosterone	cervix	endoderm	fetus
puberty	vagina	mesoderm	labor
epididymis	ovarian follicle	cytoplasmic	lactation
vas deferens	ovulation	localization	
penis	corpus luteum	mophogens	

Lecture Outline

38.1   Mind-Boggling Births
    A. Multiple births are becoming more common.
        1. The incidence has increased almost 60 percent in the past two decades.
        2. Fertility drugs and assisted reproduction technologies are partly responsible.
    B. Multiple births are a concern to doctors.
        1. There is a greater risk of miscarriage, premature delivery, and surgical delivery.
        2. Multiple newborns usually have lower birth weights and higher mortality rates.

38.2   Modes of Animal Reproduction
    A. Asexual Reproduction
        1. Asexual reproduction by budding (for example, sponge) or fission (for example, flatworm) results in offspring identical to the parents; this is a useful strategy in stable environments.
           a. By asexual reproduction, one parent has all its genes represented in its offspring.
           b. All offspring are clones.

B. Sexual Reproduction
1. Sexual reproduction permits adaptation through variation but is biologically costly because the sexes are separate; animals must produce gametes and must find each other (usually) for fertilization to occur.
2. By reproducing sexually, odds are better that the offspring will have a gene combination that suits them for the environmental conditions present.

C. Gamete Formation and Fertilization
1. Few animals are hermaphrodites; that is, they produce both the sperm and the egg for reproduction.
2. Most animals have a separate male and female organism that must meet for fertilization.
   a. External fertilization in water requires large numbers of gametes.
   b. Internal fertilization requires an investment in elaborate reproductive organs, including the penis, to transfer sperm to the female.

D. Nourishing the Developing Young
1. Energy is set aside for nourishing some number of offspring.
   a. Yolk is a thick fluid containing proteins and lipids to nourish the embryo until it can feed.
   b. Those eggs with little yolk must develop larval stages quickly.
   c. Others, such as birds, have adequate food reserves for a more lengthy development within the shell.
   d. Some eggs, such as those of humans, have no yolk; the embryo must be nourished with energy molecules drawn from the mother through a placenta.

38.3 Reproductive Function of Human Males

A. Male Reproductive Anatomy
1. Each testis contains many seminiferous tubules where sperm are continuously formed.
2. Sperm move from a testis →epididymis (for maturation and storage) → vas deferens → ejaculatory ducts → urethra (located inside the penis).
3. The sperm-bearing fluid—semen—is formed by secretions from the seminal vesicles (fructose and prostaglandins) and the prostate (buffers against acidic vagina).
4. The bulbourethral glands secrete a mucus-rich fluid into the vagina during sexual arousal.
5. During aging, many men develop an enlarged prostate, which can be a sign of cancer.

B. Sperm Formation
1. Sperm form in the walls of the seminiferous tubules of the testes.
2. Diploid spermatogonia undergo mitosis → primary spermatocytes, which undergo meiosis I → haploid secondary spermatocytes, which undergo meiosis II → haploid spermatids → mature sperm.
3. Sertoli cells in the tubule provide nourishment and chemical signals to the developing sperm.
4. Each sperm has a head (nucleus and acrosome), midpiece (mitochondria), and tail (microtubules).
5. Hormonal Controls
   a. Testosterone, produced by Leydig cells located between the lobes in the testes, stimulates spermatogenesis, the formation of reproductive organs and secondary sex characteristics, and helps to develop and maintain normal (or abnormal?) sexual behavior.
   b. Luteinizing hormone (LH) is released from the anterior pituitary (under prodding by GnRH from the hypothalamus) and stimulates testosterone production.

    c.   GnRH also causes the pituitary to release FSH, which stimulates the production of sperm, beginning at puberty.

38.4   Reproductive Function of Human Females
  A. Female Reproductive Anatomy
    1. The human female's gonads consist of a pair of ovaries that produce oocytes and secrete sex hormones.
    2. The egg is released from the ovary → oviduct → uterus (zygote will implant in its lining, the endometrium).
    3. The lower part of the uterus is the cervix, which extends into the vagina, a muscular mucosa-lined tube that in turn leads to the outer genitalia: labia majora, labia minora, and clitoris.
  B. Oocyte Maturation and Release
    1. Females are born with 2 million primary oocytes.
    2. During each cycle an oocyte matures and ovulates from the ovary and (if it is fertilized) may implant in the endometrium; if there is no implantation, the uterine lining is sloughed at the end of each cycle of (approximately) 28 days.
    3. Hormonal regulation induces a primary oocyte to divide into unequal cells: one secondary oocyte and one polar body.
    4. After ovulation of the secondary oocyte, the hormone-secreting cells produce a corpus luteum that will support the zygote after implantation.

38.5   Hormones and The Menstrual Cycle
  A. The Ovarian and Menstrual Cycles
    1. A menstrual cycle consists of several phases.
      a. The menstruation consists of the 1 to 5 day menstrual flow as the uterine lining breaks down; increased GnRH secretion leads to secretion of FSH and LH.
        i.   FSH stimulates the selection of follicles into potential eggs.
      b. This round of follicular maturation, which last from day 6 – 13, is called the follicular phase.
      c. During ovulation, LH surging in the system leads to one ovary releasing an oocyte around day 14.
      d. In the luteal phase, which lasts from day 15 to 28, the corpus luteum develops and releases progestins, causing the endometrium to thicken in preparation for pregnancy.
      e. If no implantation takes place, estrogen and progestin levels drop and lead to menstruation.
  B. Menstrual Disorders
    1. PMS, premenstrual syndrome, is related to discomfort a week or two before menstruation.
      a. Hormones cause milk ducts to enlarge, making the breasts swell and become tender.
      b. Cycle induced changes also cause depression, irritability, anxiety, headaches, and sleeping disorders.

2. Menstrual Pain
   a. Prostaglandins secreted during menstruation stimulate contractions of smooth muscle in the uterine wall.
      a. Many women do not even notice these contractions.
      b. Others may experience a dull ache or sharp pain.
   b. About 10 percent of women develop endometriosis, the growth of endometrial tissues in the wrong places. This can cause painful menstruation.
   c. Fibroids are benign uterine tumors that can cause long, painful menstrual cycles.
C. From Puberty to Menopause
   1. Puberty, the development of secondary sexual characteristics, occurs when estrogen is upregulated in the ovaries.
   2. When a female runs out of follicles, she enters menopause; hormonal changes can lead to hot flashes, and sleep disruption

38.6 When Egg and Sperm Meet
A. Sexual Intercourse
   1. In male sexual arousal, the spongy tissue spaces inside the penis become filled with blood to cause an erection.
   2. During sexual intercourse, stimulation of the penis results in involuntary contractions that force semen out and into the vagina.
   3. Ejaculation in the male and similar smooth muscle contractions in the female are called orgasm.
   4. Viagra is a medication prescribed to counter erectile dysfunction in men.
B. Fertilization
   1. Of the 150 million to 350 million sperm deposited in the vagina during coitus, only a few hundred ever reach the upper region of the oviduct where fertilization occurs.
      a. Sperm may live for about three days following ejaculation.
      b. About 30 minutes after being deposited in the vagina the sperm may reach the oviducts, the entry to the fallopian tubes.
   2. Only one sperm will successfully enter the cytoplasm of the secondary oocyte after digesting its way through the zona pellucida.
      a. The arrival of that sperm stimulates the completion of meiosis II, which yields a mature ovum.
      b. The sperm nucleus fuses with the egg nucleus to restore the diploid chromosome number.

38.7 Preventing Pregnancy
A. Fertility Control Options
   1. Abstinence is most effective, but probably unrealistic.
   2. In the rhythm method, there is no intercourse during the days when an egg is capable of being fertilized.
   3. Withdrawal before ejaculation would seem to be effective, but is not.
   4. Douching is similarly ineffective due to the speed with which sperm enter the uterus.
   5. Surgery to cut and tie the oviducts (tubal ligation) or vas deferens (vasectomy) is effective and generally considered an irreversible method to prevent sperm and egg union.
   6. Spermicidal foam and jelly are toxic to sperm but not reliable unless used in combination with a barrier device.
   7. A diaphragm fits over the cervix and prevents entry of sperm into the uterus.
   8. Condoms prevent sperm deposition in the vagina but must be used with care.

Reproduction and Development   325

9. The birth control pill (and birth control patch) contains synthetic female hormones and prevents ovulation when taken faithfully according to directions.
10. Progestin injections (Depo-Provera) or implants (Norplant) inhibit ovulation over several months.
11. "Morning-after pills" intercept pregnancy by blocking fertilization or preventing implantation.

38.8   Sexually Transmitted Diseases

A. Consequences of Infection
1. Sexually transmitted diseases (STDs) infect about 15 million Americans each year.
2. The social consequences are enormous; women develop more complications than men.

B. Major Agents of STDs
1. HPV
   a. Human Papillomavirus infection is the fastest growing STD in the U.S.
   b. Some strains cause genital warts; others can cause cervical cancer.
2. Trichomoniasis
   a. *Trichomonas vaginalis*, a protozoan, causes soreness and discharge from the vagina; males are usually symptom free.
   b. Untreated infections damage the urinary tract and invite HIV infection.
3. Chlamydia
   a. *Chlamydia trachomatis* causes the disease, with a particularly high incidence in teenagers—especially girls.
   b. It shows few symptoms but can lead to pelvic inflammatory disease.
4. Genital Herpes
   a. *Herpes simplex* virus can invade the mucous membranes of the mouth or genitals by direct contact.
   b. Blisters may form, disappear, then reappear under stressful conditions.
5. Gonorrhea
   a. *Neisseria gonorrhoeae*, a bacterium, enters the body through mucous membranes during sexual intercourse.
   b. Because the initial symptoms are mild, treatment is often delayed, allowing the bacterium to multiply out of control.
6. Syphilis
   a. The spirochete *Treponema pallidum* enters the body from an infected sexual partner.
   b. Initially the spirochetes produce a localized ulcer that heals, but the organisms continue to multiply in the spinal cord, brain, eyes, bones, joints, and mucous membranes with serious consequences.
7. AIDS
   a. Infection by the human immunodeficiency virus (HIV) leads to AIDS, an incurable STD that leads to a complete breakdown of the immune system.
   b. Opportunistic infections are the eventual cause of death.
   c. HIV spreads by anal, vaginal, and oral intercourse as well as by intravenous drug use.

38.9   Overview of Animal Development

A. There are stages stages of animal reproduction and development.
1. In the first stage, gamete formation, eggs or sperm form and mature within the parents.
2. Fertilization begins when a sperm penetrates an egg and is completed when the sperm nucleus fuses with the egg nucleus, resulting in formation of the zygote.

3. Repeated mitotic divisions—cleavage—convert the zygote to a blastula; cell numbers increase but not cell size.
4. Gastrulation results in three germ layers, or tissues.
   a. *Ectoderm* is the outer layer; it gives rise to the nervous system and the outer layers of the integument.
   b. *Endoderm* is the inner layer; it gives rise to the gut and organs derived from it.
   c. *Mesoderm* is the middle layer; muscle, organs of circulation, reproduction, excretion, and skeleton are derived from it.
5. Organ formation begins as germ layers subdivide into populations of cells destined to become unique in structure and function.
6. During growth and tissue specialization, organs acquire specialized chemical and physical properties.

B. Each stage builds upon the previous one.

38.10 Early Marching Orders

A. Components of the Sperm and Egg
   1. The sperm contributes little more than the paternal DNA.
   2. The oocyte contains the majority of materials that will affect early development.
      a. RNA transcripts will be translated into proteins that are used in chromosome replication.
      b. Ribosomal subunits necessary for protein synthesis are stockpiled.
      c. Microtubules will influence the division orientation during cleavage.
      d. Certain materials are not distributed all through the cytoplasm, they are located in one region or another, and this is called cytoplasmic localization.
   3. Cytoplasmic localization is a feature of all oocytes; some egg components are localized in the egg setting up important gradients for development.
      a. In a frog egg, microtubules move granules from the animal pole to form a *gray crescent* near the equator opposite the penetration site.
      b. Near the crescent, the body axis of the frog embryo will become established and gastrulation will begin.

B. Cleavage—The Start of Multicellularity
   1. During cleavage, a furrow appears on the cell surface and defines the plane of the cut.
      a. These divisions are not random.
      b. The pattern dictates what types and proportions of materials a blastomere will get, as well as its size.
   2. Each species has a characteristic cleavage pattern.

C. From Blastula to Gastrula
   1. From a hundred to thousands of cells may form at cleavage—depending upon the species.
   2. Starting with gastrulation, cells migrate about and rearrange themselves.
      a. In most animals, the small ball of cells formed at cleavage develops into a gastrula with three distinct germ layers: ectoderm, mesoderm, and endoderm.
      b. Specific patterns of cell migration occur within the gastrulation process.

38.11 Specialized Cells, Tissues, and Organs Form

A. Cell Differentiation
   1. All cells in an embryo descend from the same zygote and have the same genes.
      a. From gastrulation onward, selective gene expression occurs.
      b. Different cell lineages express different subsets of genes.

   c. This is the start of differentiation, where cell lineages become specialized in composition, structure, and function.

  2. An adult body has about 200 differentiated cell types.

  3. A differentiated cell retains the entire genome; this is what makes cloning possible.

B. Cell Communication in Development

  1. Morphogens are signaling molecules produced by master genes.

    a. They diffuse out and form a concentration gradient in the embryo.

    b. A morphogen's effect on target cells is proportional to its concentration.

  2. Embryonic induction occurs when embryonic cells produce signals that alter the behavior of neighboring cells.

C. Cell Movement and Apoptosis

  1. Morphogenesis is the process by which tissues and organs form.

    a. Cells migrate to specific locations.

    b. Sheets of cells expand and fold as cells change shape.

  2. Programmed cell death (apoptosis) helps sculpt body parts.

D. Pattern Formation

  1. Pattern formation is the process by which certain body parts form in a specific place.

E. Evolution and Development

  1. The basic body plans of the major animal groups have not changed due to a limited number of master genes.

  2. Positional information affects expression of homeotic genes that regulate development of specific body parts.

  3. This helps explain the similarities among animal body plans, which are influenced by three different constraints.

    a. An example of a physical constraint is the surface area to volume ratio.

    b. Architectural constraints are imposed by body axes.

    c. Phyletic constrains are those imposed by interactions among genes that regulate development in a lineage.

38.12 Early Human Development

A. Cleavage and Implantation

  1. During the first few days after fertilization, the zygote undergoes repeated cleavages as it travels down the oviduct; a blastocyst forms in about one week.

  2. By the time it reaches the uterus, it is a solid ball of cells (morula), which is transformed into a blastocyst.

    a. Implantation begins about six days after fertilization.

    b. The inner cell mass of the blastocyst is transformed into an embryonic disk that will develop into the embryo-proper within the next week.

    c. The developing placenta must produce HCG, which feeds back to the corpus luteum, in order to maintain progestin levels.

B. Extraembryonic Membranes

  1. The membranes and their functions are:

    a. The *amnion* is a fluid-filled sac that keeps the embryo from drying out and acts as a shock absorber.

    b. The *yolk sac* becomes a site for blood cell formation.

    c. The *chorion*, a protective membrane around the embryo, forms a portion of the placenta and secretes a hormone (human chorionic gonadotropin) that maintains the uterine lining after implantation.

    d. The *allantois* does not function in waste storage (as it does in birds), but is active in blood formation and formation of the urinary bladder.

C. Gastrulation and Organ Formation
  1. By the third week of development, a two-layered embryonic disk consisting of ectoderm and endoderm has formed.
     a. The "primitive streak," a forerunner of the neural tube from which the brain and spinal cord will form, has appeared.
     b. Some cells also form the notochord, from which the vertebrae will form.
  2. Toward the end of the third week, mesoderm has developed and is giving rise to somites—segments of bones and skeletal muscles.

38.13 Emergence of Distinctly Human Features
  A. By the end of the fourth week, the embryo is 500 times larger than when it started but still smaller than a centimeter in length.
  B. It has embarked on an intricate program of cell differentiation and morphogenesis, including development of limbs, circulation, and umbilical cord.
  C. The second trimester encompasses months four, five, and six; the individual is now called a fetus; the heart is beating; fuzzy hair covers the body.
  D. The third trimester extends from month seven until birth; the earliest delivery in which survival on its own is possible is the middle of this trimester.

38.14 The Function of the Placenta
  A. The placenta is a combination of uterine lining and extraembryonic membranes.
     1. At full term, the placenta will cover approximately one-fourth of the inner surface of the uterus.
     2. The placenta forms early in pregnancy.
  B. Materials are exchanged from blood capillaries of mother to fetus, and vice versa, by diffusion.
     1. The maternal blood and fetal blood do not mix!
     2. After the third month, the placenta produces large amounts of HCG, progesterone, and estrogen to maintain the uterine lining.

38.15 Birth and Lactation
  A. Giving Birth
     1. The birth process (labor) begins with contractions of the uterine muscles; the cervical canal dilates, and the amniotic sac ruptures.
        a. The hormone relaxin softens the cervical connective tissues and makes the bridges between the pelvic bones looser.
        b. The hormone oxytocin induces powerful uterine contractions.
        c. The process of labor is an example of a positive feedback mechanism.
     2. The fetus is expelled accompanied by fluid and blood; the umbilical cord is severed; and finally the placenta is expelled.
     3. Corticotropin-releasing hormone affects the timing of labor, and it may contribute to post-partum depression.
  B. Nourishing the Newborn
     1. The mammary glands first produce a special fluid for the newborn; then, under the influence of prolactin, they produce milk.
     2. Oxytocin is released in response to suckling and further increases the milk supply.
     3. Besides providing nourishment, human breast milk contains antibodies that protect a newborn from some viruses and bacteria.

Suggestions for Presenting the Material

♦ This chapter could easily be two or three chapters of information; additionally, this is usually relevant interesting information for college students. Pick and choose what is most important for your students to know and be clear about those objectives.

♦ Before diving into human reproduction and development; spend some time discussing and debating different reproductive strategies. What are the benefits and drawbacks of asexual vs. sexual reproduction?

♦ It would be easy to turn this discussion into a human sexuality talk, but focus on the biology instead of the psychology; or if time permits, have a point/counterpoint discussion with a psychologist in your class.

♦ There are numerous excellent animated figures available to help you present this material. The animated figures provide excellent visual context for your students.

♦ While this chapter focuses on the details of humans, it also presents *general terms of reproduction* (sexual versus asexual), *development* (fertilization, cleavage, gastrulation, and organogenesis), *growth, metamorphosis,* and *differentiation.*

♦ Embryonic development is best demonstrated by use of a DVD (see the Enrichment section); but if not available, pictures of Figure 39.6 will substitute, albeit not as well. If you are lucky enough, your department has a set of models that will help students understand this process.

♦ The most "abstract" sections in this chapter include the topics of morphogenesis and pattern formation. These will require some inventive use of visual aids and/or video to convey the message.

♦ Ensure that the Figures (38.4 and 38.7) of male and female reproductive systems are in view of the students during your presentation.

♦ Male and female reproductive systems provide an interesting dichotomy of potential reproductive strategies, discuss how this affects natural selection.

♦ When comparing the male and female systems, it is helpful to note that the male produces and delivers sperm, much as the female produces and delivers eggs. However, the female also provides: (a) a site for fertilization, and (b) a site for embryonic and fetal development. This provides a convenient lead-in to the discussion of the menstrual cycle.

♦ The details of the menstrual cycle are of interest to both sexes but especially to females, of course. Because events are happening simultaneously in the pituitary, ovary, and uterus, it is virtually a necessity to keep Figure 38.9 in constant view. The critical feature of this figure is the time line along the bottom, which puts all events into perspective.

♦ These points need emphasis in your lecture on female reproduction:

   a. Females are born with a finite number of eggs, which means eggs grow old (implications for causing genetic defects in offspring).

   b. Menstrual cycle can be defined as "the monthly release of an egg and all the preparations for it."

   c. Retention or sloughing of endometrium is determined by progesterone levels at the end of the menstrual cycle.

♦ Figure 38.21 and 38.22 A&B present an overview of human development. The specifics of each development in each time interval can lead to a "cataloging" approach, which can be alleviated by using the video referred to in the Enrichment section.

♦ The most practical aspect of the chapter is the section on "control of human fertility." Students are eager for this information, especially when it can be presented with special reference to the mode of action of each device. Be sure to emphasize the effectiveness of each method as shown in Table 38.2.

♦ The topic of sexual diseases is presented in this chapter in Section 38.8. Individual instructors may, or may not, wish to present this. But certainly some reference, even without details, should be made to the toll these diseases exact on society.

♦ Aging is something your youthful class will not find of much interest now. But perhaps you can find some recent research tidbit on which to base your presentation of what is really a puzzling process.

♦ **Common Student Misconceptions**

   o Most students approach the topic of reproduction with a sigh of relief and an attitude that says "finally, something I know *everything* about." The intuitive instructor will build upon what *accurate* information the students already know and will gently, but authoritatively, correct misinformation. This also prohibits any belittling of incomplete, or inaccurate, "folklore."

   o You may be able to surprise your students with the fact that only a few days of each month comprise the "fertile period." But hasten to inform your young "experimenters" that the fertile days can "move around" depending on a variety of nutritional, psychological, and health factors.

Classroom and Laboratory Enrichment

♦ If at all possible, show a DVD depicting development of some animal, and contrast/compare this with the focus on human development in this chapter. Because of the dynamic nature of this process and the rapid changes, static photographs are usually inadequate.

♦ Dissect the male and female reproductive systems of a fetal pig.

♦ Reproduction and development provide a great conceptual framework to revisit evolution, i.e. changes to homeotic genes lead to development of different body plans, etc.

♦ Although it is not always convenient to do so, the demonstration of live chick embryos is a real attention-arresting sight. Don't neglect to place an embryo under a stereomicroscope to see the heartbeat and blood flow.

♦ The early development of sea urchin embryos is not as difficult to demonstrate as that of the chick. Biological supply houses sell demonstration kits. Timing is a critical factor for viewing all the stages, so you should plan to videotape the sequence.

♦ Because you probably teach students with a great range of sexual knowledge and experience, adjust your enrichment activities accordingly. For example, many students will appreciate observing birth control devices or pictures of them. Others may be intimately familiar with their use.

♦ The topic of prenatal development will be greatly enhanced by the use of a video such as *Life's Greatest Miracle.*

♦ If you decide to present details of the physical manifestations of sexually transmitted diseases, use discretion in which slides you show.

♦ Have a roundtable of doctors, nurses/nurse practitioners, public health officials to discuss STD and contraception information and alternatives.

♦ Students enjoy bragging about their sexual knowledge. Perhaps you can bring some perspective to this by preparing a true/false quiz of common facts and fallacies associated with human reproduction. Allowing the students to remain anonymous, administer the quiz prior to your lecture. Tabulate the results, and report to the class as you give the accurate information.

Impacts, Issues Classroom Discussion Ideas

♦ Why do think the number of multiple births has increased so dramatically in the past 20 years? Have students compile a list of multiple births in their families and among their friends. Present the multiple birth statistics from earlier generations with that of the current multiple birth trends.

♦ What are the risks of mothers in their forties and even fifties (or even their 60s) giving birth? Evaluate both the risk to the mother and the fetus/child.

♦ How many ways can you think of in which the increased number of multiple births results in increased costs to society?

♦ Will Americans ever agree to controls over-fertility and reproduction as some other countries have?

Additional Ideas for Classroom Discussion

♦ What are the benefits and drawbacks of asexual vs. sexual reproduction?

♦ If sexual reproduction is so evolutionarily beneficial, why does asexual reproduction persist?

♦ Is there such a creature as a "female earthworm"? Explain your answer in anatomical terms.

♦ Some persons think the "yolk" of the chicken egg corresponds to the "nucleus." Is this true?

♦ Why does the incidence of birth defects increase for women over 35?

♦ Why would a low fat diet affect the hormonal control of the menstrual cycle?

♦ All animals reproduce at rates sufficient to maintain their populations. Humans are the only ones whose proliferation seems to be under very few limiting factors. Is this so? Why?

♦ Using anatomical terms, explain why men who have had a vasectomy operation are still able to expel normal amounts of semen but no sperm.

♦ Explain the events that result in the production of identical and fraternal twins.

♦ What propels sperm from their point of origin to the opening where they exit the body?

♦ What mechanisms prevent the entry of more than a single sperm into the egg?

♦ The placenta supplements, or completely replaces, the activity of three organ systems in the fetus. What are they?

♦ Many communities and even states restrict the teaching of human reproduction. Why do you think this body system is singled out over, say, digestion or respiration for such a prohibition?

♦ Why do the different methods of birth control work in theory?

♦ How does a fertilized egg know how to develop into a human pattern?

♦ At what point does a stem cell lack the ability to be pluripotent?

♦ Initiate a discussion on fetal alcohol syndrome. Ask students to describe similar life style habits that might create similar risks for women who are pregnant or nursing infants.

♦ Males in the class are often unfamiliar with the physiological processes associated with the menstrual cycle.

How Would You Vote? Classroom Discussion Ideas

♦ Have students complete class polling using the JoinIn clickers. The tradeoff between concerns over high risk pregnancies and assisting couples in enhancing their fertility is a difficult question to consider. Have your students break into small groups and present both the pro and con arguments. On the board or overhead projector, summarize the primary arguments and categorize them as: Personal, Social, Economic, etc.

Term Paper Topics, Library Activities, and Special Projects

♦ Sexual dysfunction is a frustrating situation for those involved, whether male or female. Prepare a list, based on your reading, of the most prevalent disorders and their treatment.

♦ We hear about "sperm banks" in the popular press every now and then. Do such repositories actually exist? Where are they? How do they function? A wonderful demonstration is to use the yellow pages from a major city in your area—look up fertility clinics. It will surprise students to learn how many there are.

♦ Any interruption in the menstrual cycle, whether temporary or permanent, is cause for concern. Report on the causes and effects of the cessation of menstruation in females who drastically reduce their body weight (anorexia) or body fat (as in body building) or through vigorous exercise regimes.

♦ Define and describe different method s of contraception and discuss their efficacy.

♦ Research the implementation of birth control campaigns in other countries.

♦ Search for the physiological explanation for the cessation of menstruation (menopause)—usually when a woman is between the ages of 40 and 50. Is there any comparable phenomenon in men?

♦ It is known that overcrowding and stressful conditions reduce reproductive behavior in rodents. Is there any published evidence of such a phenomenon in humans?

Possible Responses to *Data Analysis Activities*

1. Heart defects were the most common defect in single births.

2. Heart defects were more common in multiple births.

3. Multiple births are twice as likely to have central nervous defects.

4. Multiple births slightly increase the risk of chromosomal defects.

Possible Responses to *Critical Thinking* Questions

1. HCG, the hormone released by the placenta in order to maintain progestin production in the corpus lutem, has to travel from the uterus to the ovaries via the circulatory system. As the blood composition is maintained by the kidneys, measurable amounts of HCG that are filtered in the kidneys should start showing up in urine samples.

2. FSH stimulates the maturation of follicles. If the level of FSH were upregulated in a female, that may lead to the stimulation and maturation of more than one follicle, leading to fraternal twins.

3. Germ cells (stem cells) have two very important properties that somatic (body cells) cells do not. One characteristic is that germ cells have the potential to differentiate into many different kinds of cells in various tissues. This is one factor that makes stem cell research so attractive to those working on medical breakthroughs on heart disease, and neural damage/diseases.

39

ANIMAL BEHAVIOR

Chapter Outline

Objectives

1. Understand the components of behavior that have a genetic and/or hormonal basis.
2. Distinguish behavior that is primarily instinctive from behavior that is learned.
3. Know the aspects of behavior that have an adaptive value.
4. Describe how forms of communication organize social behavior.
5. List the costs and benefits of social life.
6. Explain the roles of self-sacrifice and altruism in social life.

Key Terms

pheromone	imprinting	sexual dimorphism	theory of inclusive
ecology	habituation	selfish herd	fitness
stimulus	communication	dominance	
instinctive behavior	signal	hierarchy	
fixed action pattern	lek	altruistic behavior	
learned behavior	territory		

Lecture Outline

39.1   An Aggressive Defense

   A.   Africanized honeybees, also known as "killer bees", are more aggressive in their stinging attacks.

      1.   Africanized bees respond faster and in greater numbers than their European cousins.

      2.   Bees release a pheromone, a chemical signal that transmits information among individuals of the same species, in response to a threat.

      3.   The pheromone signals the hive of danger and members ban together to ward of the potential predator.

   B.   This is an example of differences in animal behavior—coordinated responses that animal species make to a range of stimuli.

39.2   Behavior's Genetic Basis

   A.   How Genes Can Influence Behavior

      1.   Animal behavior involves detecting stimuli. Stimuli are some type of information about the environment that a sensory receptor has detected and responded to.

      2.   Genes contribute in an indirect way to behavior by influencing development of the nervous system.

   B.   Genetic Variation Within a Species

      1.   One way to understand the genetic basis of behavior is to examine behavioral and genetic differences among members of a single species

      2.   Illustration: Feeding preferences of garter snakes in two populations the following.

         a.   Newborn offspring of coastal parents readily ate banana slugs; offspring of inland parents rejected them.

         b.   Offspring "hybrid" snakes responded *more* to banana slug scent but *less* than did typical newborn coastal snakes.

      3.   Fruit fly larvae have a genetic difference in foraging behavior.

         a.   Rovers move as often as they feed and this represents the dominant allele of the foraging-related gene.

         b.   Sitters move infrequently as they feed and this is a homozygous recessive trait.

   C.   Genetic Variation Among Species

      1.   Comparing behavior of related species can clarify the genetic basis of behavior.

      2.   Illustration: The hormone oxytocin in two closely related species of vole can affect social behavior.

         a.   Higher oxytocin activity produces monogamy in the monogamous prairie voles.

         b.   If a monogamous female is given an oxytocin-blocking drug, she promptly dumps her long-term partner.

    c.   The more promiscuous vole species has been found to have fewer oxytocin receptors in the area of the brain associated with social learning.

  D. Human Behavior Genetics
    1. Nearly all human behavioral traits have a polygenic basis and are influenced by the environment; therefore, making them very difficult to study.
    2. Insight from studies of animal behavior can inspire human studies (for example, a lack of oxytocin activity may underlie autism).

39.3   Instinct and Learning

  A. Instinctive Behavior
    1. In instinctive behavior, components of the nervous system allow an animal to make a stereotyped, innate response to a first-time encounter with environmental cues.
      a. Each of these instinctive responses is triggered by a sign stimulus, which sets in motion a fixed action pattern, a series of instinctive movements.
      b. A fixed action pattern will emerge given specific stimuli no matter what else is happening in the environment.
    2. Fixed action patterns convey a survival advantage by permitting fast response to specific stimuli.

  B. Time-Sensitive Learning
    1. Learned behavior develops after birth and is shaped by experience.
    2. In imprinting, learning requires exposure to key stimuli in the environment during a sensitive period in the young animal's life.
      a. Young geese learned the big object leaning over it gives it food and warmth, and will afterwards follow it.
      b. Sparrows can learn some of the dialect from recordings, but do better if they have a social experience with a live "tutor."

  C. Conditioned Responses
    1. Classical conditioning occurs when an animal's involuntary response to a stimulus becomes associated with a stimulus that is presented at the same time (for example, the famous experiments conducted by Ivan Pavlov).
    2. Operant conditioning occurs when an animal modifies its voluntary behavior in response to consequences of that behavior (for example, animals learn to avoid behaviors that cause pain).

  D. Other Types of Learned Behavior
    1. With habituation, an animal learns by experience not to respond to a stimulus that has neither positive nor negative effects.
    2. Animals learn about physical landmarks in their environment, as well as details of their social landscape.
    3. With imitation/observational learning, an animal copies the behavior it observes in another individual.

39.4 Adaptive Behavior

  A. Adaptive behavior promotes the propagation of an individual's genes and tends to occur at increased frequency in successive generations.

  B. This was tested by examining the nest-decorating behavior of starlings.
    1. Starlings decorate their nests using a specific aromatic plant. It was hypothesized that the plant reduced the number of blood-sucking mites that could weaken nestlings.

2. Scientists, Larry Clark and Russell Mason, replaced the nests with some that had aromatic sprigs and some that did not.
   a. After the chicks left the nest the researchers found fewer mites in the nests decorated with aromatic sprigs.
   b. Mason and Clark concluded that decorating a nest with aromatic sprigs deterred the blood-sucking mites.

39.5   Communication Signals

A. Communication signals are cues for social behavior between members of a species.
   1. Signals may be chemical, acoustical, visual, or tactile.
   2. Pheromones are powerful chemical cues released into the air .
      a. Signaling pheromones induce a receiver to respond fast, such as the alarm pheromone of honeybees.
      b. Priming pheromones elicit long-term responses; for example, the volatile odor of male mice urine triggers and enhances estrus in female mice.
   3. Acoustical signals, such as a bird song, attract a mate or define a territory. Others are alarms that alert members to danger.
   4. Visual signals are part of courtship displays. Selection favors unambiguous displays that result in exaggerated mating displays.
   5. Tactile signals are used to communicate by some means of bodily contact.
      a. When a foraging honeybee finds food relatively close to the hive, it returns and performs a "round dance" on the honeycomb with several bees in close contact.
      b. If the forager is to communicate more precise information about the location of the food source, she performs a "waggle dance," which pinpoints the location of the food relative to the position of the sun.

B. The same signal sometimes functions in more than one context. These signals evolve and persist only if they convey benefits for both the sender and receiver.

C. Illegitimate Signalers and Receivers
   1. Male tugara frogs attract females with complex calls and frog-eating bats use these calls to locate their prey.
   2. Male fireflies attract mates by producing flashes of light and this signal is misused by predators of this species to entice/locate their prey.

39.6   Mates, Offspring, and Reproductive Success

A. Mating Behavior
   1. Sexual selection is the evolutionary outcome of competition for mates and selectivity among potential mates.
      a. Males produce large numbers of small gametes; therefore, reproductive success is measured in terms of how many females the male can inseminate.
      b. Because females produce limited numbers of eggs and can care for a small number of offspring, it is the quality of a mate that is important.
   2. The following are some examples of selection procedures.
      a. Male hangingflies kill a moth, which they then present as a gift to females, who will mate only so long as the food holds out.
      b. Female fiddler crabs stroll by the burrows of the male crabs looking for the most attractive, over-sized claw.
      c. Male sage grouse gather on a communal display ground (a lek) to strut their stuff, hoping to attract the attention of the females gathered around.

3. In these examples and many other species, it is the females that dictate the rules of male competition, with males employing tactics that will help them attract females in order to fertilize as many eggs as possible. Such systems impose strong selective pressures and result in sexual dimorphisms, differences in morphology between sexes.

4. In species in which females cluster around a necessary resource, males may hold a territory, a region that they occupy and defend from others. The territory holder will mate with all the females in his territory.

B. Parental Care

1. Parental behavior drains time and energy that might be allocated to improving their own chances of living to reproduce at another time.

2. Yet parental behavior benefits the individual by improving the likelihood that the current generation of offspring will survive.

39.7 Living in Groups

A. Defense Against Predators

1. Cooperative responses to predators reduce the net risk to all.

2. A group of animals simply provides more pairs of eyes to detect predators; they may also engage in group counterattack. Example: When disturbed sawfly caterpillars collectively rear up, writhe about, and regurgitate toxic fluids.

3. Some animals live in groups simply to "use" others as a shield against predators. This is an example of the selfish herd behavior, where individuals hide behind others. Example: The largest, most powerful bluegill fish protect the eggs in the center of the nest, while smaller males assemble around them and bear the predatory attacks that may come from bass.

B. Improved Feeding Opportunities

1. Many animals like wolves live in groups that cooperate in hunts.
   a. Group hunts are not necessarily more successful than solitary hunting because the captured prey must be shared.
   b. Hunting in groups may have other benefits such as fending off scavengers, caring for one another's young, and protection of the common territory.

2. Group living allows the transfer of cultural traits, or behaviors learned by imitation. For example, young chimpanzees learn to make a "fishing stick" from the older members of the group. The stick is placed it into a termite mound to obtain a tasty termite snack.

C. Dominance Hierarchies

1. Some animals show self-sacrificing behavior that enhances the continuity of their particular genetic lineage.

2. Why do individuals sacrifice some of their own reproductive success for the good of the group?
   a. Sacrifice may be the cost of belonging to the group.
   b. Individuals may cooperate against predators, even though the opportunities to reproduce may not be theirs.
   c. Dominance hierarchies tend to minimize aggression within the society, and dominant members leave more offspring than subordinates, who may move up if they patiently wait.

D. Regarding the Costs

1. Animals living in close association may increase their hunting success to such an extent that they deplete the local resources more rapidly than if they were spread out.

2. Sociality may also increase vulnerability to predators, parasites, and disease.

39.8   Why Sacrifice Yourself?
   A.   Social Insects
      1.   Eusocial insects, like bees, stay together for generations in a group that has a division of labor.
      2.   Consider the honeybee colony: Each member, by its self-sacrificing behavior, increases the number of genetically similar offspring produced.
         a.   Sterile guards may protect the queen by stinging an intruder and thereby committing suicide.
         b.   Worker bees feed larvae and clean and maintain the hive.
         c.   Males, stingless drones, live only to mate with the queen.
      3.   Termites also live in large, extensive family groups.
         a.   Soldier termites defend the colony by secreting substances to attract other defenders and by battling the invaders themselves.
         b.   Soldiers and workers are sterile and dedicate their lives to providing for the fertile king and queen.
   B.   Social Mole-Rats
      1.   The only eusocial mammals are the African mole rats, which live in excavated burrows.
      2.   One reproducing female dominates the clan and mates with one to three males; other non-breeders tend the "queen" and "king(s)" and their offspring.
   C.   Evolution of Altruism
      1.   Altruistic behavior involves actions that enhance another individual's reproductive success at the altruist's expense.
      2.   The theory of inclusive fitness holds that individuals can indirectly pass on their genes by helping relatives survive and reproduce.
      3.   All individuals of the insect colonies are members of an extended family involved in many activities that are altruistic.

39.9   Evolution and Human Behavior
   A.   The discussion of natural behavior in animal groups does not include a judgment of moral right or wrong.
   B.   To evolutionary biologists, "adaptive" simply means a behavior that increases reproductive success.
   C.   Infanticide is morally repugnant to humans but common in most animal groups and human cultures.

Suggestions for Presenting the Material

   ◆   This chapter deals with topics that are not strictly biological but rather encompass the realm of social interaction, concluding with a discussion on human behavior patterns that many would argue are not biological in nature.

   ◆   One approach to presenting the material is the inclusion of representative examples (with pictures) that illustrate each principle of learning.

   ◆   Stress the "interpretative" aspect of studying behavior; that is, rarely do two investigators give exactly the same interpretation of the behavior they see. The role of behavior and the interpretations rely on repetitive observations across the same species or closely related species.

- Many of the principles of animal behavior are difficult to demonstrate in the lab, although behavior textbooks and lab manuals contain possibilities for classroom lab experiments that can be used to accompany this chapter.

- Students recognize the importance of communication signals but fail to grasp how many there are and how complex they can be. Show the animated Figure 39.11 to illustrate tactile displays by honeybees and the role it plays in group behavior.

- Show videos of such aspects of animal behavior as instinctive behaviors and learned behaviors. Students can also read and report on animal behavior experiments performed by others or the careers of famous animal behaviorists.

- The topic of animal behavior can serve as an opening for discussing the challenges of experimental design, especially with regard to experiments conducted in the field.

- If you feel capable of commenting on the relationship between behavior as viewed by a biologist and as viewed by a sociologist, your students would no doubt appreciate this "bridging" of the disciplines.

- Emphasize the evolutionary value of each of the social behaviors described in the text. Students have seen many examples of adaptive traits by this point in their study of introductory biology and will be fascinated to think of behaviors as yet another example.

- Students will ask questions about aspects of human behavior that will serve as the focal points of some interesting discussions.

- Because many social behaviors are difficult to describe or demonstrate in class, films can be effectively used to present many of the more complex examples of social behavior, such as communication among honeybees.

- **Common Student Misconceptions**
    - Students often have a limited grasp of the concept of instinct and the role it plays in the animal world. Taking the time to introduce this idea using numerous examples and contrasting it with learned behavior will help.

Classroom and Laboratory Enrichment

- Ask students to consider and possibly design an animal behavior experiment that can be performed outdoors in your campus environment. Begin by listing animal species found on campus, and then design methods of observing their behaviors.

- Learn more about experiments investigating instinctive behaviors in newly hatched chicks.

- Design experiments to test the ability of mice to learn mazes.

- Can zoos or aquaria be used as laboratories for animal behavior research? Visit a nearby zoo or aquarium to observe animal behavior. What types of behaviors do you see that are a product of captivity?

- Develop lab experiments investigating territoriality among fishes using an aquarium.

- The most reliable sources of visual enhancement for these lectures are film clips.

- Although this chapter focuses on behavior in general using a variety of animals, you may want to prepare a listing of human examples for each topic and ask students to evaluate your list and supplement it.

- Have students prepare a list of human behavior actions that fit into the categories of instinctive and learned behaviors.

- Survey the class opinion on whether each of the human aspects below is controlled more by heredity or environment, or equally.

  a. Intelligence

  b. Body size

  c. Beauty

  d. Speech patterns

  e. Health

- Look up information about body language and visual cues used by humans. Design experiments to be performed on campus that will allow you to observe these and other forms of nonverbal human communication. Is nonverbal communication different in males and females? Do students use different types of body language in different campus locations (classrooms, library, cafeteria, and dormitories)?

- Design and perform a lab experiment investigating maternal behaviors in white mice. Is a mother able to quickly retrieve her pups if they are removed from the nest? Why is this an adaptive trait? What signals does she use to find her pups?

- What kinds of acoustical signaling can you hear in your area on a spring or summer evening? What kinds of acoustical signaling can you hear during the daytime hours? Determine the species responsible for the sounds you hear, and analyze the meaning of their calls.

- If the opportunity is available, consider a demonstration of firefly signaling. This may be overly ambitious but might be of interest to an honors group as a special project.

An Aggressive Defense (revisited)

- What are some of the difficulties in designing research experiments in animal behavior? Discuss problems that must be overcome when performing animal behavior research.

- Can you think of some reasons why displays of aggression between males of the same species rarely result in death?

- What part has natural selection played in the behaviors we observe in animals today?

- Why do you think true social behavior has evolved in only a few insect species?

- How does crossbreeding influence behaviors in other animals besides bees?

Additional Ideas for Classroom Discussion

- Can avoidance behavior in *Paramecium* be considered learning?

- What is the link between environment and behavior? Can environment mask instinctive behaviors? What is the role of crossbreeding in modifying behaviors in animals?

- What are the characteristics of innate behaviors? What are the characteristics of learned behaviors?

- Distinguish between associative learning and insight learning.

- How much of the animal behavior we see and interpret is the result of what "we want to see"?

- What kinds of methods are used to alter animal behavior (for example, training dogs)? Are these the same methods as used for altering behavior in children?

- In what way is human behavior altered by long-term isolation or prison incarceration?

- Discuss the ways in which elaborate mating displays benefit a species.

- In what ways do elements of sociality, such as schooling, benefit a species? What are the drawbacks of sociality?

- How do dominance hierarchies benefit those species that use them?

- What is meant by the term selfish herd? Are such behaviors evident in human society?

- How much of our human behavior is determined by our culture? What behaviors seem to be universal among all cultures? Can you think of unusual behaviors that seem to be found only among one culture?

- Can you think of some selection pressures that are responsible for the evolution of many human traits? (Some examples include selection for capturing large prey, coping with carnivorous competitors, and caring for infants.)

- Is child abuse a human behavior of modern times in western cultures? Can you think of some reasons why this might be so?

- In what respects are countries that describe themselves as "socialist" similar to truly social insects? How do they differ?

How Would You Vote? Classroom Discussion Ideas

- Have students complete class polling using the JoinIn clickers. Africanized honeybees continue to increase their range. Should study of their genetics be a high priority? It seems a reasonable request that there are benefits to increased funding for research on bees—both European and Africanized. These insects are extremely valuable participants in the balance of nature. Understanding the genetic nature of behaviors, especially aggression, might lead to pathways to intercede and breed this out of the wild populations that are considered dangerous.

Term Paper Topics, Library Activities, and Special Projects

- Describe the role of environmental cues in determining migratory behaviors in birds. Do biologists understand the physiology underlying the navigational senses of birds?

- Discuss the annual migration of salmon to spawning grounds. Select other migratory behavior and look for common elements and contrasting elements. Have students work in a group to discuss which might be instinctive and which might be learned.

- How are green sea turtles able to find their way from their home in ocean waters off Brazil to their breeding grounds hundreds of miles away on Ascension Island? Describe the latest research efforts attempting to answer this question.

- Describe the mood-altering effects of the steroid drugs sometimes taken by athletes to increase muscle mass.

- Examine the effects of any one of the so-called recreational drugs (alcohol, nicotine, marijuana, cocaine, LSD, amphetamines, barbiturates) on human behavior. How do the chemicals in these substances alter our behaviors? Have students speculate about the chemical interactions influenced.

- Describe the role of melatonin in vertebrate behavior.

- Examine the role of sex in determining human behavior. Are there some behaviors that occur with significantly greater frequency among individuals of one sex than among individuals of the opposite sex?

- Station yourself in a variety of busy spots on campus. Record the usual and unusual behaviors you see. Make note of the day of the week, time of day, gender of participants, race, weather conditions, and so on. Compare your observations with those of others in the class.

- What is unusual about monarch butterfly migrations compared to bird migrations? (Hint: Investigate the migration of the offspring.)

- Describe the chemical nature, distribution, and role of pheromones in animal behavior.

- Describe the visual communication system of fireflies.

- Describe behavioral studies of human infants.

- Using InfoTrac® College Edition, have students research one element of animal behavior interesting to them. Have them complete a single-page summary and report their findings to the class.

- How can human behaviors change as a result of brain surgery (such as a lobotomy) or injury? Describe the relationship between the different areas of the brain and human behavior.

- What examples of nonverbal communication (for example, certain gestures and facial displays) seem to be universally understood? What are some examples of nonverbal communication that exist only within a particular culture or have different meanings among different cultures?

- Examine the growing commercial use of pheromones to control insect pests. How do pheromones work? How are they produced?

- Read about Diane Fosse's research on the societies of primates in Africa.

- E. O. Wilson is well known for his synthesis of biology and sociology as presented in his book on "sociobiology." Prepare a brief synopsis of his ideas.

Answers to *Data Analysis Activities*

1. Africanized bees first became established in Texas.

2. Africanized bees appeared in Arkansas, Louisiana, and Florida for the first time in 2005.

3. Human transport of bees likely contributed to the spread of Africanized honeybees to Florida since colonies were not first found in either Mississippi or Alabama.

Possible Responses to *Critical Thinking* Questions

1. While the clustering around street lights or window panes is not considered evolutionarily adaptive, it likely persists because it is a deeply ingrained genetic trait. In addition, this behavior is unlikely to negatively effect reproduction to the point that this trait is diminished or removed.

2. If the male had engaged in sex with the female parent of the infant, infanticide on his part would possibly remove his genetic offspring from the community. This action would be counterproductive.

40

POPULATION ECOLOGY

Chapter Outline

Objectives

1. Learn the language associated with the study of population ecology.
2. Understand the factors that affect population density, distribution, and change.
3. Understand the meaning of exponential growth.
4. Understand the significance and use of life tables; interpret survivorship curves.
5. Know the impacts of the growth of human populations.
6. Tell which factors have encouraged growth in some cultures and limited growth in others.

Key Terms

population
demographics
population size
plot sampling
mark-recapture
  sampling
population
  density
population
  distribution
age structure
reproductive
  base

immigration
emigration
zero population
  growth
per capita
  growth rate
exponential
  growth
biotic potential
limiting factor
carrying
  capacity
logistic growth

density-
  dependent
  factors
density-
  independent
  factors
life history
  pattern
cohort
survivorship
  curve
r-selection
k-selection

total fertility
  rate
replacement
  fertility rate
demographic
  transition
  model
ecological
  footprint

Lecture Outline

40.1   A Honking Mess

    A. The number of Canada geese in the United States has soared since federal laws were put in place to protect them in the early 1900s.

    B. Issues with this exceptionally large population, a group of organisms of the same species that occupy a particular area, include: excessive feces is a nuisance and adds nutrients to water, thus increasing bacterial and algal growth; potential hazard to air traffic.

    C. Most Canada geese still migrate between the United States and Canada; however, some populations have lost this trait. Compared to a migratory bird, one that stays put can devote more energy to producing young. This has lead to the biggest increases in the nonmigratory Canada geese.

40.2   Population Demographics

    A. Each population—a group of individuals of the same species living in the same area (habitat)—has certain characteristics. Demographics is the statistics that describe a population, and these values often change over time.

        1. The population size is the number of individuals in a population, and this value is often estimated.

        2. Plot sampling estimates the total number of individuals in an area on the basis of direct counts in a small portion of the area. This method is best applied to organisms that are not very mobile.

        3. To estimate the population size of mobile organisms, scientist use mark-recapture sampling.

    B. Population density is the number of individuals per unit of area or volume—the habitat. Population distribution refers to the general pattern in which the population members are dispersed through its habitat.

    C. Populations can be dispersed in three patterns: clumped, near-uniform, or random.

        1. Members of a population living in clumps is very common for these reasons.

            a. Suitable physical, chemical, and biological conditions are patchy, not uniform.

            b. Many animals form social groups.

            c. Many offspring are not highly mobile and are forced to live "where they landed."

2. Near-uniform dispersion is rare in nature; when it does occur, it is usually the result of fierce competition for limited resources.
3. Random dispersion occurs in nature if environmental conditions are rather uniform in the habitat and members are neither attracting nor repelling each other.

D. The age structure of a population refers to the number of individuals in various age categories: pre-reproductive, reproductive, or post-reproductive. All age groups contribute to the reproductive base of a population, except post-reproductive organisms.

E. The scale of the area sampled and the timing of a study can influence the observed demographics.

40.3 Population Size and Exponential Growth

A. Gains and Losses in Population Size
1. Population size is dependent on births, immigration, deaths, and emigration.
2. Population size may also change on a predictable basis as a result of daily or seasonal events called migrations.

B. From Zero to Exponential Growth
1. Zero population growth designates a near balance of births and deaths.
2. Rate of increase: r = per capita growth rate.
3. The growth rate formula is: G = r x N.
   a. G is the population growth per unit time, r is the per capita growth rate, and N is the number of individuals.
   b. As long as r is positive, the population will continue to increase at ever-increasing rates (exponential growth) —easily measured by noting the "doubling time."
   c. A graphic plot of exponential growth results in a J-shaped curve that becomes steeper with advancing time.

C. What Is the Biotic Potential?
1. The biotic potential of a population is its maximum rate of increase under ideal—nonlimiting—conditions.
2. The biotic potential varies from species to species. Actual rates of growth depend upon:
   a. At what age each generation starts reproducing.
   b. How often reproduction occurs.
   c. How many offspring are born each time.

40.4 Limits on Population Growth

A. Environmental Limits on Growth
1. The actual rate of increase of a population is influenced by environmental conditions.
2. Limiting factors (nutrient supply, predation, competition for space, pollution, and metabolic wastes) provide environmental resistance to population growth.

B. Carrying Capacity and Logistic Growth
1. The sustainable supply of resources defines the carrying capacity for a particular population in a given environment.
   a. The carrying capacity can vary over time and is expressed graphically in the S-shaped curve pattern called logistic growth. The population grows slowly, then increases rapidly until it reaches carrying capacity and levels off.
   b. The formula for logistic growth is: population growth = maximum per capita population growth rate x number of individuals x proportion of resources not yet used

© 2011 Cengage Learning. All Rights Reserved. May not be copied, scanned, or duplicated, in whole or in part, except for use as permitted in a license distributed with a certain product or service or otherwise on a password-protected website for classroom use.

C. Two Categories of Limiting Factors
   1. Competition for limited resources causes density-dependent effects, as does disease.
      a. Density-dependent factors lower reproductive success, via decreased birth rates or increased death rates, and appear or worsen with crowding.
      b. These factors exert their effects in proportion to the number of individuals present.
   2. Density-independent f actors decrease reproductive success too, but the likelihood of occurring and magnitude are unrelated to population densities.
      a. Some events, such as weather, tend to increase the death rate without respect to the number of individuals present.
      b. Lightning, floods, snowstorms, and the like affect large populations as well as small groups.

40.5 Life History Patterns

A. Each species has a life history pattern, events between birth and death that influences survival, fertility, and the age of first reproduction.

B. Patterns of Survival and Reproduction
   1. Life history traits within a population can be studied by recording what happens to a specific cohort, a group to individuals born near the same time.
   2. Survivorship curves are plots of the age-specific patterns of death for a given cohort.3. Most animals are characterized by one of these types of survivorship curves.
      a. A *Type I* curve is typical of large mammals where few offspring are produced and cared for so that infant mortality is low; death usually comes after an extended life.
      b. A *Type II* curve is typical of many animals where the chances of survival or death are about the same at any age.
      c. A *Type III* curve indicates low survivorship, or conversely, high mortality in early life.

C. Natural selection influences the timing of reproduction and how much a parent invests in each offspring.
   1. At a low population density, there is little competition for resources and r-selection predominates: individuals who turn resources into offspring fastest have a selective advantage.
   2. K-selection predominates occurs when a population is near carrying capacity and individuals who produce offspring capable of outcompeting others for limited resources have a selective advantage.

40.6 Evidence of Evolving Life History Patterns

A. Evolutionary biologists, David Reznick and John Endler, studied the differences in size and survival of guppies in Trinidad.
   1. They were interested in the effects of predation on guppy populations in two streams with different predators.
   2. Their hypothesis was that predation by killifish and cichlids represent a selective agent that acted to shape guppy lifehistory patterns. Noting that killifish prey mostly on immature guppies and cichlids tend to pursue mature guppies.

B. They discovered that differences in growth rate and reproductive maturity have a genetic basis because the effects were the same in lab-reared guppies as compared to the natural populations.

C. The experimenters performed other field experiments that stretched over 11 years.
   1. Guppies that had been exposed to one predator, and then moved to another, displayed changes.
   2. Reznick and Endler showed that life history traits can be inherited, but these traits may also evolve.

D. The evolution of life history traits is not simply an academic exercise, it has important commercial applications.
    1. Human pressures on the North Atlantic cod fishery have altered the age at which these fish reach sexual maturity.
    2. Life history changes can indicate larger scale population troubles, for example the steep decline in the cod population.

40.7 Human Population Growth
    A. Human growth rate grew very slowly until about 10,000 years ago. Three trends promoted the large increases:
        1. Humans expanded into new habitats and climatic zones.
        2. Humans developed new technologies that increased the carrying capacity of existing habitats.
        3. Humans sidestepped some limiting factors that restrain growth of other species, including growing food, controlling disease, and tapping into fossil fuels.
    B. Consider this: It took 2.5 million years for the world's human population to reach 1 billion; it took only 12 years to reach the sixth billion.
    C. Fertility Rates and Future Growth
        1. The total fertility rate of a human population is the average number of children born to a woman during her reproductive years. Although this has decreased, it still remains above the replacement fertility rate.
        2. The human population will continue to increase as long as total fertility rate exceeds the replacement rate. World population is expected to reach 8.9 billion by 2050. The greatest population growth will be seen in India, China, Pakistan, Nigeria Bangladesh, and Indonesia.

40.8 Population Growth and Economic Effects
    A. Development and Demographics
        1. In the demographic transition model, changes in population growth are linked to four stages of economic development.
            a. In the preindustrial stage, living conditions are harsh; birth and death rates are high; and there is little increase in population size.
            b. In the transitional stage, living conditions improve; death rate drops; and birth rate remains high.
            c. In the industrial stage, growth slows due to couples tendency to have smaller families as city dwellers.
            d. In the postindustrial stage, zero population growth is reached; birth rate falls below death rate.
        2. Some developed countries are in the industrial stage (for example, the United States; some countries (for example, Mexico) are in the transitional stage; some countries are in the postindustrial stage (for example, Japan).
    B. Development and Consumption
        1. On a per capita basis, people in highly developed countries use far more resources than those in less developed countries, and they also generate more waste and pollution.
        2. An ecological footprint is the amount of Earth's surface required to support a particular level of development and consumption in a sustainable fashion.
            a. The United States uses about a quarter of the world's mineral and energy supplies, produces about 21 percent of all goods and services, but constitutes only 4.6 percent of the world's population.
            b. Other countries such as India and China are asking for a greater share of the economic pie.

Suggestions for Presenting the Material

♦ This is the second chapter in the book to discuss *populations*. Chapter 17 discussed the *genetics* of populations; the present one reports on the *ecology* of populations.

♦ The bulk of the chapter concerns general aspects of populations: density/distribution, dynamics, survival, and limits.

♦ Students will perhaps be most interested in studies of population as they affect human population growth, a subject covered at the end of this chapter. Examination of the changes in worldwide patterns of population growth since the turn of the century and in the last 20 years in particular will surprise students and highlight the overwhelming need for humans to find ways to control the global population growth rate. The inclusion of human population growth studies in this chapter allows students to see that we are not exempt from the rules and limitations that govern all populations.

♦ Exploration of population ecology also sets the stage for interesting discussions of the socioeconomic impacts of population growth and the ethical questions related to regulating population growth.

♦ **Common Student Misconceptions**

  o Students often have a difficult time keeping straight the environmental limits on population growth and the idea of a shifting carrying capacity.

  o Table 40.1 and 40.2 should be used to help students understand the concept of life history patterns, another area they have some difficulty with.

Classroom and Laboratory Enrichment

♦ Use flowcharts on the board or on the overhead projector to show the relationships among the different components of an ecosystem.

♦ Select an ecosystem that consists of all or part of the campus or a nearby area. List as many of the biotic and abiotic components of that ecosystem as you can. Students could work in teams, with each team assigned to different ecosystem components.

♦ Graph the rates of population growth for several of the nations of the world. Discuss reasons for the differences between nations.

♦ Use the animated Figure 40.4 to visually reinforce the idea of exponential growth. Using the biotic potential of bacteria is a classic way to illustrate the phenomenal growth in some populations over very short periods of time.

♦ Compare and contrast survivorship curves of different organisms. Ask students to first guess whether the organism you have named has a Type I, II, or III survivorship curve. Then use transparent overlays on the overhead projector to show survivorship curves for each species.

♦ Design and implement experiments examining the effects of resource availability, time lags, and competition on population densities of small organisms easily raised in the laboratory.

♦ Calculate population densities for a plant species in several small, defined areas with varying environmental conditions. What pattern(s) of spatial distribution do you see? Identify factors that you believe might influence species distribution (some examples might be nutrient availability, amount of sunlight, moisture, and openings created by disturbance). Design experiments that would evaluate the role of each environmental factor in species distribution.

- Show overhead transparencies of age structure diagrams for human populations of different nations.
- If you have a collection of slides, search for a scene that will include clearly visible examples of a population, the four participating groups in a community, an ecosystem, and the biosphere. As you project each slide, ask students to identify each element.
- Use the classroom and its occupants to illustrate density and distribution:

  a. Head count (size)   a. 50 students
  b. Density   b. 50 students per room
  c. Clumped distribution   c. 50 students in rear half of room
  d. Random distribution   d. 50 students milling around before class begins
  e. Uniform distribution   e. 50 students in evenly spaced rows of chairs
  f. Distribution over time   f. 50 students dispersed to all parts of campus after class

- Show a copy of a life table as published in a modern entomology textbook. These are especially good examples because of the differential death rates in the various stages of metamorphosis.
- The three types of survivorship curves have rather abstract designations (I, II, and III). The following may aid retention:

  a. Type I: Think "hi"   Signifying high survivorship during most of a lifetime
  b. Type II: Think "middle"   Death rate constant
  c. Type II: Think "low"   "III" resembles "low" (both have three items and indicate low survivorship)

- Stimulate interest in the future of human population dynamics by asking your class to vote on one of three possibilities listed below (using Figure 40.7 as a guide).

  a. The S-curve will not "flatten out" as it reaches a carrying capacity but will continue to climb indefinitely.
  b. The curve will oscillate near the carrying capacity.
  c. The curve will plunge downward in a "crash."

A Honking Mess (revisited)

- Describe how migratory organisms are subject to harsher conditions as compared to their nonmigratory counterparts. Is it always beneficial to be a nonmigratory organism? What are the benefits to being a migratory organism?
- Discuss the methodology for determining the origin of the bird feathers found in the engines of the plane that had to land in the Hudson River in 2009. How many naturally occurring hydrogen isotopes exist? Use this opportunity to show students how important chemistry is to the study of biology.

  Discuss DNA analysis. DNA typing began in the mid-1980s, prior to this technique how would the cause of this plane crash into the Hudson River be analyzed? How did the analysis pinpoint the damage to two female and one male Canada goose?

Additional Ideas for Classroom Discussion

♦ Do you think the United States should play a role in disseminating birth control information and supplies to other nations?

♦ What is your opinion about the stance of various religious groups against birth control?

♦ Discuss with students the role life tables and environmental limits on populations play in wildlife management agencies. How the populations are estimated, and carrying capacities determined? How are removal numbers (and sex) calculated for a hunt?

♦ How has modern medical care changed the survivorship curve for humans since the turn of the century?

♦ Some organisms (bamboo, cicadas) reproduce only at a single, very brief interlude during their life span but produce a large number of seeds or offspring during this short period of time. Can you think of some ways in which this pattern benefits a species?

♦ What is the relationship between the size of offspring and their number per reproductive event?

♦ What socioeconomic challenges will the current population structure in the United States someday pose to future generations?

♦ How might the current trend toward delayed childbearing change the population growth in the United States? Why would an increase in parental age change the population structure?

♦ What feature distinguishes each of the following categories from the others?

    a. community   b. population c. ecosystem

How Would You Vote? Classroom Discussion Ideas

♦ Monitor the voting for the online question or have students complete class polling using the JoinIn clickers. One way to decrease the number of nonmigratory Canada geese is by encouraging hunting when migratory birds are unlikely to be present. Would you support relaxing hunting restrictions in regions where Canada geese have become pests?

Term Paper Topics, Library Activities, and Special Projects

♦ Examine how the widespread wave of immigrants in the late 1800s and early 1900s changed the size and rate of growth in the U.S. population.

♦ Examine the effects of the Black Plague on the subsequent size and growth of the human population in Europe.

♦ Have students use Thomson's InfoTrac College Edition to research current articles on population growth in humans. Have them summarize an article in a short paper.

♦ Have students take pro or con sides and discuss population controls in some regional animal population. Have them discuss alternatives to hunting, and the economics and social impacts of such controls.

♦ Look up information about organizations concerned with world overpopulation.

♦ Compare reproductive rates among different cultural and ethnic subgroups of people in the United States. Construct age structure diagrams for each subgroup.

- Look up information on population densities of several rural areas scattered randomly throughout the United States, and also the population densities of several randomly located urban areas. Then find figures on the rates of alcoholism, crime, suicide, and divorce for each area. Is there a statistically significant correlation between population density and any one of these four social problems?

- Locate current data on human population growth in several countries around the world. Which countries are growing faster than the world average? Slower? Are any countries experiencing a negative population growth?

- Investigate the success of the world's most extensive human population limiting program—China's.

- Read several essays on human populations to learn the relationship between numbers of people and rate of consumption of nonrenewable resources. Which countries waste the most? The least?

Responses to *Data Analysis Activities*

1. At the time of the first census, Santa Fe Island had more marked iguanas.
2. The population size did not change on Genovesa Island, and the population decreased by half on Santa Fe Island.
3. If an adverse event had affected both islands, then the December census ought to reveal an equal decline in the population of marked iguanas on both islands.

Possible Responses to *Critical Thinking* Questions

1. The color change observed in the male guppies moved from pools with cichlids to pools with killifish was due to predation. If highly colorful male guppies were not the first prey choice for the killifish, then over many generations more and more male guppies would express this phenotype. This color change may have directly or indirectly lead to variable selection, since the trait may have "piggy-backed" with another trait which directly provided a reproductive advantage.

2. The desert environment is supportive to both the saguaro and the poppies. The saguaro has a very long life history; therefore, it can endure the vagaries of desert life—heat, cold, lack of water—because it will grow slowly and not be affected by transient changes. On the other hand, the poppy takes advantage of the environment of the moment, grows rapidly, reproduces, and dies.

3. The age structure diagram on the left is a population with the greatest numbers of people being young and significantly less older people. This population is able to support the older people, with so many younger citizens; however, in years to come this population may have too little resources to support the growth as the current the population of young begin to reproduce. The age structure diagram on the right is a population with very similar populations of young, middle-aged, and older people. This population is stable and will continue to be stable, as long as the appropriate resources are available.

41

COMMUNITY ECOLOGY

Chapter Outline

Objectives

1. Define the following ecological terms: habitat, niche, community, symbiotic, competition, predation, parasitism, and mutualism.

2. List and distinguish among the several types of species interactions.

3. Discuss the positive aspects and negative aspects of predation on prey populations.

4. List the various types of prey defenses against predators.

5. Describe how communities are organized, how they develop, and how they diversify.

6. Discuss the concept of ecological succession.

Key Terms

community	commensalism	mutualism	interspecific competition
habitat	symbiosis	ecological niche	

competitive exclusion

character displacement

resource partitioning

predation

camouflage

mimicry

herbivory

parasitism

brood parasites

parasitoids

primary succession

secondary succession

pioneer species

intermediate disturbance hypothesis

keystone species

indicator species

exotic species

species richness

equilibrium model of island biogeography

area effect

distance effect

Lecture Outline

41.1   Fighting Foreign Fire Ants

   A. Fire ants have invaded the United States.
     1. The species entered from South America in the 1930s.
     2. They aggressively defend their nests by stinging invaders, injecting venom which causes a burning sensation.
     3. Invasive ants displace natural ant communities and the animals that feed on them.
       a. The invasive fire ants eat voraciously, mowing down plants and feeding on other insects and small animals.
       b. In Texas, the Texas horned lizard has disappeared from most of its range because its primary food, a native ant, had been displaced by invasive fire ants.

   B. Ecologists are using biological controls.
     1. Phorid flies: Inside the fire ant, the parasitoid lays her eggs, which hatch to a larva that consumes the ant's vital tissues. After the larva gets big enough, it secretes an enzyme that makes the ant's head fall off. The larva develops into an adult within the shelter of the detached head.
     2. Another idea is to use microbes that will infect fire ants but not native species.
     3. Species interactions such as those between ants and flies are the focus of community ecology. A community is all the species that live in a region.

41.2   Community Structure

   A. A habitat is a place where an organism lives; it is characterized by distinctive physical features, vegetation, and the array of species living in it.
     1. A community is an association of interacting populations of different species living in a particular habitat.
     2. Each community has a dynamic structure, showing shifting patterns of species diversity, which are the relative abundances of species in a habitat.
     3. Several factors shape the structure of the community.
       a. Interactions between climate and topography dictate rainfall, temperature, soil composition, and so on.
       b. Availability of food and resources affects inhabitants.
       c. Adaptive traits enable individuals to exploit specific resources.
       d. Interactions of various kinds occur among the inhabitants.

   B. Introduction to Species Interactions
     1. Interactions can occur between any two species in a community and between entire communities.

2. There are several types of species interactions.
   a. Commensalism: one species benefits while the other is not affected (for example, a bird's nest in a tree).
   b. Symbiosis refers to the often close association among species during their lives.
3. Two organisms that have close interactions for extended periods of time will coevolve.

41.3 Mutualism

A. Mutualism is an interspecific interaction that benefits both species, and is common in nature.
   1. In some mutualisms, neither species can complete its life cycle without the other. The yucca moth feeds only on the yucca plant, which is completely dependent on the moth for pollination—a classic example of mutualism that is obligatory.
   2. In other cases the mutualism is helpful, but not a life or death requirement; for example, most plants have more than one pollinator.

B. For some mutualists, the main benefit of association is defense; for example the sea anemone protects the anemone fish with its tentacles and the fish repays its partner by chasing off other fishes that wish to eat the sea anemone.

C. Reflect on the theory of endosymbiosis presented in Chapter 18 and the development of organelles like mitochondria. All eukaryotes are the product of ancient mutualisms.

41.4 Competitive Interactions

A. There are two major categories of competition.
   1. Competition within a population of the same species (intraspecific) is usually fierce and may result in depletion of a resource. This is due to the members of a species sharing the same ecological niche, physical and biological requirements.
   2. Interspecific competition is typically less intense, as the ecological niches are less similar between the competitors. However, the more similar the niches of two species are, the more intensely the species will compete.
   3. There are two types of competitive interactions regardless of whether they are inter- or intraspecific.
      a. In interference competition, some individuals limit others' access to the resource.
      b. In exploitation competition, all individuals have equal access to a resource but differ in their ability (speed or efficiency) to exploit that resource.

B. Effects of Competition
   1. Competitive exclusion suggests that complete competitors, those that require the same resources to survive and reproduce, cannot coexist indefinitely.
   2. When competitors' niches do not overlap quite as much, the coexistence is more probable, checking the growth of both populations.

C. Resource Partitioning
   1. Resource partitioning refers to the subdividing of an essential resource that reduces the competition among species that require it.
   2. In each species, those that differ the most from the competing species are favored.
      a. Character displacement occurs when, over the generations, a trait of one species diverges in a way that lowers the intensity of competition with the other species.
      b. Modification of the trait has promoted the portioning of a resource.

41.5 Predation and Herbivory

A. Predator and Prey Abundance
   1. Predators are consumers that obtain energy and nutrients from prey, the living organisms that predators capture, kill, and eat.

2. The quantity and types of prey species affect predator diversity and abundance, and predator types and numbers do the same for prey.
3. The extent to which the changes in the two populations rely on each other is a function of how predators respond to changes in prey populations. There are three basic models.
   a. Each individual predator will consume a constant number of prey individuals over time, regardless of prey abundance.
   b. The consumption of prey by each predator increases, but not as fast as increases in prey density.
   c. A predator response is lowest when prey density is at its lowest level and predation pressure lessens.
4. The Canadian Lynx and Snowshoe Hare
   a. Stable coexistence results when predators prevent prey from overshooting the carrying capacity.
   b. Fluctuations in population density tend to occur when predators do not reproduce as fast as their prey, when they can eat only so many prey, and when carrying capacity for prey is high.

B. Coevolution of Predators and Prey
   1. Interactions among predators and prey influence characteristic species traits.
   2. Many of the adaptations of predators and their victims arose through coevolution via exerting selective pressure on one another.
   3. Prey defenses include the following:
      a. Some prey species have hard or sharp parts to make them difficult to consume.
      b. Many prey species (animals and plants) contain chemicals that taste bad or sicken predators.
      c. Warning coloration in toxic prey offer bright colors or bold patterns that serve as a warning to predators.
      d. In mimicry, prey not equipped with defenses may escape predators by resembling toxic prey.
      e. Some prey animals defend themselves by startling or intimidating the predator with display behavior.
      f. Camouflaging is any adaptation in form, color, patterning, or behavior that allows a prey or predator to blend with its surroundings.
      g. Some predators can just plain outrun their prey.

C. Coevolution of Herbivores and Plants
   1. With herbivory, an animal eats a plant or plant parts; therefore, the number and type of plants in a community can influence the number and type of herbivores present.
   2. Two types of defenses have evolved in response to herbivory:
      a. Some plants have adapted to withstand and recover quickly.
      b. Some plants have spines, thorns, tough leaves, or bad tasting chemicals to deter herbivores.

41.6 Parasites, Brood Parasites, and Parasitoids

A. Parasitism
   1. Parasites are species that spend all or part of their life in or on other species (the host), and pilfer nutrients from them.
   2. There are several kinds of parasites.
      a. All viruses, some bacteria, protists, and fungi are parasites, even a few plants.
      b. Many tapeworms, flukes, roundworms, insects, and of course, those nasty ticks are also parasites.

3. Natural selection tends to favor parasite and host adaptations that promote some level of mutual tolerance and less-than-lethal effects.
4. Parasites have an important impact on a host population
   a. Most are small, and many are pathogens which cause disease in the host.
   b. Parasites affect host numbers by altering birth and death rates.

B. Strangers in the Nest
1. With brood parasitism, one egg-laying species benefits by having another raise its offspring.
2. Brood parasitism decreases the reproductive rate of the host species and favors host individuals that can detect and eject foreign young.
3. This form of parasitism has also evolved in some bee species.

C. Parasitoids
1. Parasitoids are insects that develop inside other insects, which they devour and kill.
2. Parasitoids reduce the size of a host population in two ways
   a. As the parasitoid larvae grow inside the host, they withdraw nutrients and prevent it from reproducing.
   b. The presence of the larvae eventually leads to the death of the host.

D. Biological Controls
1. Parasites and parasitoids have five attributes that make them good control agents.
   a. They are well adapted to the host species and their habitat.
   b. They are exceptionally good at searching for hosts.
   c. Their growth rate is comparable to that of the host species.
   d. The offspring are mobile enough for adequate dispersal.
2. Care must be taken in releasing a control agent in a given area due to the possibility of affecting nontargeted species.

41.7 Ecological Succession

A. Successional Change
1. Pioneer species are opportunistic colonizers of new or newly vacated habitats.
   a. They have high dispersal rates, grow and mature quickly, and produce many offspring.
   b. More competitive species replace them; then in turn the replacements are replaced.
2. Primary succession happens in an area that was devoid of life.
   a. Pioneer species help to improve soil fertility; they are usually small, low-growing plants with a short life cycle and an abundance of seeds.
   b. Gradually other, usually larger, species join or replace the pioneer species.
3. In secondary succession, a community reestablishes itself after a disturbance (for example, burned forest) that allows sunlight to penetrate.

B. Factors that Influence Succession
1. It was once thought that a stable climax community would always develop in a given region because of constraints imposed by climate.
2. According to the climax pattern model, a community is adapted to a total pattern of environmental factors—climate, soil, topography, wind, fires, etc.—to create a continuum of climax stages of succession.
3. Scientists now realize that the species composition of a community changes frequently, often in unpredictable ways.
   a. Communities do not journey in a single path to a predetermined climax community.
   b. Random events influence the order in which species arrive in a habitat and thus affect the course of succession.

4. In the intermediate disturbance hypothesis, species richness is the greatest in habitats where disturbances are moderate in their intensity or frequency.

5. The modern view of succession holds that the species composition of a community is affected by:

    a. Physical factors such as soil and climate.

    b. Chance events such as the order in which species arrive.

    c. The extent of disturbances in a habitat.

41.8 Species Interactions and Community Instability

A. The Role of Keystone Species

    1. A keystone species influences community structure in a disproportionally large way relative to its abundance.

        a. For example, when sea stars (keystone predator of mussels) were removed from a habitat, mussels increased in number, and in turn preyed on enough other species to reduce the community diversity.

    2. Keystone species need not be predators.

        a. For example, beavers cut down trees by gnawing through their trunks and use these trees to build a dam. The beaver alters the physical environment and affects the types of fish and aquatic invertebrates living in the area.

B. Adapting to Disturbance

    1. In communities repeatedly subjected to a particular type of disturbance, individuals that withstand or benefit from that disturbance have a selective advantage.

    2. Some species are very sensitive to disturbances. Indicator species are the first to do poorly when conditions change, so they can provide an early warning of environmental degradation.

C. Species Introductions

    1. An exotic species is a resident of an established community that dispersed from its home range and became established elsewhere.

    2. Some introduced species have proved beneficial: soybeans, rice, wheat, corn, and potatoes.

    3. Other exotic species have greatly altered the community structure—for the worse: kudzu plant, gypsy moths, and nutrias.

41.9 Biogeographic Patterns in Community Structure

A. Biogeography is the study of how species richness, the number of species in an area, is distributed in the natural world.

B. Latitudinal Patterns

    1. The number of species increases from the Arctic regions to the temperate zone to the tropics.

    2. Biodiversity is favored in the tropics for three reasons.

        a. More rainfall and sunlight provides more food reserves.

        b. Species diversity is self-reinforcing from herbivores to predators and parasites.

        c. Traditionally, the rate of speciation has exceeded the rate of extinction.

C. Island Patterns

    1. The equilibrium model of island biogeography upholds that species numbers increase on new islands and reach a stable number that is a balance between immigration rate for species new to the island and the extinction rate for established species.

    2. Islands distant from source areas receive fewer colonizing species (distance effect).

    3. Larger islands tend to support more species (area effect).

Suggestions for Presenting the Material

♦ While the previous chapter covered population structure and growth, this chapter discusses the interactions among the species of a community.

♦ Most students feel fairly comfortable with the broad concepts of community structure (predator-prey relationships) and the issue of biodiversity. The familiarity tends to be fairly shallow, and you will need to reinforce the specific nature of the terminology and the relative complexity of interactions even in seemingly simple communities.

♦ The elaborate, finely tuned species interactions described here offer another excellent opportunity to discuss coevolution. Examples such as the array of yucca species in Colorado, each pollinated exclusively by one kind of yucca moth species, emphasize the point that individuals don't evolve, populations do. Students will see many good examples of adaptive traits in this chapter.

♦ The animated Figure 41.6 provides a solid reference for students who may fail to grasp the process of competitive exclusion. Perhaps one of the best ways to maintain student interest in biodiversity is to pepper your lectures with examples, preferably illustrated with visual material.

♦ **Common Student Misconceptions**

  o Students often have difficulty with applying the concept of coevolution to specific examples of predator-prey relationships. Specifically, they are confused about the ongoing nature of these dynamic interactions that vary in complex ways. Students often want to view this concept in the short-term failing to tie it back to longer-term impacts on allele frequencies.

Classroom and Laboratory Enrichment

♦ Design an experiment to be carried out in the lab or in the field that would test the principle of competitive exclusion.

♦ Develop a method of graphing habitat usage and niche overlap among two or more species living in the same habitat.

♦ Examine a vegetated area on campus or in an area nearby. How are the plants in the area competing for resources? Illustrate the competition for mineral and water resources by excavating the root zone. Students are often amazed by the density of roots. Suggest some ways in which competition has shaped the plant community.

♦ Show numerous pictures and videos of examples of camouflage; ask students to distinguish the camouflaged organism.

♦ Select any ecosystem, and look for examples of resource partitioning.

♦ Design and implement a study of succession. This can be done on a small scale in the lab or on a larger scale in the field. List the species and their approximate densities at the beginning of the study; follow the changes in species composition and density as the study progresses. Students may establish a baseline study to be followed in later semesters by other students.

♦ Examine road cuts, construction sites, flooded river banks, plowed fields, and other places that have recently been disturbed. Can you find several plant species that you would describe as pioneer species?

♦ Describe patterns of succession at edges of stream beds, rivers, or coastlines.

- Ask your students to classify each of the items below as belonging to a human "habitat" or "niche."

    a. President

    b. Dorm room

    c. Secretary

    d. Lounge

    e. Counselor

    f. Student

- As each topic in the chapter is discussed, slides should be in view, because these topics are best taught and remembered by the examples given.

- Show the graphs (animated Figure 41.6) of the classic experiments of *Paramecium* growth that Gause performed. Why did *P. caudatum* decrease to near extinction in the containers but thrive in nature?

- Using the observation that grass quickly establishes itself in the cracks in the pavement of a highway in which traffic has been blocked for some time, describe what is happening using terms from the chapter.

Fighting Foreign Fire Ants (revisited)

- How do parasites help to regulate host populations in nature?

- Why do insects, plants, or animals introduced into the United States become such pests when they were not so in their native country? Ask students to provide examples from your region where introduced diseases or animals have resulted in some ecological impact.

- Global climate change is an international concern. Discuss how the very broad concept of climate change will affect the habitat of the red imported fire ants (RIFA), as well as the effects of this change on the prey populations of the RIFAs.

Additional Ideas for Classroom Discussion

- Would you expect competition between two finches of different species to be less intense or more intense than competition between two finches of the same species? Explain your answer.

- How does a shift in niche benefit competing species sharing the same environment?

- Discuss predator–prey interactions. Why are the cycles of predator and prey abundance shown in Figure 41.8 described as "idealized"? What do you think a predator would do if deprived of its primary prey item? Examine the actual diets of several predatory species; how do these diets change from one month to the next throughout the year? How can environmental disturbances such as fires, floods, climate fluctuations, and insect outbreaks influence the predator–prey cycle? What are some of the other variables that may be overlooked in predator–prey interactions?

- What is the difference between parasites and parasitoids?

- Why is resource partitioning essential for groups of functionally similar species living together?

- What is the ecological role of mimicry? What processes drive mimicry to develop and persist in certain populations? Is mimicry confined to insect populations or do we see examples in the mammal populations?

- What characteristics distinguish a pioneer species? Are pioneer species good competitors against later successional species? Why are pioneer species dependent on the frequent advent of open, disturbed places?

- In the classic graph of lynx and hare populations (Figure 41.8), what was the basis of the numerical count on the *x*-axis? How valid was this compared to actual field counts of these two animals?

- The monarch butterfly is orange and black and tastes bad (birds eating them spit them out immediately); viceroy butterflies are almost indistinguishable from monarchs but taste good. Which of these is the "model" and which is the "mimic"?

- "In primary succession," according to your text, "changes begin when pioneer species colonize a barren habitat." Are there any uninhabited places left on the Earth for pioneer plants and animals to colonize? What would create such a setting?

How Would You Vote? Classroom Discussion Ideas

- Have students complete class polling using the JoinIn clickers. Increased global trade and faster ships are contributing to a rise in the rate of species introductions into North America. Faster ships mean shorter trips, increasing the likelihood that pests will survive a voyage. Wood-eating insects from Asia turn up with alarming frequency in the wood packing crates and spools for steel wire. Some of these insects, such as the Asian long-horned beetle, now pose a serious threat to North America's forests. Currently, only a small fraction of the crates imported into the United States are inspected to see if they contain exotic species. Should inspections increase? The answer to the question of more extensive inspection programs gets an affirmative nod. However, this will increase the cost of imported goods. Nobody likes to pay more for something, especially when they see no direct result or benefit in the purchased product. Most consumers fail to consider the ecological costs associated with the importation of exotic species.

Term Paper Topics, Library Activities, and Special Projects

- Have your students use Thomson's InfoTrac College Edition service to find current articles that examine exotic introduced species in the United States. Ask them to summarize the article (s) and present their findings in a one-page paper.

- Summarize several of the classic studies involving predator–prey interactions.

- Describe several species of parasites commonly found among humans in the United States earlier in this century, prior to the advent of improved hygiene and widespread medical care. What parasites are still commonly found among human populations today? What are some of the steps that can be taken to reduce parasitic infections?

- Write a report on the effects of interspecific competition on a native species whose populations have been adversely affected by an introduced species.

- Describe succession as it has occurred following a major disaster such as a flood, debris slide, fire, or volcanic eruption.

- Discuss examples of mutualism among plants and animals.

- How did disturbance by human intervention help to initiate secondary succession in American prairies?

- At what point will the growing number of plant species in a previously disturbed area stop increasing? What factors will halt the rise in species composition? Examine studies of island ecology that seek to answer this question.

- Select a group of related species for which distribution data are available, and construct a graph of patterns of species diversity corresponding to latitude.

- Search for specific examples of insects that are parasitoids of other insects. Are the parasitoids "effective" controls?

- Report on the succession that has occurred since the widespread fires in the Yellowstone National Park ecosystem in 1988.

Responses to *Data Analysis Activities*

1. The population size in the control plots increased 40% during the first four months of the study.

2. The population size in the two types of treated plots decreased during the first four months of the study.

3. If the study had ended after the first year, it would have demonstrated a modest benefit for the plots treated with the biological controls plus pesticide, as compared to pesticide alone.

4. Treatment with biological controls plus pesticide is the most effective method for up to 28 months. Plots only treated with pesticide began to increase ant numbers by 1.5 years following the onset of the experiment.

Possible Responses to *Critical Thinking* Questions

1. In this scenario in which beneficial bacteria out-compete harmful bacteria, the principle of competitive exclusion is operating. The massive quantities of beneficial bacteria given to the cattle, coupled with the extremely rapid reproduction rate, make it less likely that the harmful bacteria will thrive.

2. The phasmids, walking sticks, have been remarkably successful by simply remaining very quiet, motionless, and stick-like. That would seem to be an easy task, but they pull it off better than most imitators. A simple experiment to show the adaptive value of the walking stick's little bag of tricks would involve countering the camouflage effect. For example, we could apply some non-toxic paint of various colors ranging from bright to dull to several phasmids and record the reaction of potential predators.

42

ECOSYSTEMS

Chapter Outline

Objectives

1. Understand how materials and energy enter, pass through, and exit an ecosystem.
2. Understand how ecosystems are organized and the various trophic roles and levels.
3. Describe the movement of materials through the biogeochemical cycles.

Key Terms

eutrophication	food web	aquifer	nitrogen cycle
primary producer	grazing food chain	groundwater	nitrogen fixation
primary production	detrital food chain	runoff	nitrification
consumer	biogeochemical	carbon cycle	denitrification
detritivore	cycle	atmospheric cycle	phosphorus cycle
decomposer	water cycle	greenhouse effect	sedimentary cycle
trophic level	watershed	global　　climate	
food chain	soil water	change	

Lecture Outline

42.1 Too Much of a Good Thing
  A. Phosphorus is an essential nutrient in all organisms.
    1. Plants meet their phosphorus requirement by taking up dissolved phosphates in soil water.
    2. Animals obtain phosphorus by eating plants or by eating other animals.
  B. High-phosphorus products (laundry and dish detergents, lawn fertilizers) are affecting the normal cyclical movement of phosphorus in aquatic ecosystems.
    1. Eutrophication is the addition of nutrients to an aquatic ecosystem.
    2. A sudden increase in the phosphorus content leads to population explosions of algae and cyanobacteria in the aquatic environment.
    3. Eutrophication with phosphorus negatively impacts the aquatic ecosystem.

42.2 The Nature of Ecosystems
  A. All ecosystems share some fundamental aspects of their structure and function. Ecosystems are defined by the array of organisms that exist in the physical environment, interacting through a one-way flow of energy and a cycling of nutrients.
  B. Primary Producers and Production
    1. Primary producers are autotrophs that can capture sunlight energy and incorporate it into organic compounds.
    2. Primary production is the rate at which producers (plants, algae, photosynthetic bacteria, and chemoautrophs) capture and store energy.
  C. The Role of Consumers
    1. *Consumers* are heterotrophs that feed on tissues of other organisms to obtain energy and carbon.
      a. Herbivores eat plants.
      b. Carnivores eat animals.
      c. Parasites reside in or on living hosts .
      d. Omnivores eat both plants and animals.
    2. Detritivores include small invertebrates that feed on partly decomposed particles of organic matter (detritus).
    3. Decomposers are also heterotrophs and include fungi and bacteria that extract energy from the remains or products of organisms.
  D. Energy Flow and Nutrient Cycling
    1. Energy transfer within an ecosystem is in a one-way direction and cannot be 100 percent efficient. Most energy gets lost in the form of heat.
    2. Nutrients, however, do get recycled within an ecosystem.

42.3 Food Chains
  A. Trophic ("nourishment") levels are a hierarchy of energy transfers, or bluntly stated, "Who eats whom?"
    1. Level 1 (closest to the energy input) consists of producers; level 2 comprises herbivores; and levels 3 and above are carnivores.
    2. Decomposers feed on organisms from all levels.
  B. A food chain is a sequence of steps by which some energy captured by primary producers is transferred to higher trophic levels.
    1. For example, Kansas tallgrass to grasshopper to sparrow to coyote.
    2. Energy captured by producers usually passes through no more than four or five trophic levels, due to the inefficiency of energy transfers.

42.4 Food Webs

A. Interconnected food chains comprise food webs in which the same food resource is often part of more than one food chain.

B. There are two categories of food webs.
1. Energy flows into ecosystems from the sun.
   a. Energy flows through ecosystems by way of grazing food webs, in which energy flows from plants to herbivores and then to carnivores.
   b. In detrital food webs, it flows mainly from plants through decomposers and detritivores.
2. In nearly all ecosystems, both kinds of webs cross-connect.
3. Diagrams of food webs help ecologists predict how ecosystems respond to disturbance.

42.5 Ecological Pyramids

A. Trophic structure can be diagrammed as a pyramid in which producers form a base for successive tiers of consumers above them.

B. Pyramids can be of two basic types.
1. A biomass pyramid makes provision for differences in size of organisms by using the dry weight of the members in each trophic level.
2. An energy pyramid reflects the trophic structure most accurately because it is based on energy losses at each level.

42.6 Biogeochemical Cycles

A. Biogeochemical cycles describe the movement of essential elements from one or more environmental reservoir through ecosystems and back to reservoirs.
1. Transfers to and from reservoirs are far slower than rates of exchange among organisms of an ecosystem.
2. Solid forms of elements are tied up in rock.
3. Nutrient reserves are maintained by environmental inputs and recycling activities.

B. Biogeochemical cycles are reservoirs for key elements. There are three types.
1. In the hydrologic cycle, oxygen and hydrogen move on a global scale in molecules of water.
2. In atmospheric cycles, gasses like carbon and nitrogen are available.
3. In sedimentary cycles, nutrients like phosphorous move with the Earth's crust.

42.7 The Water Cycle

A. How and Where Water Moves
1. Water is moved or stored by the processes of evaporation, precipitation, condensation, and transpiration. The cycle is from the ocean to the atmosphere, onto land, and back to oceans.
2. A watershed funnels rain or snow into a single river.
   a. Most water that falls in a watershed seeps into the ground and is called soil water.
   b. Some collects in permeable rock layers called aquifers.
   c. Groundwater is the water in soil and aquifers.
   d. Runoff occurs when the ground is saturated.
3. Flowing water moves dissolved nutrients into and out of a watershed.

B. Limited Fresh Water
1. Large-scale agriculture accounts for nearly two-thirds of the human population's use of freshwater.
   a. Salt buildup (salinization) of the soil can result.
   b. Withdrawal of ground water faster than it is replenished causes water tables to drop.
2. Most of the Earth's water is too salty for human consumption or for agriculture.

    a.   Desalinization processes are available and can be used when absolutely necessary.

    b.   However, desalinization is not cost effective in most locales, and it uses valuable fuel reserves to provide the energy for the desalination equipment.

42.8   The Carbon Cycle

A. Carbon moves in an atmospheric cycle through the atmosphere, oceans, soils and into and out of food webs.
1. Plants take up carbon dioxide from the atmosphere.
2. Carbon dioxide is released into the atmosphere during aerobic respiration.
3. Most of the annual cycling takes place between the atmosphere and the ocean.
4. Single greatest reservoir of carbon is Earth's rocks.
5. Carbon release from burning fossil fuels contributes to atmospheric build up of carbon dioxide, a major greenhouse gas.

B. Carbon, the Greenhouse Effect, and Global Warming
1. The greenhouse effect is the name for the warming action of the Earth due to trapped heat.
    a. The greenhouse gases (carbon dioxide, water vapor, ozone, methane, nitrous oxide, and CFCs) trap heat as they escape from the Earth back into space.
    b. Heat builds in the lower atmosphere—the greenhouse effect.
2. We are in the midst of a period of global climate change, a rise in temperature and shifts in other climate patterns.
    a. Levels of atmospheric carbon dioxide are among the highest in the last 420,000 years.
    b. Increased greenhouse gas concentrations may be a factor in global warming.

42.9   The Nitrogen Cycle

A. Nitrogen Reservoirs and Movements
1. Gaseous nitrogen makes up about 80 percent of the atmosphere. Nitrogen is a part of several steps in a cycling process.
2. In nitrogen fixation, bacteria convert nitrogen gas (N_2) to ammonia (NH_3) which is then ionized in water to ammonium (NH_4^+).
3. Nitrification is a type of chemosynthesis where NH_3 or NH_4^+ is converted to nitrite (NO_2^-); other nitrifying bacteria use the nitrite for energy and release nitrate (NO_3^-).
4. Ecosystems lose nitrogen through denitrification. *Denitrification* is the release of nitrogen gas to the atmosphere by the action of bacteria (NO_2^- and $NO_3^- \rightarrow N_2$).

B. Human Effects on the Nitrogen Cycle
1. About half of all nitrogen applied in fertilizers to crops runs off, contributing to groundwater pollution.
2. Burning fossil fuels releases nitrogen oxides.
    a. These chemicals contribute to global warming.
    b. Nitrogen in acid rain can have equally bad effects.

42.10 Phosphorus Cycle

A. Phosphorus moves from land, to sediments in the seas, and back to the land in its long-term geochemical phase of the cycle. Since there is no commonly occurring gaseous form of phosphorus, the cycle is called a sedimentary cycle.
1. In the ecosystem phase, plants take up the phosphorus from the soil.
2. In the biological portion, producers take up phosphorus it is then transferred to herbivores and carnivores, which excrete it in wastes and their own decomposing bodies.

B. Of all minerals, phosphorus is often the most limiting factor for plant growth in all natural ecosystems.

Suggestions for Presenting the Material

♦ The material presented in this chapter will help students understand that any ecosystem is composed of many interdependent parts. After learning about how an ecosystem can be described in terms of its food webs, trophic levels, and biogeochemical cycles, students will be aware of the unity that joins all organisms.

♦ Use as many local examples of ecosystems as possible in discussions, demonstrations, and lab work. While it may seem overly simplistic and sometimes inaccurate to identify and describe the different levels of an ecosystem, students should see that it is useful because it helps us to understand the functioning of an ecosystem as a whole. Such ecosystem descriptions provide a valuable baseline against which we can measure the effects of change.

♦ In various sections of the chapter, the author shows how humans have altered the natural ecosystems and their functioning. Stress the nature of the human changes to natural processes, the best example being the current global focus on climate change and the contributions humans are making to the atmospheric carbon dioxide pool.

♦ Be sure to use animated Figure 42.11 to visually illustrate the concept of how greenhouse gases contribute to trapping long wave heat radiation in our lower atmosphere. Most students have heard about the greenhouse effect but have little idea of the physics involved.

♦ **Common Student Misconceptions**

o Students often have difficulties understanding that energy moves one way through an ecosystem and nutrients are recycled. They want to believe that energy gets recycled in a similar manner with nutrients. By stressing the inefficient energy transfer process inherent in food webs you can reinforce this concept.

o Students may confuse food web with food chain, thinking the terms are synonymous. Stress that food chains are linear exchanges of energy and that food webs describe complex relationships in an ecosystem.

Classroom and Laboratory Enrichment

♦ Working individually or in teams, students should select a local ecosystem in a laboratory or a field setting and identify which organisms make up each trophic level of the ecosystem.

♦ Have the students create an organismal profile describing one of the primary producers and one of the consumers in a local ecosystem.

♦ Devise an experiment in which one of the trophic levels of an ecosystem is removed or disrupted and the effects are measured and described. What happens when the disruption occurs at different trophic levels?

♦ Set up aquatic ecosystems in the lab, and monitor them throughout the semester. Identify the trophic levels of the ecosystem, and analyze the cycling of minerals and nutrients within it. In what ways are the aquatic ecosystems in the lab similar to/different from real aquatic ecosystems?

♦ Discuss the primary productivities of different regions of the United States. How can human intervention change primary productivity?

♦ Construct a detrital food web for a typical forest or open field ecosystem. Students can list the decomposers and detritivores one might find in such areas (or identify as many of the detritivores as possible in lab) and then find out how each organism would be arranged in a food web.

- Use figures and animations to present and reinforce the biogeochemical cycles.

- Using an inexpensive soil test kit, analyze local soils to determine the mineral and organic contents. Do the same with a water testing kit with local pond water, or better yet, water from a surface water runoff retention pond. Compare and contrast results.

- Using animated Figure 42.4 as your point of departure, show several examples of each trophic level using pictures.

- Using an overhead transparency of Figure 42.4, clarify the fact that the primary consumer is actually at the second trophic level. What group of organisms necessary for nutrient recycling is not indicated in this figure?

- Assuming that a flat 10 percent of the energy in one trophic level is conserved to the next and the producer represents 100 percent, calculate what percent is received by a marsh hawk as a fourth level consumer in an ecosystem.

- Using pictures and figures for the major biogeochemical cycles (nitrogen, carbon, and water), indicate where humans are active or passive participants. How have human activities altered the "natural" cycles?

- Monitor the quality of air in your area. What has been the impact of humans on the air in your community?

- What happens to your trash? Trace the fate of the garbage that leaves your campus daily. What about wastes containing dangerous chemicals from research labs or medical wastes from the campus infirmary or university hospital? Does your institution have a set of rules and guidelines governing waste disposal?

- Visit a sewage treatment plant. Discuss the biological steps involved in the treatment of your local sewage. In what ways could sewage treatment be improved?

- Collect water samples from your classroom building and have the samples analyzed. Discuss the results with your class.

- Working in small groups, debate the pros and cons of carbon-based energy sources versus renewable energy sources. Each group should be prepared to discuss the merits and drawbacks of several examples.

- Ask a representative from a local environmental group to address the class.

- Prepare a list of environmental concerns in your area and state. Ask students what should be done, then ask them what realistically can be done.

- Obtain a map of the United States showing the areas of highest cancer rates. Ask students to speculate about the link between environmental quality and human disease.

Too Much of a Good Thing (revisited)

- Water treatment for the removal of phosphates is very effective yet very costly. Discuss who should bear this cost. The consumer? The government? The companies producing the phosphate-laden products?

- Laundry detergents without phosphates utilize the power of enzymes for cleaning power. Compare and contrast the differences between type of detergent. Think about mechanisms, cost, efficacy of cleaning, and environmental safety.

- Phosphate is used to fertilize lawns. Why is phosphate necessary for lawn maintenance? Could an alternative fertilize be as effective? How does the phosphate in fertilizers avoid water treatment plants?

Additional Ideas for Classroom Discussion

♦ Discuss what would happen to an ecosystem if all of the producers disappeared. What would happen to the ecosystem if all of the consumers or decomposers or detritivores disappeared? Can you think of examples of ecosystems in which any of these events has occurred? How can an ecosystem recover from such a disturbance?

♦ Describe several trophic levels of a typical ecosystem, and ask students to arrange them in the correct order.

♦ Introduce students to the concept of residence time for the different greenhouse gasses and the role of water vapor as the most abundant greenhouse gas.

♦ What is the one ingredient required by all ecosystems that cannot be recycled?

♦ Why is the term food chain rarely used when describing actual ecosystems?

♦ What do you think were the first producers to evolve on the Earth?

♦ Does the loss of tropical forests throughout South America affect us? How?

♦ Why is a pyramid of biomass a more accurate representation of an ecosystem than is a pyramid of numbers?

♦ Why are many marine pyramids of biomass often upside down?

♦ Why does a pyramid of energy narrow as it goes up?

♦ Is it environmentally wise to rely on large quantities of nitrogen-rich fertilizers for crop production? What are some alternatives? Discuss the pros and cons of commercial fertilizers.

♦ Analyze each of the segments of the following expression: "bio—geo—chemical cycle."

♦ For each of the biogeochemical cycles, indicate the route each component takes in recycling. What "invisible" component is not recyclable?

♦ How have coal-burning power plants changed in the past 20 years?

♦ What is a "clean" energy source? Can you think of an example?

♦ Why is the ozone layer of the Earth's atmosphere shrinking at the same time that excessive amounts of ozone at the Earth's surface are present in photochemical smog?

♦ Do you think our laws regarding air pollution are too lenient? What changes would you make in the laws or their enforcement?

♦ Why does normal rainwater have a pH of around 5.6?

♦ Ask students to consider examples of renewable energy sources.

♦ How many students in the class recycle their aluminum cans? Newspapers? Glass? Take a hand count. Ask students for reasons why they do (or do not) recycle these materials.

♦ Ask students to make a list of ways in which they could modify their own lifestyles and behaviors to reduce environmental pollution.

How Would You Vote? Classroom Discussion Ideas

♦ Have students complete class polling using the JoinIn clickers. Is banning high-phosphate products the best way to prevent phosphate-related eutrophication, or are consumer education programs a better option?

Term Paper Topics, Library Activities, and Special Projects

♦ Assess public understanding of environmental pollution issues by designing a brief questionnaire. Divide the public into several different groups, and compare the levels of understanding among the groups. Some possible groupings are: students in this course, past students of the course, university or college students at large, university employees, different age groups, local residents not employed by the college or university, and groups created on the basis of differences in factors such as socioeconomic status, political affiliation, age, and education. How well informed are the different groups? Did they know more or less about environmental issues than you thought they would? Can you identify any myths about environmental pollution that appear to be widely held?

♦ Have students investigate marine ecosystems using Thomson's InfoTrac College Edition. Have them complete a short report on ecosystems deep on the ocean floor at depths impenetrable by light. What kinds of organisms make up the first trophic level in such ecosystems? How are these organisms obtaining energy?

♦ What happens to an ecosystem if any one of its levels is removed? Find descriptions of ecosystems in which this has happened, and describe the results.

♦ Describe the biochemical steps used by chemosynthetic autotrophs to produce energy.

♦ List and describe some of the primary producers in an open ocean ecosystem off the U.S. coast.

♦ Discuss the primary productivities of various regions around the world. Which areas have the highest and lowest primary productivities? Why?

♦ Look up the root/shoot ratios of several plant species, and graph these values against the latitudes of their geographic ranges.

♦ Describe nitrogen fixation. What kinds of organisms can perform nitrogen fixation? Discuss genetic engineering research in this area.

♦ Discuss farming techniques designed to minimize nitrogen loss in the soil.

♦ Obtain records of the yearly average temperatures and rainfall amounts from your local weather bureau. Graph the data. Are there any trends?

♦ Examine the statistical link between air quality and rates of respiratory disease. Discuss the chemical composition of smog and how it relates to greenhouse gasses.

♦ Discuss the success of recycling programs in states (such as New Jersey) with laws requiring mandatory recycling.

♦ Write a report describing the discovery and use of new plastics that will degrade when exposed to sunlight or can be decomposed by microorganisms.

♦ Summarize the federal laws against pollution.

♦ Who are your local polluters? Find out which industries release pollutants into the atmosphere. List the pollutants, and describe what steps the companies have taken to reduce emission of pollutants.

- Describe the process of illegal dumping. Why is it done? Has it been done in your area? What are the penalties for illegal dumping?

- Have a member of the local government hazardous waste disposal site come and speak to the class about how such chemicals are handled and disposed of.

- What are the current alternatives for storing nuclear waste? What are some proposed methods that might be used to store nuclear waste in the future?

- Just a handful of states have mandatory refundable deposits on drink containers. The highest (10 cents per container) is in Michigan. Investigate the effect this law has had on the soft drink industry, the retailers, and the environment.

- Tap water in all metropolitan areas is certified as "safe," but that doesn't necessarily mean you would want to drink it. In your library, find the yellow pages listings for suppliers of bottled water for these cities: New York, Chicago, Los Angeles, New Orleans, and Atlanta. Compare the number of these suppliers with the population to obtain a ratio. Did you find any surprises?

Responses to *Data Analysis Activities*

1. The highest carbon dioxide level was approximately 300 part per million (ppm).
2. At no time between 400,000 B.C. and 0 A.D. did the level of carbon dioxide in the atmosphere reach the level directly measured in 1980.
3. Prior to the industrial revolution in 1800, the amount of carbon dioxide in the atmosphere was relatively the same at approximately 280 ppm. Since the industrial revolution, the amount of carbon dioxide in the atmosphere has steadily increased.
4. The rise in the amount of carbon dioxide in the atmosphere rose more quickly in the years between 1800 and 1975 as compared to 1980 and 2007.

Possible Responses to *Critical Thinking* Questions

1. Remember that primary production relates to the amount of carbon sequestered in photosynthesizing organisms. In each location this process is a function of seasonal cycles in temperature, and moisture, as well as the type of soils and mineral nutrition available from those soils.

2. Visit the Science in your Watershed site at http://water.usgs.gov/wsc; research and answer the questions.

3. Phosphorus and nitrogen are key elements in all known forms of life. Phosphorus is necessary for the production of DNA, RNA, ATP, and phospholipids. Also, phosphorylation is a key mechanism for intracellular regulation of protein activity. Nitrogen is an essential building block of amino acids, DNA, and RNA.

4. Growing the same crop year-after-year depletes the soil of nutrients. A crop that leaches the soil of one kind of nutrient is followed during the next growing season by a dissimilar crop that returns that nutrient to the soil or draws a different ratio of nutrients.

43

THE BIOSPHERE

Chapter Outline

Objectives

1. Describe the ways in which climate affects the biomes of Earth and influences how organisms are shaped and how they behave.
2. Characterize each of the world's major biomes with respect to climate, plant life, and animal life.
3. Contrast life in lake ecosystems with that in oceans and estuaries.
4. Discover ways in which human activities have put many ecosystems in peril.

Key Terms

El Niño	desert	arctic tundra	benthic province
La Niña	grassland	permafrost	seamount
biosphere	chaparral	alpine tundra	hydrothermal vent
climate	temperate	estuary	
rain shadow	deciduous forest	coral reef	
monsoon	tropical rain forest	coral bleaching	
biome	boreal forest	pelagic province	

Lecture Outline

43.1 El Niño Effects

  A. El Niño is a periodic warming of equatorial Pacific waters and the associated shifts in global weather patterns.

  B. El Niño can have drastic effects.

    1. In 1997–1998, half of the sea lions disappeared in the Galápagos Islands.

    2. The number of Northern fur seal births plummeted in California.

  C. In that winter a massive volume of warm water from the southwestern Pacific moved east.

    1. Currents that would have churned up nutrients were displaced.

    2. Violent storms affect sea life and coastal human dwellings.

    3. Monster hurricanes, ice storms, flooding, and drought were in the news.

  D. La Niña is a periodic cooling of equatorial Pacific waters and the associated shifts in global weather patterns.

  E. The biosphere includes all places where we find life on Earth.

43.2 Air Circulation Patterns

  A. Climate refers to average weather conditions, such as temperature, humidity, wind speed, cloud cover, and rainfall, over time.

  B. Seasonal Effects

    1. Seasonal variations in climate result from the Earth's revolution around the sun.

    2. The amount of solar radiation reaching the Earth's surface changes in the Northern and Southern hemispheres; this results in seasonal changes in climate.

    3. In each hemisphere, the degree of seasonal change in day length increases with latitude.

  C. Air Circulation and Rainfall

    1. The sun differentially heats equatorial and polar regions, creating the world's major air currents and temperature zones.

    2. Warm equatorial air rises, cools, releases its moisture, and spreads northward and southward where it descends at 30° latitudes as very dry air (results in deserts).

    3. The air is warmed again and ascends at 60° latitude; as it moves toward the poles, regional areas receive varying amounts of rainfall that in turn influence ecosystems.

    4. In temperate regions, organisms respond most to changes in day length and temperature; in deserts and tropical regions, they respond more to seasonal changes in rainfall.

  D. Surface Wind Patterns

    1. Major wind patterns arise as air in the lower atmosphere move continually from latitudes where air is sinking toward those where air is rising.

    2. Earth's rotation affects the trajectory of these winds.

      a. In the Northern Hemisphere, winds curve toward the right.

      b. In the Southern Hemisphere, winds curve toward the left.

43.3 The Ocean, Landforms, and Climates

A. Ocean Currents

   1. Ocean water covers almost three-fourths of the Earth's surface.

   2. Latitudinal and seasonal variations in solar heating cause ocean water to warm and cool on a vast scale.

      a. Surface waters tend to move from the equator to the poles, warming the air above.

      b. Currents form because of the Earth's rotation, winds, variations in temperature, and distribution of land masses.

   3. Immense circular water movements in the Atlantic and Pacific Oceans influence climate zones and the distribution of ecosystems.

   4. Ocean circulation patterns shift over geologic time as land masses move.

B. Regional Effects Rain Shadows and Monsoons

   1. Topography refers to physical features such as elevation.

   2. Mountains, valleys, and other features influence regional climates.

      a. The mountains of the western United States cause the winds from the ocean to rise, cool, and lose their moisture.

      b. As the winds descend on the leeward (eastern) slopes, they are devoid of moisture, causing a rain shadow effect, a semiarid or arid region of sparse rainfall.

      c. Monsoon rains occur when warm winds pick up ocean moisture and release it over the cooler landmasses of Asia and Africa.

      d. The dramatic differences in moisture cause significant differences in vegetation patterns as a function of rain shadows.

43.4 Biomes

A. Differences Between Biomes

   1. Biomes are large vegetational subdivisions including all animals and other organisms.

   2. Biome distribution corresponds with climate, topography, and soil type.

   3. The form of the dominant plants tells us something of the weather conditions.

B. Similarities Within a Biome

   1. Climatic factors determine patterns of vegetation and why unrelated species may have similar adaptations although separated by thousands of miles.

   2. Evolution often produces similar solutions to environmental challenges

43.5 Deserts

A. Desert Locations and Conditions

   1. Annual rainfall is less than 10 centimeters.

   2. Most deserts form near 30° north and south latitudes.

   3. Day/night temperatures fluctuate widely due to the low humidity in deserts.

   4. Soils have little topsoil and are somewhat salty.

B. Adaptations to Desert Conditions

   1. Most deserts support some plant life, with the greatest diversity in regions where moisture is available more than one season.

   2. Adaptations include methods to reduce water loss (spines or hairs), enhanced water storage mechanisms, specialized root systems, and alternative carbon-fixing pathways.

C. The Crust Community

   1. A desert crust includes cyanobacteria, lichens, mosses, and fungi.

   2. These organisms secrete substances to bind them together and to the soil, creating a crust.

   3. The crust acts to fix nitrogen and hold soil particles in place.

43.6   Grasslands
A. Grasslands form across much of the interior of continents, in the zones between deserts and temperate forests.
1. Soils are rich with deep topsoil.
2. Annual rainfall supports low-growing grasses and other nonwoody plants, but cannot sustain woodlands.
3. Growth tends to be seasonal.
B. Temperate Grasslands
1. Summers are warm and winters tend to be cold. Annual rainfall is 25–100 cm.
2. There are two basic types in North America.
a. Shortgrass prairie of the American Midwest is typified by short, drought-resistant grasses that have been replaced by grains that require irrigation.
b. Tallgrass prairie was originally found in the American West where water was more plentiful.
C. The African savannas are hot, dry, and bear small bushes among the grass.

43.7   Dry Shrublands and Woodlands
A. Dry shrublands prevail when rainfall is less than 25–60 cm (for example, the California chaparral).
1. The climate is semiarid.
2. Rains occur seasonally during mild winter months; summers are long, hot, and dry; and dominant plants have tough evergreen leaves.
2. Dry woodlands occur when rainfall is about 40–100 cm; there are trees but not in dense forests.

43.8   Broadleaf Forests

A. Semi-Evergreen and Deciduous Forests
1. Semi-evergreen forests form between 10 and 25 degrees of latitude where the dry season lasts longer and decomposition is slower.
2. In the tropical deciduous forest, many trees drop some or all of their leaves during the pronounced dry season.
3. In the temperate deciduous forests of North America, conditions of temperature and rainfall do not favor rapid decomposition; thus, nutrients are conserved to provide fertile soil.

B. Tropical Rain Forests
1. Evergreen broadleaf forests occur between 10° N and S latitude.
a. Most typical is the tropical rain forest where temperatures, rainfall, and humidity are all high with rainfall averaging 130-200 cm per year.
b. These biomes are structurally complex and highly diverse.
2. Decomposition and nutrient cycling happen very fast.
a. Litter does not accumulate.
b. Soils are highly weathered, nutrient poor, and highly leached.
3. Fast growing populations that exist in areas with tropical rainforests rely heavily on those forests for economic development.
a. The result is a continuing loss of rainforest.
b. Rainforests contain tremendous animal and plant diversity.
c. Products of rainforests save and enhance human lives, including several cancer drugs derived from organic compounds discovered in tropical rainforest plants.

4. The loss of rainforests may influence the atmosphere.
    a. Rainforests are vast storehouses of atmospheric carbon.
    b. Burning the tropical rainforest to develop agriculture releases large amounts of carbon.

43.9 Coniferous Forests

A. Conifers, evergreen trees that bear cones dominate the coniferous forests.
    1. The typical "tree" in these forests is some variety of evergreen with needlelike leaves.
    2. Conifers are able to tolerate poorer soils and drier habitats than deciduous trees.
B. Coniferous forests are found in widely divergent geographic areas.
    1. Boreal forests (or taiga) are found in the cool to cold northern regions of North America, Europe, and Asia; spruce and balsam fir are dominant.
    2. Montane coniferous forests extend southward through the great mountain ranges; fir and pine dominate.
    3. Pine barrens make up about a quarter of New Jersey, while about one-third of the southeast U.S. supports fast-growing pine stands.

43.10 Tundra

A. Arctic tundra lies to the north of the boreal forests; it is a vast treeless plain, very cold, with low moisture; it is characterized by permafrost, which prevents growth of large trees.
B. Alpine tundra is a similar biome that occurs at high elevations in mountains throughout the world. The alpine soil lacks permafrost, is well drained, thin, and nutrient poor.

43.11 Freshwater Ecosystems

A. Lakes
    1. A lake is a body of standing freshwater produced by geologic processes, as when an advancing glacier carves a basin in the earth.
        a. The littoral zone extends from the shore to where rooted plants stop growing.
        b. The limnetic zone includes open, sunlit waters beyond the littoral to a depth where photosynthesis is no longer significant; phytoplankton life is abundant.
        c. The profundal zone is the deep, open water below the depth of light penetration; detritus sinks from the limnetic and is acted upon by decomposers.
    2. Nutrient Content and Succession
        a. Lakes undergo successional changes just like terrestrial ecosystems.
        b. Oligotrophic lakes are deep, nutrient-poor, and low in primary productivity.
        c. Eutrophic lakes are shallow and nutrient-rich often due to agricultural and urban runoff wastes.
    3. Seasonal Changes
        a. In temperate regions, lakes undergo changes in density and temperature.
        b. In winter, ice (less dense) forms on the surface over water that is warmer, much of it at 4° C (greatest density), and heavier.
        c. During the spring overturn, warming and winds cause oxygen to be carried downward and nutrients to the surface.
        d. By midsummer, a thermocline between the upper warmer layers and lower cooler layers prevents vertical warming.
        e. During autumn, the upper layers cool and sink causing a fall overturn.
B. Streams and Rivers
    1. Streams start out as freshwater springs or seeps.
    2. As steams flow downslope they grow and merge.

3. Several factors affect streams.
   a. Average flow and temperature are influenced by geography, altitude, and forest shade.
   b. A stream imports nutrients into many food webs.
4. A river is a flowing water ecosystem that usually starts when streams converge.
   a. Along its length, rivers vary in depth, speed, and flow.
   b. The land area that drains into a river is called its watershed.

C. The Importance of Dissolved Oxygen
   1. The dissolved oxygen content is greatest in cooler, faster-flowing water than in warmer, still water.
   2. In freshwater habitats, the aquatic organisms are all affected by changes in the dissolved oxygen content; however, some are more sensitive than others.

43.12 Coastal Ecosystems

A. Coastal Wetlands
   1. Estuaries are partially enclosed regions where fresh and saltwater meet.
      a. Estuaries are incredibly productive feeding and breeding grounds for many animals.
      b. Many estuaries are declining because of upstream diversion of the freshwater that is necessary for their maintenance.
   2. Mangrove wetlands refer to forests in sheltered regions along tropical coasts.
      a. These forests consist of salt tolerant woody plants.
      b. These plants develop prop roots that extend out from the trunk of the tree for support.

B. Rocky and Sandy Shores
   1. The inhabitants of the intertidal-zone are alternately exposed and submerged; existence is difficult.
   2. Rocky shores have three vertically arranged zones.
      a. The upper littoral is submerged only during the highest possible lunar tide; it is sparsely populated.
      b. The mid-littoral is submerged during the regular tide and exposed at the lowest tide of the day.
      c. The lower littoral is exposed only during the lowest lunar tide.

43.13 Coral Reefs

A. Coral reefs are wave-resistant formations that consist of accumulated remains of marine organisms.
   1. Coral reefs develop primarily between 25° north and south in clear warm waters.
   2. Corals, dinoflagellates, fishes, algae, and any many other organisms live in a delicate balance.

B. Coral reefs are diverse, vast underwater ecosystems.
   1. Dinoflagellates live in the coral polyps, providing oxygen and recycling of nutrients.
   2. When corals are stressed, however, they expel their symbionts.

C. When corals die, only the hardened chambers remain.
   1. This is called coral bleaching.
   2. It is on the rise all over the world, partly due to higher sea surface temperatures.

D. Human activities such as oil exploration, fishing, and the introduction of invasive species all threaten biodiversity in these fragile ecosystems.

43.14 The Open Ocean
  A. The Pelagic Province
    1. The ocean's open waters are the pelagic province.
    2. Phytoplankton are the beginning of ocean food webs and plentiful in the upper, bright waters.
       a. Phytoplankton include vast amounts of photosynthetic bacteria.
       b. Phytoplankton account for most of the ocean's primary productivity.
  B. The Benthic Province
    1. The ocean bottom, its rocks and sediments are the benthic province.
    2. Seamounts are undersea mountains which attract large numbers of fishes and marine invertebrates.
    3. Hydrothermal vent ecosystems occur on the ocean floor.
       a. Here, very cold water at the ocean bottom seeps into fissures, is heated, and then is spewed forth mixed with minerals.
       b. Chemoautotrophic bacteria provide the starting point for complex communities of tube worms, crustaceans, clams, and fishes.

Suggestions for Presenting the Material

♦ Use the animated Figure 43.5 to help students understand the broad interaction between climates, the oceans, and topography. Students are likely familiar with the Gulf Stream, but may not realize that it is only one of many grand ocean currents that influence global weather patterns.

♦ Many of the subjects discussed in this chapter can be presented very effectively with the aid of pictures and videos. Many of the biomes are unfamiliar to most students, but they can be made memorable by use of pictures illustrating their different features.

♦ After reading about ecosystems in the previous chapter, students should be able to identify ecosystem components in the biomes and aquatic ecosystems discussed here. Use familiar examples related to local weather patterns, if possible, when discussing climate.

♦ Students will be interested in learning more about tropical deforestation, El Niño, and ocean pollution—subjects that are consistently in the news.

♦ Several aspects of human impact on the biosphere are discussed in the next chapter; you and your students may wish to wait until then before exploring some of the topics and activities suggested here.

♦ **Common Student Misconceptions**
  o Most students fail to connect climate or large scale weather patterns to the impact on the development of ecosystems. Rarely do students step back and try to visualize the big picture when it comes to climate and the distribution of plants and animals.

Classroom and Laboratory Enrichment

♦ Use a globe and the information you have learned about global patterns of air circulation to explain the reasons for your latest weather conditions. Explain why your region has the weather it does.

- Discuss the latest advances in meteorology. Describe the role of satellites in assisting weather prediction.

- Select an example of a high-elevation ecosystem, and examine the plant and animal communities that are found at different elevational ranges. Examine the effects of elevation, slope, or aspect on plant community composition by taking a field trip.

- Prepare a diagram showing how the effects of increasing elevation are similar to those of decreasing latitude.

- View road cuts or dig trenches in different local plant communities, and examine the exposed soil profiles. Identify the soil horizons. Students can perform additional soil science experiments if desired.

- Examine changes in terrestrial plant community composition along moisture gradients.

- Study zonation in a local pond or lake. List the plants, animals, protists, and other microorganisms you find in each zone. Students in subsequent semesters could sample the lake again and describe what changes occur from season to season.

- Design and implement a study of lake stratification. Measure the temperature, dissolved oxygen, and nutrients in each layer of the lake.

- Examine zonation in a marine ecosystem. Visit a coastline area to observe shoreline species, if possible, look at slides and films, or visit a marine aquarium.

- Construct small-scale replications of freshwater or marine ecosystems in the lab.

- Ask a weather specialist to speak to the class concerning global and local weather and trends in climate change.

- If you do not feel qualified to present the climatological information, secure a film or videotape that will explain it fully and concisely.

- If you are located near an intergrade between biomes (such as temperate deciduous forest to grassland), draw this to the students' attention. Remind them to observe the changes in plant life as they drive through the area and note some highway marker or nearby town for reference.

- To most people, the American desert is viewed as a biodiversity wasteland of sand and cactus to be bypassed, as the early settlers did to reach the promise of the west coast. Gather information on how weekend revelers are destroying this fragile biome that "heals" itself very slowly.

- Prepare a table listing: (a) each biome, (b) its principal location, and (c) its chief plant and animal life.

- Collect water samples from your classroom building, and have the samples analyzed. Discuss the results with your class.

- Ask a representative from a local park to address the class about biodiversity issues in your region.

Effects of El Niño (revisited)

- What is cholera and how does an El Niño event relate to the prevalence of this disease?

- How are the small crustacean, copepods, related to the connection between cholera outbreaks and El Niño events? Discuss the concept of "reservoir of a disease."

- What other types of disease may be affected by climate change?

Additional Ideas for Classroom Discussion

- As each biome is discussed, ask students who have visited that biome to share their observations with the class. What changes did they notice in plant and animal communities? Have them speculate about what environmental factors drove those differences.

- Discuss some of the ways to improve soils considered too poor for agriculture. What are some of the characteristics of desert soils and tropical soils that make them poorly suited for long-term agriculture?

- Discuss the ways in which animal morphology might differ from one biome to the next. What role does annual mean temperature play in determining animal morphology? What differences in plant morphology can you see among the different biomes?

- Have students speculate about the reasons that tropical soils are considered nutrient poor when there are so many species of plants and animals present.

- Why is species diversity so high in tropical rain forests?

- Describe the rates of nutrient cycling in the tundra and in the tropical forest. How can you explain the different rates of nutrient cycling in these two biomes?

- What is meant when a lake is described as "dead"? How does such a condition come about? How can a "dead" lake be rejuvenated?

- What is the most readily observable feature that distinguishes one biome from another?

- As a child, you may have believed that if you could leave the Earth's surface and fly toward the sun, you would get warmer and warmer. But of course just the opposite is true; why?

- Should modern technology change desert habitats such as Palm Springs, California, where lawns are green only because they are maintained by artificial means?

- Why would it be unwise to clear tropical forests and irrigate arid lands for conversion to agriculture?

- What do you think will be the most important areas of science in the next decade? In 50 years?

How Would You Vote? Classroom Discussion Ideas

- Have students complete class polling using the JoinIn clickers. Is supporting studies of El Niño and the other long-term climate cycles a good use of government funds?

Term Paper Topics, Library Activities, and Special Projects

- Describe how plant and animal communities are influenced by climate. How do long-term climatic changes influence evolution in these communities?

- Write a description of your local climate. List and describe all of the factors responsible for your local climate.

- Use soil science reports from the National Resource Conservation Service to help you write a description of local soil types.

- Describe where prairie remnants are found today in the United States. Prepare plant species lists of the shortgrass prairie and the tallgrass prairie.

- Write a report about historical descriptions of the Dust Bowl. Download an oral history from someone who farmed through the dustbowl era.

- What changes in plant species composition would you see among deciduous forests as you traveled from the eastern United States to the western coast?

- Describe the latest efforts made by governments around the world to slow the rate of tropical deforestation.

- What happens to the arctic tundra when the permafrost becomes damaged? Discuss the effects of human habitation on the arctic tundra.

- Describe what happens when a lake undergoes eutrophication. Discuss examples of situations in which eutrophication was reversed. What changes in aquatic species composition will occur as a result of eutrophication?

- Discuss the rejuvenation of lake ecosystems that were formerly polluted.

- Describe the role of estuaries in commercial fisheries. Discuss the ecology of one of the commercially important estuaries in the United States.

- In the Northern Hemisphere, we experience warm summer temperatures when the Earth is tilted toward the sun. In winter, the tilt is just the opposite. But during which season is the Earth slightly closer to the sun? Don't assume you know this one—look it up!

- Irrigation has brought "bloom to the deserts." But is there a negative side to this practice? Search for a balanced perspective.

Responses to *Data Analysis Activities*

1. The greatest positive temperature deviation occurred in 1998.

2. During the winter of 1982-1983, an El Niño event occurred. A La Niña event was ending and returning to neutral conditions, during the winter of 2001-2002.

3. The longest interval without a La Niña event was between 1977 and 1984.

4. In the fall of 2007, California was experiencing a La Niña event.

Possible Responses to *Critical Thinking* Questions

1. Chernoboyl is located in the Northern Hemisphere; therefore, the winds carried the fallout towards the right.

2. To most people, there is nothing more desolate and useless than a desert. It just seems to be lying there waiting for "terror-tourists" on off-road vehicles. Perhaps it is not their fault, it is ours—the biologists—for not educating them on the fragility of the desert biome. What is most sobering, however, is the long periods of time necessary to undo the damage these vehicles cause and to restore the ecosystem. In many desert communities, you can still observe evidence from wagon traffic that occurred in the 19th century.

3. Global warming may cause an increase in cholera outbreaks because the higher temperature will increase phytoplankton, thus increasing the number of disease-carrying copepods (a vector of this disease).

44

HUMAN EFFECTS ON THE BIOSPHERE

Chapter Outline

Objectives

1. Understand the difference between the natural process of extinction and the effects of human activities on extinction events.
2. Describe how harmful land uses today can have long-term and long-range effects.
3. Distinguish among the types of pollutants and recognize the effects on the biosphere.
4. Understand how conservation biologists are working to keep Earth's biodiversity.
5. List ways to reduce the negative impact of human activities on the biosphere.

Key Terms

endangered species	pollutants	ozone layer	ecological restoration
threatened species	acid rain	biodiversity	
endemic species	bioaccumulation	conservation biology	
desertification	biological magnification	hot spots	

Lecture Outline

44.1 A Long Reach

    A. Humans have extended their reach and influence into all the biomes on Earth.

    B. The temperature of Earth's atmosphere and seas are rising.

        1. In the Arctic, this affects the seasonal cycle of sea ice formation and melting.

        2. The Arctic polar bears are experiencing shorter periods of hunting and potential for becoming stranded too far from solid land, as a consequence of climate changes.

    B. Even though profound changes on Earth have occurred for eons, the increasing pace of change and the capacity of our own species to recognize and affect its role are new.

44.2 A Global Extinction Crisis

    A. Threatened and Endangered Species

        1. Extinction is a natural process. The rate of extinction is dramatically increased during a mass extinction event, such as the one we are currently experiencing.

           a. Unlike historical mass extinctions, this one does not stem from a natural catastrophe.

           b. The current mass extinction is the outcome of the success of humans and our effects on Earth.

        2. An endangered species is a species that faces extinction in all or part of its range.

        3. A threatened species is one that is likely to become endangered in the near future.

    B. Causes of Species Declines

        1. Overharvesting of species has been a major cause of species decline (for example, passenger pigeons, Atlantic codfish, and white abalone).

        2. Destruction or degradation of a habitat causes species decline. An edemic species, one that is confined to the limited area in which it evolved, is more likely to go extinct that a species with a more widespread distribution (for example, giant pandas , ivory-billed woodpeckers, and plant life).e

        3. Deliberate or accidental species introductions also cause species decline (for example, koa bug).

    C. The Unknown Losses

        1. The International Union for Conservation of Nature and Natural Resources estimates that 36% of the 47,677 species they had accessed were threatened or endangered.

        2. The extent of extinction in invertebrates, plants, protists, and fungi is relatively unknown.

44.3 Harmful Land Use Practices

    A. Desertification

        1. Desertification is the conversion of a dry grassland or woodland to a desert.

        2. Occurs when plowing or grazing removes plants and so exposes topsoil to wind erosion.

        3. Plant cannot thrive and are blown away

        4. Drought also contributes to the onset and maintenance of desertification.

B. Deforestation
1. Tropical rain forests are disappearing at an alarming rate due to logging activities.
2. Deforestation causes loss of forest organisms, contributes to landslides and encourages flooding.

44.4   Acid Rain

A. Pollutants are natural or man-made substances released into soil, air, or water in greater than natural amounts. The presence of a pollutant disrupts the physiological processes of organism that are not adapted to tolerate it.

B. Acid rain, or wet acid deposition, occurs when pollutants combine with water and fall as acidic precipitation.
1. Acid rain can be ten times more acidic than unpolluted rainwater.
2. Acid rain burns tree leaves and alters the composition of soils.
3. Acid rain makes forests more susceptible to insects and pathogens.

44.5   Biological Effects of Chemical Pollutants

A. Accumulation and Magnification
1. Bioaccumulation processes cause an organism's tissues to store a pollutant taken up from the environment, causing the amount in the body to increase over time.
2. Biological magnification processes cause the amount of a chemical pollutant to become increasingly more concentrated as it moves up through the food chains.
   a. DDT, a pesticide no longer in use in the United States, was measured from various members of a food chain in a salt marsh ecosystem on Long Island, Ney York.b.   The concentration of DDT in osprey tissues, a top predator in this ecosystem, was 276,000 times higher than that in the water.

B. Point and Nonpoint Sources
1. Point sources of pollutants come from a few easily identifiable sites and are the easiest to control.
2. Pollution from nonpoint sources is more challenging to control, as this pollution stems from widespread release of a pollutant.

44.6   The Trouble With Trash

A. Historically, unwanted material was simply buried in the ground or dumped out at sea. The lead to groundwater contamination, and widespread harm to marine life.

B. Nonrecycled trash now gets burned in high-temperature incinerators or placed in engineered landfills. No solid municipal waste can legally be dumped at sea.

44.7   Ozone Depletion and Pollution

A. Depletion of the Ozone Layer
1. The ozone layer is a high atmospheric layer with a high concentration of ozone (O_3) that prevents much ultraviolet (UV) radiation from reaching the Earth's surface.
2. UV radiation damages DNA and causes mutations, and with a thinner ozone layer people are exposed to more UV radiation.
3. Exposure to excessive UV radiation is detrimental to animals as well as plants and other producers.
4. Chlorofluorocarbons, or CFCs, are the main ozone destroyers, and countries worldwide agreed in 1987 to phase out production of these chemical propellants.

Human Effects on the Biosphere   **385**

B. Near-Ground Ozone Pollution
  1. Near the ground, ozone is considered a pollutant and acts to irritate the eyes and respiratory tracts of humans and wildlife.
  2. To reduce ozone pollution, avoid actions that put fossil fuels or their combustion products (for example, filling your gas tank or running a gas-powered lawn mower) into the air on hot, sunny days.

44.8   Global Climate Change
  A. Average temperatures are increasing, and warming is more pronounced at temperate and polar latitudes.
  B. Rising temperatures raise the sea level and some coastal wetlands are disappearing underwater.
  C. Warmer temperatures are affecting deciduous forests, animal migration patterns, alteration of breeding seasons, and weather patterns.

44.9   Conservation Biology
  A. The Value of Biodiversity
    1. Biodiversity is the biological wealth of a region measured by the genetic diversity within species, species diversity, and ecosystem diversity.
    2. Biodiversity is currently declining, and conservation biology addresses these declines.
    3. Protection of biodiversity is essential to the survival of our species, as other organisms produce the oxygen we breathe and the food we eat.
    4. Additionally, there are ethical reasons to preserve biodiversity since the extinction of a species removes its unique collection of traits from the Earth.
  B. Setting Priorities
    1. Conservation biologists identify hot spots, places that are home to species found nowhere else and are under great threat of destruction.   These areas can take priority in worldwide conservation efforts.
    2. Conservation biologists identify ecoregions, land or aquatic regions characterized by climate, geography, and the species found within them. Endangered ecoregions become top priority for conservation efforts.
  C. Preservation and Restoration
    1. Through ecological restoration, we re-create or renew a biologically diverse ecosystem that has been destroyed or degraded.

44.10 Reducing Negative Impacts
  A. The health of our planet depends on our ability to recognize that the principles of energy flow and of resource limitation, which govern the survival of all systems of life, do not change. We must find a way to live within our limits.
  B. Promoting sustainability, meeting the needs of the present generation without reducing the ability of future generations to meet their own needs, begins with recognizing the environmental consequences of one's own lifestyle.
  C. You can save energy and other resources by reducing energy consumption, recycling, and reusing materials.

Suggestions for Presenting the Material

♦ This chapter is based on the premise that human activities are negatively affecting the biosphere. Allow and encourage students that oppose this proposal to discuss/debate their views.

♦ Present images of the Arctic perennial sea ice in the 1970s versus current images. This will provide a concrete example of the effects of global warming.

♦ Show images of various types of skin cancer, a visual demonstration of the effects of ultraviolet radiation. Discuss the importance of protection and prevention by wearing hats, sunglasses, and creams with sun-protection factor. Then relate this "protection and prevention" to the environment.

♦ Have students keep a log of the number of times and in what circumstances they heard, spoke about, or saw something relating to environmental concerns.

♦ Invite a conservation biologist and/or a conservationist to speak to the class.

♦ The concept of "going green" is prevalent in mainstream vernacular. Ask students what this means to them and how does this pop-culture term relate to the discipline of conservation biology.

♦ This chapter may leave students feeling that the Earth is so badly damaged and nothing can be done to repair it. Make certain to include positive examples of ecological preservation and restoration. Emphasize the effects one person can have.

♦ **Common Student Misconceptions**

o Students may deem global climate changes, the extinction crisis, and pollution as intangible and innocuous. Take time to provide concrete ways that these issues directly affect their lives, the lives of their children, and the lives of all future generations.

Classroom and Laboratory Enrichment

♦ Use images and videos to demonstrate the effects of global climate change on the Arctic.

♦ Research and map the polar bear habitat. Could this species be transplanted to other types of habitats successfully? Why or why not?

♦ In the United States, what are the steps that must be taken to place a plant or animal on the endangered species list?

♦ Comprise a list of endangered, threatened, and endemic species in your area, region, or state.

♦ Working in groups, thoroughly research a local ecosystem and how human activities directly and indirectly affect the ecosystem.

♦ To examine air quality, have students coat a microscope slide with petroleum jelly and place these slides at different locations in the building, on campus, and at home. Compare slides, to a control slide placed in a closed box, under light microscopy.

♦ Plant a series of bean plants in soil with varying pH, changing no other factors. Students should monitor the effects of pH throughout the course and relate the results to the effects of acid rain.

♦ Ground-level ozone is an air pollutant with harmful effects on the respiratory systems of animals. Have students place ozone test strips at different distances from highways, on campus, or near gas stations

- Test the effects of experimentally produced acid rain (vinegar or a solution of pH=3) on a variety of building materials, including: marble, pea stone, red sandstone, and granite. The effects of acid rain can be compared to the same material being placed in tap water. Submerge the materials and weigh the remaining solids at various time points.

- Have students determine their "ecological footprint." There are a variety of online sources to assist in this calculation. Class data can be shared and analyzed for trends, such as students who deem themselves as eco-friendly versus those who do not.

- Monitor the quality of air in your area. What has been the impact of humans on the air in your community?

- Prepare a list of environmental concerns in your area and state. Ask students what should be done, then ask them what realistically can be done.

A Long Reach (revisited)

- How is the Arctic different from Antarctica? Discuss the issues of land and resource rights in a sovereign country versus a geographic area.

- Discuss the link between global climate change and removal of resources from the Arctic region. Why is it becoming easier for people to remove minerals and fossil fuels from this region?

- How should international disputes over land and resource rights be solved? Is there an international governing body in place to rectify theses issues?

- Explain the impact of removing resources from the Arctic region. Consider issues relating to food chains/webs, animal life and biodiversity, and the impact of more human involvement in this area (for example, machinery to mine resources).

Additional Ideas for Classroom Discussion

- Are human activities the only cause of global change?

- Defend and refute the statement, "Extinction, like speciation, is a natural process."

- Can an endangered plant species lead to an endangered animal species?

- How has China's vast human population been a factor in the desertification of the Gobi Desert?

- Discuss ways to reduce pollutants.

- How can acid rain be neutralized to reduce its devastating effects?

- In terms of biological magnification, is it better to be a strict vegetarian or omnivorous?

- Discuss point and nonpoint sources of pollution in your area, region, or state.

- What are the drawbacks to renewable energy sources?

- Discuss the biodiversity in your area, region, or state. How has the biodiversity changed in the past 10 years?

- Why is the ozone layer of the Earth's atmosphere shrinking at the same time that excessive amounts of ozone at the Earth's surface are present in photochemical smog?

- Where does the tap water in your classroom building come from? Where does the wastewater created on your campus end up?

- Why would it be unwise to clear tropical forests and irrigate arid lands for conversion to agriculture?

- Ask students to make a list of ways in which they could modify their own lifestyles and behaviors to reduce environmental pollution.

- Do you think that our current environmental pollution problems reflect a fundamental shift in human values over the past 50 years? Why or why not?

How Would You Vote? Classroom Discussion Ideas

- Have students complete class polling using the JoinIn clickers. The Arctic has extensive deposits of minerals and fossil fuel, but tapping into these resources might pose a risk to species already threatened by global climate change. Should the United States exploit its share of the Arctic resources or advocate for protection of the region?

Term Paper Topics, Library Activities, and Special Projects

- Research the history of expeditions in the Arctic region. How have these investigations helped bring international attention to issues faced in this area of the world? Have these investigations had negative consequences?

- Compare and contrast historical mass extinctions with the current mass extinction.

- Review a current list of endangered species. Select one or two of these animals and describe the reasons these species are facing extinction. Are human activities to blame or is this a natural extinction process? Is this simply an uncommon species?

- Some species have been removed from the endangered list due to the efforts of conservation biology. Research a species that was removed from the endangered list and examine the efforts employed in the conservation of this species.

- Describe the role of the International Union for Conservation of Nature and Natural Resources in the global extinction crisis.

- Describe the distinction among the following terminology: endangered species, threatened species, and endemic species. Provide an example of each and report on measures being taken to safeguard these organisms.

- Describe the desertification process as it relates to Africa's Sahara Desert.

- Compare desertification and deforestation. Could one lead to the other?

- Describe the series of events that causes acid rain. Include the initial production/source of pollutants, atmospheric considerations, and the outcome as the rain falls back to the Earth.

- Report on the 1967 study, conducted by Woodwell, Wurster and Isaacson, of an estuary on Long Island, New York. Include the current ecological conditions in this area.

- Describe the methods used to remove garbage and debris from the oceans of the world.

- How does ultraviolet radiation cause skin cancer? Describe the series of events and the role melanin plays in this process.

- Describe the measures currently being taken to "repair the ozone layer."

- Describe the relationship among carbon dioxide, fossil fuels, and global climate change.

- What are biofuels? How will these affect the biosphere?

- Research an ecological "hot spot" in your area. Describe the measures conservational biologists are taking to assist this area. Assess public understanding of environmental pollution issues by designing a brief questionnaire. Divide the public into several different groups, and compare the levels of understanding among the groups. Some possible groupings are: students in this course, past students of the course, university or college students at large, university employees, different age groups, local residents not employed by the college or university, and groups created on the basis of differences in factors such as socioeconomic status, political affiliation, age, and education. How well informed are the different groups? Did they know more or less about environmental issues than you thought they would? Can you identify any myths about environmental pollution that appear to be widely held?

- Describe the actual contents of industrial smog or photochemical smog in the nearest city with an air pollution problem. Describe the ways in which the air pollution affects the health of area residents.

- What are the biological effects of acid rain on fish populations?

- Examine the statistical link between air quality and rates of respiratory disease in your community, state, and region.

- Describe successful community recycling programs. List the features of successful programs, and describe obstacles that must be overcome to ensure success.

- Who are your local polluters? Investigate local water quality issues related to development.

- Describe the process of illegal dumping. Why is it done? Has it been done in your area? What are the penalties for illegal dumping.

Answers to *Data Analysis Activities*

1. Males were more common offspring of women with less than 1 microgram per milliliter of PCB.

2. Females were more common offspring of women with greater than 4 micrograms per milliliter of PCB.

3. In villages with nearly all female newborns, you would expect PCB levels to be above 4 micrograms per milliliter.

Possible Responses to *Critical Thinking* Questions

1. Responses will vary with students either supporting the protection of endangered birds or our feline companions, cats. The students are asked to support their opinion and encourage them to examine the opposing view.

2. Plants utilize carbon dioxide as a substrate for the production of glucose and oxygen gas, via the process of photosynthesis. A global decrease in the amount of vegetation will cause the carbon dioxide levels to rise as less and less of this substrate is used for photosynthesis.

3. The presence of certain types of rocks mitigate the effects of acid rain since alkaline (basic) soils can neutralize the acid directly.

4. With biological magnification, a pollutant increases in concentration as it is passed up a food chain; therefore, it would appear that bowhead whales are lower on the food chain as compared to ringed seals.

Appendix

WRITING ESSAYS AND TERM PAPERS

A term paper is really just a long essay, its greater length reflecting more extensive treatment of a broader issue. Both assignments present critical evaluations of what you have read. In preparing an essay, you synthesize information, explore relationships, analyze, compare, contrast, evaluate, and organize your own arguments clearly, logically, and persuasively, gradually leading up to an assessment of your own. A good term paper or short essay is a creative work; you must interpret thoughtfully what you have read and come up with something that goes beyond what is presented in any single article or book consulted.

Getting Started

You must first decide on a general subject of interest. Often your instructor will suggest topics that former students have successfully exploited. Use these suggestions as guides, but do not feel compelled to select one of these topics unless so instructed. Be sure to choose or develop a subject that interests you. It is much easier to write successfully about something of interest than about something that bores you. All you need for getting started is a general subject, not a specific topic. Stay flexible. As you research your selected subject, you usually will find that you must narrow your focus to a particular topic because you encounter an unmanageable number of references pertinent to your original idea. You cannot, for instance, write about the entire field of primate behavior because the field has many different facets, each associated with a large and growing literature. In such a case, you will find a smaller topic, such as the social significance of primate grooming behavior, to be more appropriate; as you continue your literature search, you may even find it necessary to restrict your attention to a few primate species. Alternatively, you may find that the topic originally selected is too narrow and that you cannot find enough information on which to base a substantial paper. You must then broaden your topic, or switch topics entirely, so that you will end up with something to discuss. Don't be afraid to discard a topic on which you cannot find much information. Choose a topic you can understand fully. You can't possibly write clearly and convincingly on something beyond your grasp. Don't set out to impress your instructor with complexity; instead, dazzle your instructor with clarity and understanding. Simple topics often make the best ones for essays.

Researching Your Topic

Begin by carefully reading the appropriate section of your textbook to get an overview of the general subject of which your topic is a part. It is usually wise to then consult one or two additional textbooks before venturing into the recent literature; a solid construction requires a firm foundation. Your instructor may have placed a number of pertinent textbooks on reserve in your college library. Alternatively, you can consult your librarian, or the library card file or computer system, looking for books listed under the topic you have chosen to investigate.

This section is adapted from *A Short Guide to Writing About Biology* by Jan A. Pechenik. Copyright ©1987 by Jan A. Pechenik. Reprinted by permission of Scott, Foresman and Company.

Plagiarism and Note Taking

The essay or term paper you submit for evaluation must be original work: yours. Submitting anyone else's work under your name is plagiarism and can get you expelled from college. Presenting someone else's ideas as your own is also plagiarism. Consider the following two paragraphs.

> Smith (1981) suggests that this discrepancy in feeding rates may reflect differences in light levels used in the two different experiments. Jones (1984), however, found that light level did not influence the feeding rates of these animals and suggested that the rate differences reflect differences in the density at which the animals were held during the two experiments.

> This discrepancy in feeding rates might reflect differences in light levels. Jones (1984), however, found that light level did not influence feeding rates. Perhaps the difference in rates reflects differences in the density at which the animals were held during the two experiments.

The first example is fine. In the second example, however, the writer takes credit for the ideas of Smith and Jones; the writer has plagiarized.

Plagiarism sometimes occurs unintentionally, through faulty note taking. Photocopying an article or book chapter does not constitute note taking; neither does copying a passage by hand, occasionally substituting a synonym for a word used by the source's author. Take notes using your own words; you must get away from being awed by other people's words and move toward building confidence in your own thoughts and phrasings. Note taking involves critical evaluation; as you read, you must decide either that particular facts or ideas are relevant to your topic or that they are irrelevant. As Sylvan Barnet says in *A Short Guide to Writing About Art* (1981. Little, Brown and Company, second edition, p. 142), "You are not doing stenography; rather, you are assimilating knowledge and you are thinking, and so for the most part your source should be digested rather than engorged whole." If an idea is relevant, you should jot down a summary using your own words. Avoid writing complete sentences as you take notes; this will help prevent unintentional plagiarism later and will encourage you to see through to the essence of a statement while note taking.

Sometimes the authors' words seem so perfect that you cannot see how they might be revised to the best advantage for your paper. In this case, you may wish to copy a phrase or a sentence or two verbatim, but be sure to enclose this material in quotation marks as you write, and clearly indicate the source and page number from which the quotation derives. If you modify the original wording slightly as you take notes, you should indicate this as well, perhaps by using modified quotation marks: " . . . . . ". If your notes on a particular passage are in your own words, you should also indicate this as you write. I precede such notes, reflecting my own ideas or my own choice of words, with the word *Me* and a colon; my wife, who is also a biologist, uses her initials. If you take notes in this manner you will avoid the unintentional plagiarism that occurs when you later forget who is actually responsible for the wording of your notes or who is really responsible for the origin of an idea.

You probably cannot take notes in your own words if you do not understand what you are reading. Similarly, it is also difficult to be selective in your note taking until you have achieved a general understanding of the material. I suggest that you first consult at least one general reference text and read the material carefully, as recommended earlier. Once you have located a particularly promising scientific article, read the entire paper through at least once without taking any notes. Resist the (strong) temptation to annotate and take notes during this first reading, even though you may feel that without a pen in your hand you are accomplishing nothing. Put your pencils, pens, and notecards or paper away and read. Read slowly and with care. Read to understand. Study the illustrations, figure captions, tables, and graphs carefully, and try to develop your own interpretations before reading those of the author(s). Don't be frustrated by not understanding the paper at the first reading; understanding scientific literature takes time and patience.

By the time you have completed your first reading of the paper, you may find that the article is not really relevant to your topic after all or is of little help in developing your theme. If so, the preliminary read-through will have saved you from wasted note taking.

Some people suggest taking notes on index cards, with one idea per card so that the notes can be sorted readily into categories at a later stage of the paper's development. If you prefer to take notes on full-sized paper, beginning a separate page for each new source and writing on only one side of each page will facilitate sorting later.

As you take notes, be sure to make a complete record of each source used: author(s), year of publication, volume and page numbers (if consulting a scientific journal), title of article or book, publisher, and total number of pages (if consulting a book). It is not always easy to relocate a source once returned to the library stacks; the source you forget to record completely is always the one that vanishes as soon as you realize that you need it again. Also, before you finish with a source, it is good practice to read the source through one last time to be sure that your notes accurately reflect the content of what you have read.

Writing the Paper

Begin by reading all your notes. Again, do this without pen or pencil in hand. Having completed a reading of your notes to get an overview of what you have accomplished, reread them, this time with the intention of sorting your ideas into categories. Notes taken on index cards are particularly easy to sort, provided that you have not written many different ideas on a single card; one idea per card is a good rule to follow. To arrange notes written on full-sized sheets of paper, some people suggest annotating the notes with pens of different colors or using a variety of symbols, with each color or symbol representing a particular aspect of the topic. Still other people simply use scissors to snip out sections of the notes and then group the resulting scraps of paper into piles of related ideas. You should experiment to find a system that works well for you.

At this point you must eliminate those notes that are irrelevant to the specific topic you have finally decided to write about. No matter how interesting a fact or an idea is, it has no place in your paper unless it clearly relates to the rest of the paper and therefore helps you develop your argument. Some of the notes you took early on in your exploration of the literature are especially likely to be irrelevant to your essay, since these notes were taken before you had developed a firm focus. Put these irrelevant notes in a safe place for later use; don't let them coax their way into your paper.

You must next decide how best to arrange your categorized notes, so that your essay or term paper progresses toward some conclusion. The direction your paper will take should be clearly and specifically indicated in the opening paragraph, as in the following example written by Student A:

> Most shelled molluscs, including clams, oysters, muscles, snails, and chitons, are sedentary; they live either attached to hard substrate (like rock) or in soft-substrate burrows. A few bivalve species, however, can actually swim, by expelling water from their mantle cavities. One such swimming mollusc is the scallop *Pecten manmus*. This paper will describe the morphological features that make swimming possible in *P. maximus* and will consider some of the evolutionary pressures that might have selected for these adaptations.

The nature of the problem being addressed is clearly indicated in this first paragraph, and Student A tells us clearly why the problem is of interest: (1) the typical bivalve doesn't move and certainly doesn't swim; (2) a few bivalves can swim; (3) so what is there about these exceptional species that enables them to do what other species can't; and (4) why might this swimming ability have evolved? Note that use of the pronoun I is now perfectly acceptable in scientific writing.

The first paragraph of your paper must state clearly what you are setting out to accomplish and why. Every paragraph that follows the first paragraph should advance your argument clearly and logically toward the stated goal.

State your case, and build it carefully. Use your information and ideas to build an argument, to develop a point, to synthesize. Avoid the tendency to simply summarize papers one by one: They did this, then they did that, and then they suggested the following explanation. Instead, set out to compare, to contrast, to illustrate, to discuss.

In referring to specific experiments, don't simply state that a particular experiment supports some particular hypothesis; describe the relevant parts of the experiment and explain how the results relate to the hypothesis under question.

In all writing, avoid quotations unless they are absolutely necessary; use your own words whenever possible. At the end of your essay, summarize the problem addressed and the major points you have made so that the reader will remember the key elements of your paper.

Never introduce any new information in your summary paragraph.

Citing Sources

Unless you are told otherwise, do not footnote. Instead, cite references directly in the text by author and date of publication. For example: Landscapes can be classified according to the dominant plant species (Slobodkin, 1988). Jones (1981), for example, refers to white oak forests.

At the end of your paper, include a section entitled Literature Cited, listing all references you have referred to in your paper. Do not include any references you have not actually read. Each reference listed must give author(s), date of publication, title of article, title of journal, and volume and page numbers. If the reference is a book, the citation must include the publisher, place of publication, and total number of pages in the book, or the page numbers pertinent to the citation. Your instructor may specify a particular format for preparing this section of your paper.

Creating a Title

By the time you have finished writing, you should be ready to title your creation. Give the essay or term paper a title that is appropriate and interesting, one that conveys significant information about the specific topic of your paper.

Good title: Behavioral and Chemical Defense Mechanisms of Gastropods and Bivalves

Poor title: Molluscan Defenses

Good title: The Effects of Spilled Fuel Oil on the Breeding of Shorebirds

Poor title: Pollutants and Birds

The following are good sources of information for developing essays and term papers:

General biology textbooks

Specialized textbooks, such as general texts on human physiology, invertebrate zoology, marine biology, and ecology.

Science section of major newspapers, such as the *Boston Globe,* the *New York Times,* and the *Los Angeles Times.* Most major daily newspapers have a science section once each week.

BioScience

The New England Journal of Medicine

Oceans

Science News

Scientific American

Sea Frontiers